20. Colloquium
der Gesellschaft für Biologische Chemie
14.–16. April 1969 in Mosbach/Baden

Inhibitors
Tools in Cell Research

Edited by Th. Bücher and H. Sies

With 150 Figures

Springer-Verlag Berlin · Heidelberg · New York 1969

Th. Bücher and H. Sies
Institut für Physiologische Chemie und Physikalische Chemie
der Universität München
D-8000 München 15, Goethestr. 33

The Proceedings of the 20th Mosbach Colloquium were unanimously dedicated by the participants to

OTTO HEINRICH WARBURG

in his 86th year of life.

„... die Fermente unter ihren natürlichsten Wirkungsbedingungen, in der lebenden Zelle selbst, zu untersuchen. Sie sind hier zwar im Sinn der präparativen Chemie so unrein wie möglich. Findet man aber Reagenzien, die nur mit den Fermenten und nicht mit den übrigen Zellbestandteilen reagieren, so stört die inaktive Zellsubstanz ebensowenig, wie bei chemischen Reaktionen die Gefäße stören, in denen man die Reaktionen ausführt.“
(Über die katalytischen Wirkungen der lebendigen Substanz 1928)

Preface

The scope of the 20th Mosbach Colloquium may be best illustrated by the following notes sent to the speakers when the colloquium was organized.

"1) The application of inhibitors in cell biology has led to decisive insight into the organisation of cellular units. The subject should be treated against a background of current aspects of cell biology. In some areas of research, a fairly complete picture of the functions and cooperative interactions of the units has already emerged. We will discuss mainly these areas.

2) At this colloquium we want to contribute illustrations of the useful application of inhibitors to biological problems. Due to limited knowledge, inhibitors are sometimes incorrectly employed. This applies both to the planning of investigations and to the conclusions drawn ("use of inhibitors by uninhibited workers").

3) Inhibitors themselves are interesting substances and their mechanisms of action constitute fascinating problems."

The colloquium has been subdivided into five sections. The known chemical structures of the inhibitors discussed are given in an *Appendix*.

We gratefully appreciate the cooperation of the speakers. To a great extent, they managed the coordination of contributions to each of the five subdivisions.

We regret that no contributors from Eastern Europe were able to participate.

We are pleased to acknowledge the advice of E. Auhagen, L. Ernster, P. Fromageot, G. Hartmann, M. Klingenberg, O. Westphal, and H. Zachau in the preparation of the colloquium, and the efficient help of members of the staff of our Institute. The colloquium was generously supported by the Stiftung Volkswagenwerk and by the continuing sponsorship of the firms who are corporate members of the Gesellschaft für Biologische Chemie.

We sincerely hope that this book justifies the effort involved in its publication and fulfills its purpose as a tool for future research.

Munich, July 1969

THEODOR BÜCHER
HELMUT SIES

Contents

I. DNA-Dependent Processes

II. Protein Synthesis

V. Cytoplasmic Compartmentation

VI. Appendix

I. DNA-Dependent Processes

DNA-Replication in vivo and in vitro

H. SCHALLER

Max-Planck-Institut für Virusforschung, Tübingen

With 7 Figures

What is the present state of knowledge about the mechanism of DNA replication? In all organisms studied, DNA replication was found to be semiconservative [26]. In addition, we now have a solid knowledge about the enzyme DNA polymerase [16]. However, nobody has been able so far to simulate semiconservative replication of double-stranded DNA in vitro. To develop a satisfactory model of the replication mechanism, we must, therefore, take into account the data obtained both in vivo and in vitro. In the following I would like to restrict myself to the replication of the DNA of the bacterium E. coli, as most of the data have been obtained from work with this organism, and no fundamental differences have been observed in other systems.

Fig. 1 shows the general scheme of semiconservative DNA replication. During replication the DNA strands separate. At the same time synthesis of new DNA occurs, yielding as a final product two daughter duplexes with the parental single strands as conserved subunits. The presence of Y-shaped intermediates has best been demonstrated by the autoradiographs of CAIRNS [4]. There is usually only a single growing point in a replicating E. coli DNA molecule [2, 4]. The rate of the DNA synthesis can, therefore, be obtained from the total number of nucleotide pairs (4×10^6) divided by the duplication time (40 min) to yield about 10^5 nucleotide pairs per min.

For a biochemist there are three main questions to be answered:

1. What is the nature of the low molecular weight precursors?

2. Which enzymes are involved in the polymerization reactions?

3. What is the mechanism of polymerization, and are different mechanisms required to synthesize the two DNA chains at the growth point? A unidirectional replication of the antiparallel double helix would require chain elongation both at the 3′- and the 5′-termini of the growing chains.

There are several lines of evidence indicating that both DNA chains are synthesized from the 5′-deoxynucleotide pools of the cell [22, 25]. Of these, the deoxynucleoside triphosphates seem to be the most likely direct precursors for DNA synthesis. This latter conclusion is drawn from pulse labelling experiments with tritiated

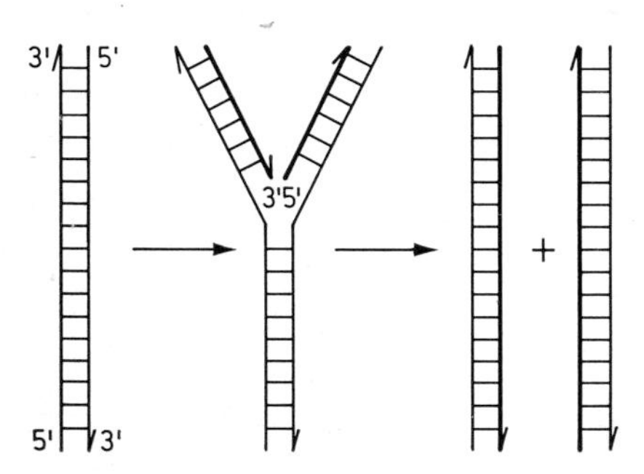

Fig. 1. Scheme of semiconservative DNA replication. The parental DNA duplex is indicated by two lines each representing a polydeoxyribonucleotide chain. The polarity of the chains is indicated by an arrow which marks the 3′-end

thymidine (Fig. 2). When ^{3}H thymidine is added to the culture of logarithmically growing E. coli cells, the label is incorporated into the DNA only after a lag period of about 15 sec. Analysis of the acid-soluble nucleotide pools shows that the monophosphate is completely labelled after 5 sec, considerably before the incorporation rate into DNA reaches its maximum. On the other hand, the labelling of the triphosphate pool can very well be correlated with the rate of DNA synthesis. Since thymidine 3′-triphosphate cannot be detected in extracts from E. coli [25], it seems likely that only the 5′-deoxyribonucleoside triphosphates are the natural precursors of DNA replication in vivo.

Which enzymes catalyse the polymerization of the deoxynucleoside triphosphates to form a polynucleotide chain? The only candidate to carry out this reaction is DNA polymerase, the Kornberg enzyme [15]. As shown in Fig. 3, this enzyme requires for reaction not only a DNA template, but also a primer DNA chain terminating in a 3′-OH group. Deoxyribonucleoside triphosphates are assembled according to the Watson-Crick rules, and pyro-

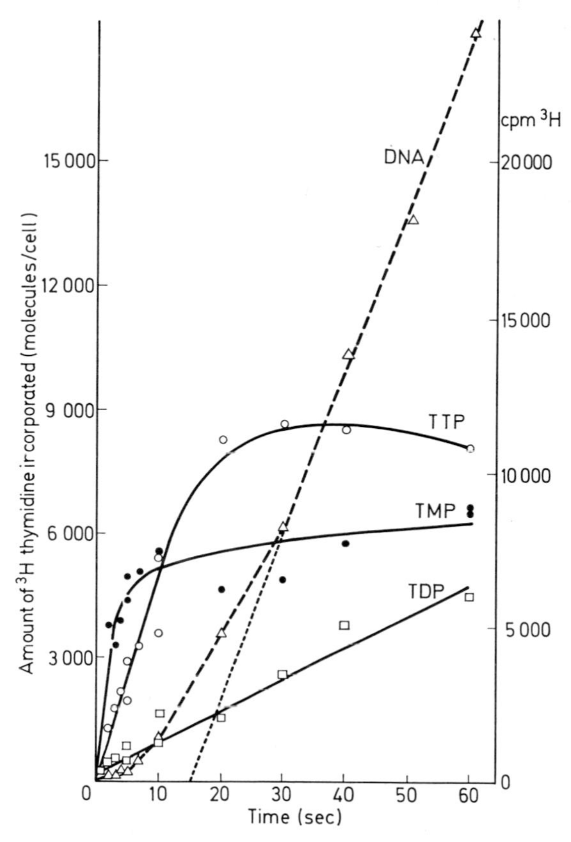

Fig. 2. Incorporation of ^{3}H thymidine (120 μμ moles, 2μC) into E. coli TAU 2×10^{8} cells) at 37° [23]. (The number of labelled molecules is based on the original specific activity of the nucleoside)

phosphate is split off. The selection of the bases is highly specific, as has been demonstrated by the recent in vitro synthesis of infectious Φ X DNA [8], a circular DNA molecule composed of about 5000 nucleotide units. The rate of DNA synthesis in the in vitro system is, however, only 10^3 nucleotides per min, which is two orders of magnitude below the rate observed in vivo.

Thanks to the extensive studies carried out during the past decade by KORNBERG and his colleagues at Stanford University, detailed information has been obtained concerning the properties of the enzyme E. coli DNA polymerase [16]. Recent improvements of the isolation procedure have made the enzyme available as a homogeneous protein in gram quantities, so that chemical and physicochemical studies became possible [5]. Molecular weight determinations in various solvents indicate that DNA polymerase consists of a single polypeptide chain with a molecular weight of

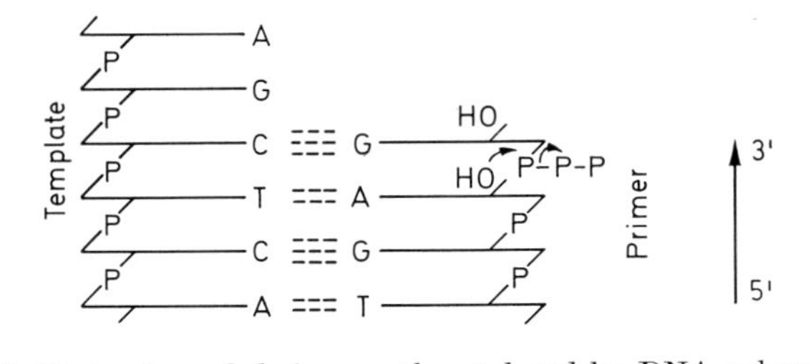

Fig. 3. Mechanism of chain growth catalysed by DNA polymerase

109,000. The amino acid composition shows the remarkably low value of three half cystein residues per molecule, two of which form a disulfide linkage which is essential for the correct secondary structure. The third sulfhydryl group can be reacted with mercury ions without loss of the enzymatic activity. This fact has been used to obtain a radioactively labelled enzyme [10], especially useful in studying the formation of enzyme-DNA complexes [5]. The data were interpreted to mean that DNA polymerase has two separate binding sites for the template and the primer DNA chains. In addition, a site for the primer chain terminus and a single binding site for the four deoxynucleoside triphosphates were detected [16].

The enzyme does not bind to double-stranded DNA except at single strand chain interruptions (nicks) or at termini [13]. In contrast, enzyme molecules can be bound to many sites along a single-stranded DNA molecule [13]. However, no DNA synthesis can be initiated in the absence of a complementary primer chain [7, 18]. Therefore, primer-free DNA single strands (like circular

Φ X DNA or fd DNA) competitively inhibit DNA polymerase activity [18].

The various ways in which DNA polymerase can act on a nicked double-stranded DNA molecule are shown in Fig. 4. Four different types of reactions have been detected: (1) DNA synthesis at the 3′-end with a concomitant peeling off of the 5′-terminated parental DNA chain [17]. (2) The degradation of the DNA chain at its 3′-terminus. This can be caused by the reverse reaction of the polymerization, i.e. pyrophosphorolysis, or by hydrolysis. Competition studies indicate that both reactions are carried out at the same active center [1, 5]. (3) Hydrolysis of the DNA chain from its

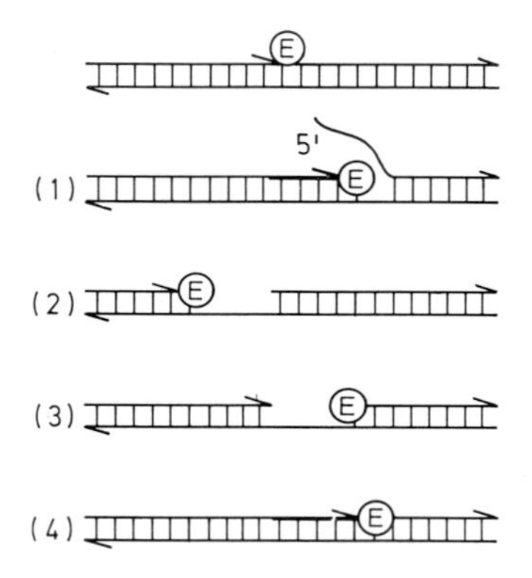

Fig. 4. Reactions carried out by DNA polymerase on a nicked DNA duplex

5′-end [14, 5]. This reaction appears to be carried out at an active site which is different from the site of polymerization [16]. (4) A reaction of both type (3) and type (1), in which DNA degradation at the 5′-end and DNA synthesis at the 3′-OH end of a nicked DNA duplex occur at the same time. The result is the "translation" of a single strand chain scission along a DNA chain. This reaction seems to be the preferential early reaction of DNA polymerase with a double-stranded DNA template in vitro [12]. Such a mechanism of DNA synthesis would explain repair synthesis, but not DNA replication.

So what is the role of the DNA polymerase in replication ? There are basically two mechanisms which could explain the in vivo data (Fig. 5). According to mechanism A, the DNA polymerase would carry out a continuous chain elongation by condensing nucleotide residues to both the 3′- and the 5′-end of the chain. If chain elongation can only be carried out at the 3′-OH end, the anti-parallel strand must be synthesized by a discontinuous mechanism (model B or model C). According to mechanism A, one DNA primer chain is elongated by addition of 5′-nucleoside triphosphates to its 3′-OH end, a reaction catalysed by DNA polymerase

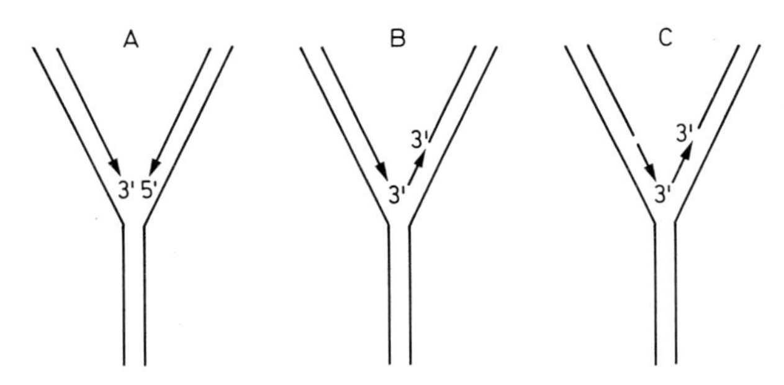

Fig. 5. Alternative mechanisms for continuous and discontinuous chain elongation at the growth point

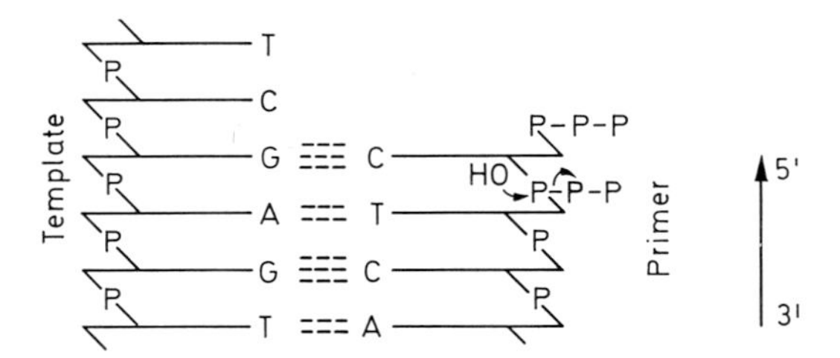

Fig. 6. Postulated mechanism of chain growth at 5′-terminus

(Fig. 3). In a postulated additional mechanism the complementary strand is elongated by adding 5′-triphosphates to a 5′-triphosphate terminus of the primer (Fig. 6). Unfortunately, such a reaction cannot be carried out in vitro by the DNA polymerase [12]. If we don't believe that another unknown DNA polymerase exists, we must accept a discontinuous mechanism of DNA synthesis at the growing region. According to such a mechanism, nascent DNA must be partly (B) or totally (C) of low molecular weight. Specific labelling of the growth point by extremely short pulses of ^{3}H

thymidine has revealed that newly synthesized DNA indeed is of low molecular weight [19]. Variable amounts of pulse labelled DNA fragments have been reported from various research groups [8, 19, 27]. Therefore, at present no decision can be made between mechanisms B and C. In this context it may be worth mentioning that a discontinuous DNA synthesis of both DNA strands would allow the action of many polymerase molecules to speed up the rate of DNA synthesis, and thus would possibly explain the rate differences between in vivo and in vitro synthesis. A mechanism of discontinuous DNA synthesis, however, requires two functions which cannot be carried out by the DNA polymerase itself: initiation on a single-stranded DNA template, and joining of the newly synthesized DNA fragments to the high molecular polymer. This

$$
\begin{array}{l}
\text{NAD} + \text{enzyme} \rightleftharpoons \text{AMP-enzyme} + \text{NMN} \\
\text{AMP-enzyme} + \text{nicked DNA} \longrightarrow \text{AMP-DNA} + \text{enzyme} \\
\text{AMP-DNA} \longrightarrow \text{joined DNA} + \text{AMP} \\
\hline
\text{NAD} + \text{nicked DNA} \longrightarrow \text{NMN} + \text{AMP} + \text{joined DNA}
\end{array}
$$

Fig. 7. Postulated mechanism of the reaction catalysed by E. coli polynucleotide ligase [20]

latter reaction can be carried out in vitro by the enzyme E. coli polynucleotide ligase [21, 6, 28], which utilizes the energy of the pyrophosphate linkage in NAD to rejoin the 5′-phosphate and the 3′-OH termini in a nicked DNA duplex (Fig. 7). As intermediates of this reaction, an enzyme-adenylate and a DNA-adenylate have been identified [20].

Now we know enzymes for polymerization and for joining, what about initiation? This reaction can be studied in vitro by using a circular single-stranded DNA (e. g., fd DNA) which is free from a complementary primer DNA as a template for DNA polymerase. As already mentioned above, in this system the enzyme does bind to DNA, but DNA synthesis can occur only if a complementary oligonucleotide is added to the reaction mixture to create the required combination of primer and template. As an alternative, one can also postulate an initiator protein which could replace the oligonucleotide primer. At present no decision can be made as to which of these possible mechanisms operate in vivo. All have in common that they require at least one additional unknown protein. That in addition to DNA polymerase and polynucleotide ligase other proteins play a role in DNA replication has also become evident by the isolation of bacterial mutants in which DNA replication is thermosensitive [3, 9]. When a great number of such mutants was analysed at the nonpermissive temperature, most of these mutants showed normal levels of the four deoxynucleoside triphosphates, and all strains showed normal activities of DNA polymerase and polynucleotide ligase [24]. In conclusion I would, therefore, like to emphasize that inhibitors which block DNA synthesis may act on quite different parts of the DNA replication mechanism. They may act on the DNA template directly, they may interfere with the precursor synthesizing system, they may act on the enzymes DNA polymerase and polynucleotide ligase, or on one of the other hitherto unknown components of the replicating system.

References

1. Beyersmann, D., and G. Schramm: Biochim. biophys. Acta **159**, 64 (1968).
2. Bonhoeffer, F., and A. Gierer: J. molec. Biol. **7**, 534 (1963).
3. —, and H. Schaller: Biochem. biophys. Res. Commun. **20**, 93 (1965).
4. Cairns, J.: Cold Spr. Harb. Symp. quant. Biol. **28**, 43 (1963).
5. Eglund, P. T., M. P. Deutscher, T. M. Jovin, R. B. Kelly, N. R. Cozzarelli, and A. Kornberg: Cold Spr. Harb. Symp. quant. Biol. **33**, 1 (1968).
6. Gefter, M., A. Becker, and J. Hurwitz: Proc. nat. Acad. Sci. (Wash.) **58**, 240 (1967).
7. Goulian, M.: Proc. nat. Acad. Sci. (Wash.) **61**, 284 (1968).
8. —, A. Kornberg, and R. L. Sinsheimer: Proc. nat. Acad. Sci. (Wash.) **58**, 232 (1967).
9. Gross, J. D., D. Karamata, and P. Hempstead: Cold Spr. Harb. Symp. quant. Biol. **33**, 307 (1968).
10. Jovin, T. M., P. T. Eglund, and L. L. Bertsch: J. biol. Chem. **244**, 2996 (1969).
11. — —, and A. Kornberg: J. biol. Chem. **244**, 3009 (1969).
12. Kelly, R. B., N. R. Cozzarelli, and A. Kornberg: Fed. Proc. **1969**, WPM-B2.
13. —, P. T. Eglund, and A. Kornberg: Fed. Proc. **1969**, TPM-B6.
14. Klett, R. P., A. Cerami, and E. Reich: Proc. nat. Acad. Sci. (Wash.) **60**, 943 (1968).
15. Kornberg, A.: Enzymatic synthesis of DNA. New York: John Wiley 1962.
16. — Science **163**, 1410 (1969).

17. Mitra, S., and A. Kornberg: J. gen. Physiol. **49** (6), 59 (1966).
18. Oertel, W., and H. Schaller: Unpublished results.
19. Okazaki, R., T. Okazaki, K. Sakabe, K. Sugimoto, and A. Sugimoto: Proc. nat. Acad. Sci. (Wash.) **59**, 598 (1968).
20. Olivera, B. M., Z. W. Hall, and I. R. Lehman: Proc. nat. Acad. Sci. (Wash.) **61**, 237 (1968).
21. —, and I. R. Lehman: Proc. nat. Acad. Sci. (Wash.) **57**, 1426 (1967).
22. Price, T. D., R. A. Darmstadt, H. A. Hinds, and S. Zamenhof: J. biol. Chem. **242**, 140 (1967).
23. Schaller, H., and H. Voss: Paper in preparation.
24. —, H. Seiler, and F. Bonhoeffer: Unpublished results.
25. Seiler, H.: Dissertation, Tübingen 1968.
26. Taylor, J. H.: In: Probleme der biologischen Reduplikation, p. 9 (P. Sitte, Ed.). Berlin-Heidelberg-New York: Springer 1966.
27. Yudelevich, A., B. Ginsberg, and J. Hurwitz: Proc. nat. Acad. Sci. (Wash.) **61**, 1129 (1968).

Note added in proof:

Very recently an E. coli strain with an (amber) mutation in its Kornberg polymerase gene has been isolated. Extracts of this bacterium show less than 0.5% DNA polymerase activity while in vivo DNA replication and cell division are normal; the strain is sensitive to UV light. These findings indicate that the Kornberg enzyme functions in vivo only as a repair enzyme, but not as a part of the replicating system. (J. Cairns, F. Miescher-Symposium Tübingen, 1969.)

Discussion

Zahn (Mainz): I cannot see why Dr. Schaller dislikes the idea of oligonucleotides being the initiators for single-strand directed synthesis. It is known that we find DNases at the points of DNA synthesis, so oligonucleotides might be found, too.

Schaller (Tübingen): To produce complementary oligonucleotides by a random process you would have to degrade a lot of DNA. In addition, DNA fragments are released from a DNA duplex only if their chain length is below ten nucleotide residues. Therefore, you would have to postulate a specific oligonucleotide generating system. There are no indications for such a reaction *in vivo*.

Geider (Heidelberg): In addition to the mechanism of *in vivo* replication with DNA polymerase (mechanism C in Fig. 5), there is a model of Kornberg [1] where the enzyme jumps after replication of a short piece of one strand to the single-stranded part of the complementary strand. There it runs in 3′-direction, till the double-stranded region is reached. A specific (unknown) nickase splits the newly polymerized strand between the two strands and polynucleotide ligase joins the new and the old replicated

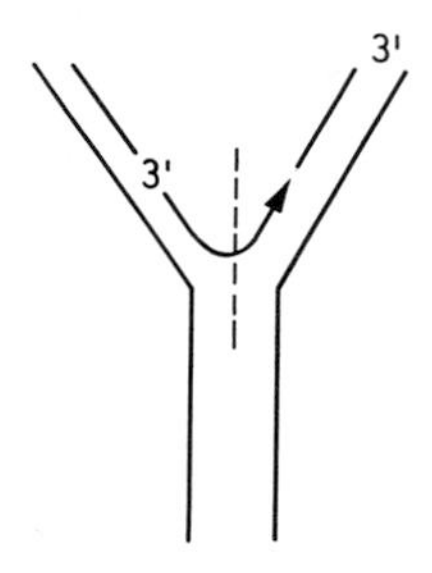

strand. For *in vitro* replication of DNA polymerase, this idea has been proposed several years ago (branched pieces of replicated phage DNA).

Schaller: I left this out due to lack of time and since it seems to be just another way to postulate an unknown enzyme.

Jovin (Göttingen): In attempting to correlate *in vivo* with *in vitro* studies of DNA replication, I believe it is necessary to keep in mind the possibly contrasting influences of various factors. In the first place the internal milieu of the cell is manifestly different from that in the test tube. Chromosomal DNA is present at high local concentrations and in a topological state not approximated in solution. Interactions with proteins and other cellular factors such as membranes are manifold and certainly of importance in initiating, maintaining, and modulating replication. Perhaps related to these considerations is the large discrepancy between *in vivo* and *in vitro* rates of synthesis which remains to be explained. Invoking the simultaneous participation of many polymerase molecules magnifies the as yet unresolved question as to how new strands are initiated. It is of interest that linear duplex molecules rendered particularly free of single strand breaks by careful isolation (alternatively, it has been suggested, by ligase action) are particularly inert as primers [2]. It is for this and related reasons that "nicks" have been proposed as the natural structures encountered and utilized by polymerase [1], a proposal quite consistent with most plausible mechanisms for replication. Yet model schemes involving strand "switchover" in order to circumvent the polarity problem [1] generate many questions regarding the detailed nature of the replicative fork under the condition that register between template and product must be ultimately preserved. The concerted action of many enzymes must be invoked with a corresponding large risk of error in the process.

References

1. Kornberg, A.: Science **163**, 1410 (1969).
2. Kelly, R. B., N. R. Cozzarelli, and A. Kornberg: Unpublished results.

Inhibitors Acting on DNA and their Use to Study DNA Replication and Repair

H. KERSTEN and W. KERSTEN

Institut für Physiologische Chemie Münster
Institut für Physiologische Chemie Erlangen

With 16 Figures

At the Cold Spring Harbor Symposium of 1947, LEONOR MICHAELIS [1] discussed DNA induced changes in the absorption spectra of dyes. Intuitively, he anticipated the intercalation hypothesis at a time when the structure of double stranded DNA was yet unknown. In 1952, changes in the absorption spectrum of the antimalarial drug chloroquine upon addition of DNA were demonstrated [2]. From these experiments it was suggested that a binding of chloroquine to DNA was related to the chemotherapeutic action of the drug. This was still a year before the Watson and Crick model of DNA structure became known [3]. Subsequently, the complex formations between acridines and DNA [4, 5] and actinomycin and DNA have been studied in detail [6—12]. Several other drugs have been found to affect the structure and function of DNA (for review see Ref. [13—15]). These studies have contributed to our understanding of the molecular mechanism by which drugs interfere with nucleic acid metabolism. Moreover, antimicrobial agents have become important tools to study DNA dependent processes during replication and transcription of the DNA molecule. A landmark in the development of this field was the discovery of mutations of the phage T_4, caused by acridines, from which CRICK proposed the triplet code and its properties [16].

This presentation is subdivided into the following parts:

1. A brief survey of inhibitors acting on DNA.

2. The damage of DNA caused by alkylating agents, especially mitomycins, and the possible mechanism of repair replication of DNA.

3. The molecular mechanism by which different functional groups of the mitomycins interfere with nucleic acid metabolism.

Survey of Inhibitors Acting on DNA

In Fig. 1 substances which interact with DNA are listed. Those which have some importance as drugs or which have been used as tools to inhibit DNA-dependent synthesis of DNA or RNA were

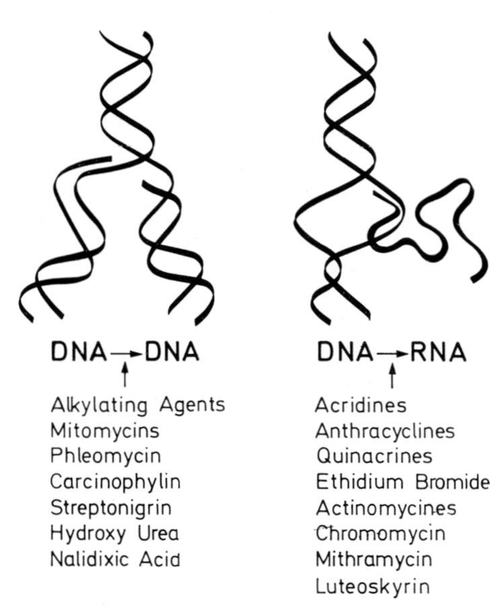

Fig. 1. Inhibitors acting on DNA and DNA dependent synthesis of DNA and RNA

selected. In cell free systems as well as in living cells these inhibitors show preference for one or the other process, but none of these substances selectively inhibits DNA or RNA synthesis in vivo. The biological consequence of the interaction with DNA is a matter of the concentration of the inhibitor and can be influenced by the biological system used. For example, in B. subtilis chromomycin [17] affects the synthesis of DNA and RNA equally well. On the other hand, mitomycin can be converted easily into a substance which preferentially inhibits the synthesis of RNA. Experimental evidence for this will be presented below.

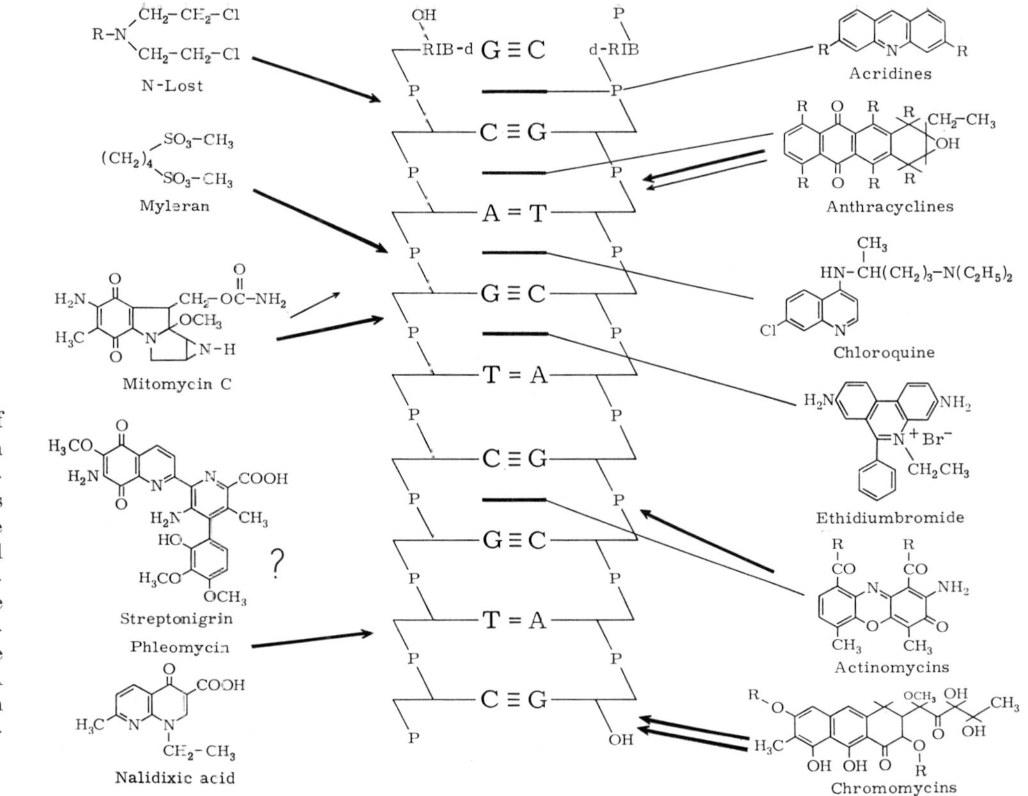

Fig. 2. Structure of inhibitors acting on DNA. Schematic representation of bases or base pairs of the DNA double strand involved in association or binding of the inhibitors. The arrows indicate the site of attack in the DNA molecule. The sign ⌐ is used to indicate intercalation

Acridines can cause the formation of altered RNA [18]. Anthracyclines, chromomycin and mithramycin [19, 20, 13], quinacrines [21, 22], ethidium bromide [23], actinomycin [19, 20], and luteoskyrin [24] preferentially inhibit DNA dependent synthesis of RNA. Inhibitors with preference for RNA synthesis have planar ring systems in common (Fig. 2). With exception of the tetrahydroanthracene-derivatives, chromomycin and mithramycin, there is increasing evidence that these inhibitors are inserted between adjacent base pairs. Details of the interaction of these substances with DNA have been discussed extensively [13—15].

In cell free systems as well as in living cells alkylating agents [25], mitomycins [26, 27], phleomycin [28, 29], carcinophylin [30], streptonigrin [31], hydroxyurea [32] and nalidixic acid [33] have been observed to inhibit the DNA-dependent synthesis of DNA preferentially. The mode of interaction of streptonigrin, hydroxyurea and nalidixic acid with DNA is still unexplained. Phleomycin, a copper containing antibiotic of as yet unknown structure has been shown to compete with Hg^{2+} in binding to the carbonyl group in 2′ position of thymidine [34, 35].

Mitomycins have in common with streptonigrin a quinone ring system; the functional role of this will be discussed later. In one important respect mitomycins differ from all the inhibitors described so far. Like the alkylating agents, for example, N-mustard derivatives and myleran (see Fig. 2), the mitomycins are covalently bound to DNA, thus causing irreversible changes in the DNA molecule [36].

The Damage of DNA Caused by Alkylating Agents and Mitomycins and the Possible Mechanism of DNA Repair

Mitomycins must first be reduced to form active difunctional alkylating agents as is shown in Fig. 3. In vivo NADPH and a quinone reductase are involved in the reductive step. The reactive sites are probably the opened aziridine ring and the -CH_2-group of the methylurethane side chain. The substituent in position 7 might as well be involved in the reaction with DNA.

Only double stranded but not single stranded DNA, when reacted in vitro with difunctional alkylating agents such as N-mustard, result upon hydrolysis in di-(-7-guaninyl) derivatives; the structure of one is shown in Fig. 4. From this result it was concluded that the product formed must originate from interstrand crosslinks [37]. In addition to crosslinking, part of the difunctional alkylating agents alkylate N_7 of guanine like monofunctional alkylating agents. Small amounts of 1-alkyl-adenine and 3-alkyl-adenine have also been observed. Mitomycins also show preference in binding for guanine [38, 39]; however, the participation of diguanyl-mitomycin in interstrand crosslinking is still a suggestion.

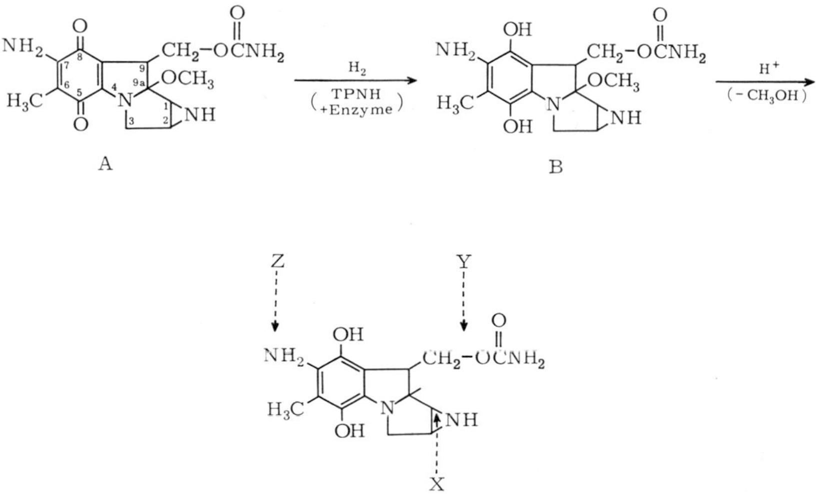

Fig. 3. Structure of mitomycin (A), the primary product after chemical or enzymatic reduction (B), postulated structure after secondary rearrangement (C), X and Y and Z are the possible reaction sites of the difunctional alkylating product (SZYBALSKI and IYER [36])

As with some other difunctional alkylating agents of short lengths it is extremely difficult to fit the mitomycin molecule as a crosslink between the complementary strands of DNA without assuming a large distortion of the double helix.

One crosslink per DNA molecule can be a lethal event for the cell, since the replication of DNA is blocked at this point. However, this damage of DNA must not be lethal. As has already been discussed in the preceding paper, microorganisms contain enzyme systems capable of repairing DNA. Therefore, mitomycins and

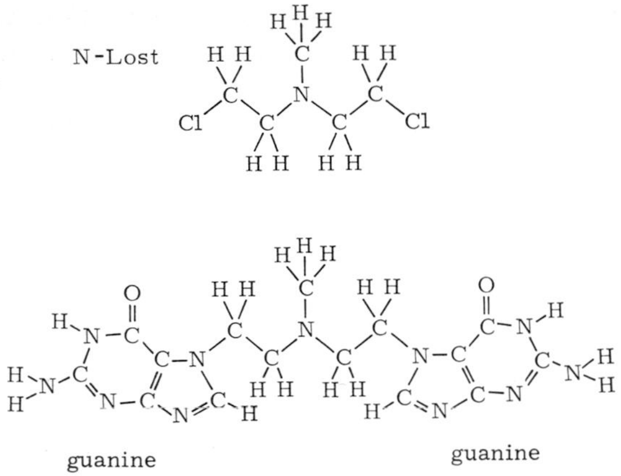

N-Lost

guanine guanine

Fig. 4: Di-(-7-guaninyl) product resulting from the reaction of double stranded DNA in vitro with alkylating agents, e.g. N-mustard (LAWLEY and BROOKES [37])

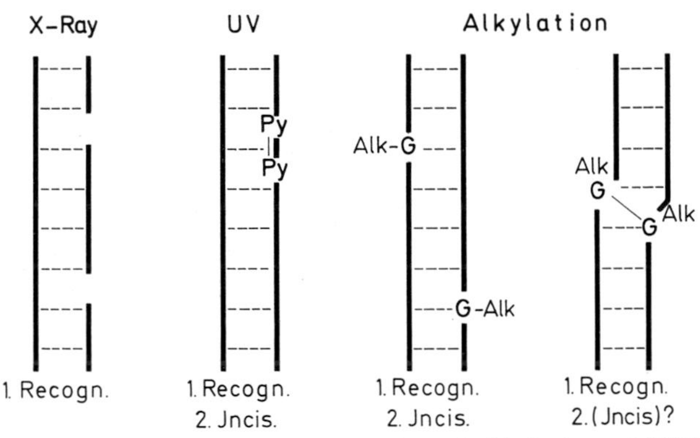

Fig. 5. Schematic representation of repairable lesions of DNA

alkylating agents have become important tools for studying mechanisms of the repair replication of the genetic material.

DNA is the target upon which several mutagenic and lethal agents act to produce damages. The nature of repairable lesions is quite different, as is schematically shown in Fig. 5.

Single strand breaks are produced by X-rays. In addition, free radicals formed upon X irradiation result in chemical changes of the pyrimidines [40]. UV irradiation leads to the formation of covalently linked pyrimidine dimers, mainly thymine dimers [41, 42]. Damage by mono- and difunctional alkylating agents has already been discussed.

The different types of damage can be repaired. An important question to be asked is: Does there exist only one mechanism of dark repair for all types of lesions? (Photoreactivation should not be discussed.) Let us assume that whatever the damage might be, it has already been recognized and an incision has occurred at the damaged places by an endonuclease. In this case the proceeding

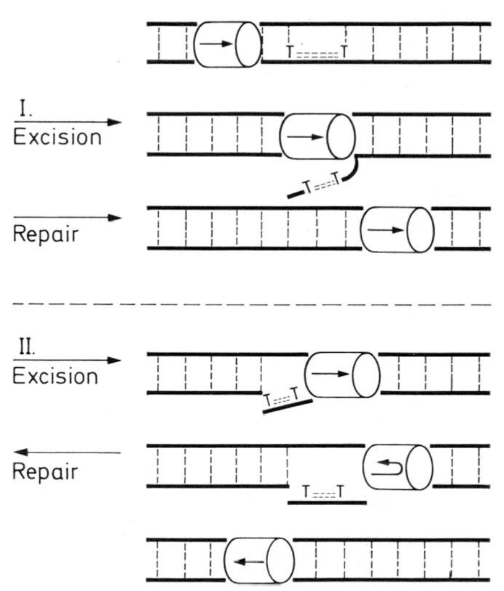

Fig. 6. Schematic representation of the excision repair mechanism

steps of repair only need a single error correcting mechanism, schematically shown in Fig. 6:

1. an exonuclease to remove the damaged bases and contiguous nucleotides (excision),

2. the DNA polymerase to replace the excised bases, using the undamaged strand as a template, and

3. the ligase to join the newly synthesized strand with the old one (repair).

Excision and repair probably do not proceed in opposite but rather in one fixed direction, since the DNA polymerase might function as exonuclease as well (see the preceding paper). These three steps in the mechanism of repair were first proposed for UV induced pyrimidine dimers [48, 49]. Investigations with UV sensitive and UV resistant mutants of different types revealed that the ability to excise dimers was much less in the sensitive strain.

If a single mechanism of repair operates for all types of lesions, UV resistant mutants should also be resistant to X irradiation, monofunctional and difunctional alkylating agents. Though in

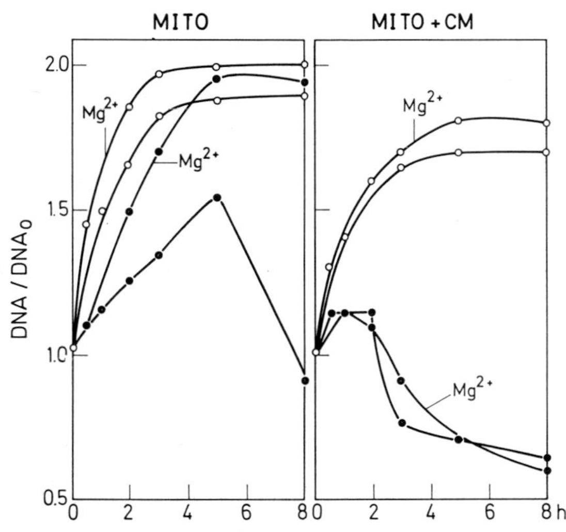

Fig. 7. Degradation of DNA in E. coli in the presence of mitomycin, or mitomycin + chloramphenicol ●——●; control o——o. Increase in stability of DNA in the presence of Mg^{2+}, $1.6 \cdot 10^{-3}$ m. [78]

many cases mutants have been isolated which are sensitive to both UV and alkylating agents, other types of mutants do not show this correlation. On the other hand, organisms which are unable to repair UV damage can repair damage induced by alkylating agents or X-rays [48—50].

Several mutants have been found with cross-resistance to X-rays and monofunctional alkylating agents (for summary see Ref. [58]). Since a depurination after alkylation of purine bases can occur directly without enzymes, thus leaving single strand breaks, the 3-step excision repair might then operate without the initial steps of recognition and incision as well as after X irradiation.

It is obvious that different enzymes are involved in the initial stages of repair. Consistent with this conclusion are the following observations: Nucleases have been found in bacterial extracts with specificity for alkylation-induced damage, which do not attack UV treated DNA containing pyrimidine dimers [51]. Thus mitomycin and alkylating agents will become helpful as tools to differentiate the enzymes of recognition and to elucidate the initial steps of DNA repair replication.

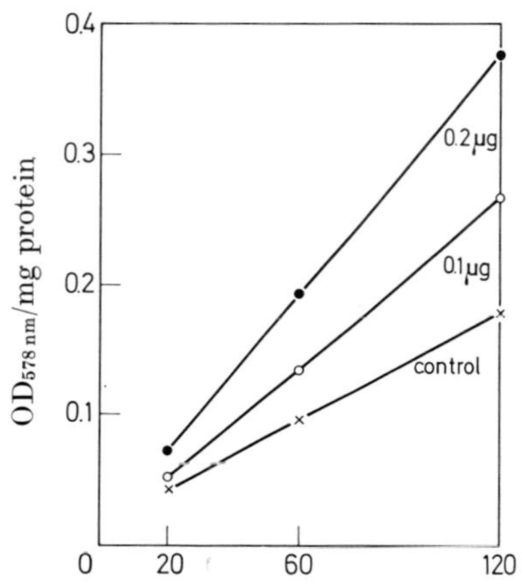

Fig. 8. Increased activity of a DNAase in E. coli upon treatment with mitomycin A (KERSTEN et al., Ref. [54]). Concentration of mitomycin A in µg/ml culture

Excision repair is always accompanied by a degradation of DNA which is most extensive in the presence of chloramphenicol [52]. This now explains our earlier findings [53] that in mitomycin treated E. coli, DNA becomes partially degraded, and that this degradation is enhanced by chloramphenicol (Fig. 7). The increased activity of a DNAase in E. coli, observed upon treatment with mitomycin (Fig. 8), might be an endonuclease involved in the as yet unknown initiation steps of repair [54].

In addition to excision repair, another mechanism has been proposed to control DNA replication. In an excision defective strain of E. coli K_{12} (UVr A6) the frequency of recombination is enhanced by UV. DNA containing several dimers can be replicated without excision. A schematic representation of this repair is shown in Fig. 9. Both strands of the DNA contain damaged bases. During replication a gap is left at these points. It is apparent that the region containing a gap in one daughter strand is intact in the sister strand. It is assumed that the free ends at the gap induce a sister exchange, so that the correct base is inserted into the gap opposite the damage. It is evident that a following step of replication and sister exchange results in the formation of intact DNA [55].

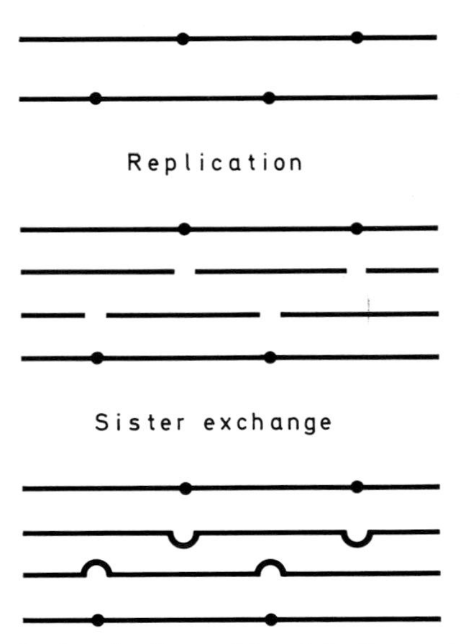

Fig. 9. Repair mechanism in the excision defective mutant strain E. coli K_{12} UVr A6 with increased frequency in recombination after UV irradiation (HOWARD-FLANDERS et al., Ref. [55])

For detailed information on DNA replication and repair see Ref. [56—59].

The usefulness of mitomycin in studies on the replication of DNA is not restricted to the repair replication of DNA. We want to discuss briefly the effect of mitomycin on the synthesis of bacterial and episomal DNA, including viral DNA. Several investigators have presented evidence that viral or episomal DNA can be produced in the presence of the inhibitor, that the viral DNA is stable, and that in many cases, however, the viruses were not infective [60—65]. No explanation has been found for the striking phenomenon of differential sensitivity of host versus virus DNA.

A defective phage PBSX of B. subtilis was obtained by induction with mitomycin [66, 67]. Upon treatment of the bacteria with mitomycin, phage coat protein is synthesized in the absence of synthesis of phage DNA. As long as the phage protein is made, the DNA of the host becomes degraded to subunits of homogeneous size, probably by action of a phage specific DNAase. The degraded DNA of the host is then packed into phage specific protein, thus producing morphologically recognizable phage particles, which can be placed taxonomically between bacteriocins and bacteriophages. These particles are defective in two aspects: they fail to inject their DNA and lack phage specific DNA. These observations show that "phage particles" can originate in the absence of the synthesis of DNA.

The Molecular Mechanism by which Different Functional Groups of the Mitomycins Interfere with Cell Metabolism

To avoid the misuse of inhibitors, the following questions should be considered: 1. Does the inhibitor interfere with only one or with several steps of cell metabolism ? 2. What are the functional groups involved in the inhibition of a biological process ? Mitomycin again is a good example for discussion of these problems.

In addition to its effect on "DNA": DNA-synthesis, DNA breakdown, increase in activity of DNAase and DNA-polymerase (see Fig. 10 and review Ref. [36]), the inhibitor can affect the synthesis of RNA [68, 69], and can cause a breakdown of RNA and ribosomes [70, 71], and an increase in RNAase activity [72]. Thus more than one active site of the molecule might function in different biochemical processes. It must be questioned whether the reductive step is necessary to exhibit biological activity of mitomycins.

Derivatives of mitomycin, lacking the aziridine ring — for example, see the compound shown in the *Appendix* — are still active inhibitors of the growth of microorganisms and animal cells including tumors [73]. The quinone ring and/or the methylurethane side chain might play a role in the function of the molecule. If the methylurethane side chain and the substituent at the 7-position of the quinone ring were involved in crosslinking of DNA, this derivative should behave like mitomycin after reduction in vitro. When DNA after reaction with mitomycin in the presence of a reducing agent is denatured by heat, it renatures easily upon cooling because the two cross-linked strands do not separate [19]. Native and denatured DNA can be distinguished by their buoyant density in CsCl. As is shown in Fig. 11, the mitomycin treated DNA

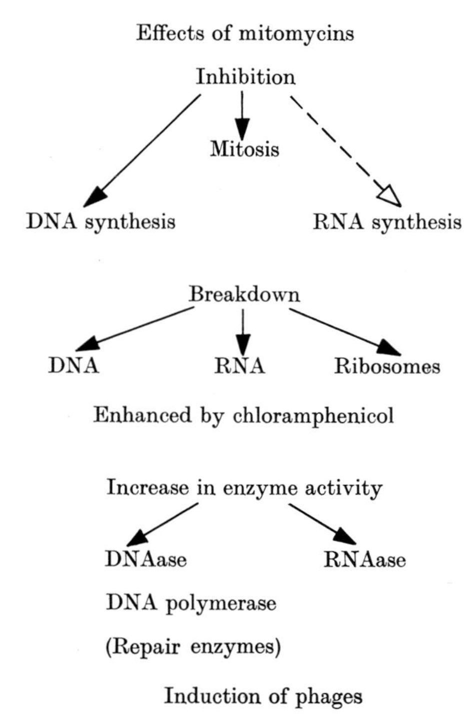

Fig. 10. Biological events following treatment of microorganisms with mitomycin antibiotics

renatures easily and bands closely to the native DNA. DNA exposed to the derivative remains denatured, indicating that the derivative has no cross-linking properties.

However, like mitomycin, the derivative also affects nucleic acid synthesis in microorganisms (Fig. 12). In contrast to mitomycin the derivative preferentially inhibits the synthesis of RNA. Both substances have only little effect on protein synthesis. The quinone ring, or the methylurethane side chain, or both, could be responsible for the inhibitory effect. What are the functional groups involved?

Comparative studies were performed using the quinones of quite different structures, for example, the quinone-antibiotic granaticin (see *Appendix*), the structure of which has recently been

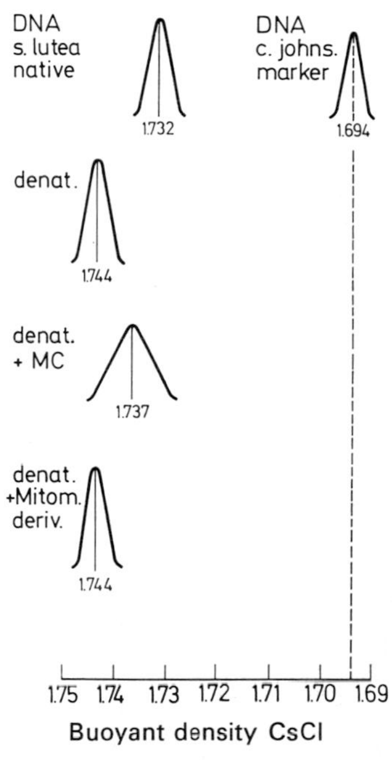

Fig. 11. The ability of heated DNA to renature after treatment with mitomycin or mitomycin derivatives in presence of a reducing agent. Native and denatured DNA are characterized by their buoyant density in CsCl

elucidated [74], and two aminoquinones, kindly supplied by Bayer, Leverkusen. The different quinones exhibit the same effect on nucleic acid synthesis as the mitomycin-derivative. At concentrations which totally inhibit RNA synthesis, the synthesis of DNA is decreased to about 50%, whereas protein synthesis is only slightly affected (Fig. 13). Thus the quinone ring in the mitomycins also functions as an inhibitor of nucleic acid synthesis. To see whether quinones preferentially affect the synthesis of a certain type of RNA, sRNA, 16 S rRNA and 23 S rRNA were separated by chromatography, and the incorporation of ^{3}H-uridine into the different RNA fractions was measured. RNA was isolated from B. subtilis treated with different concentrations of granaticin (see

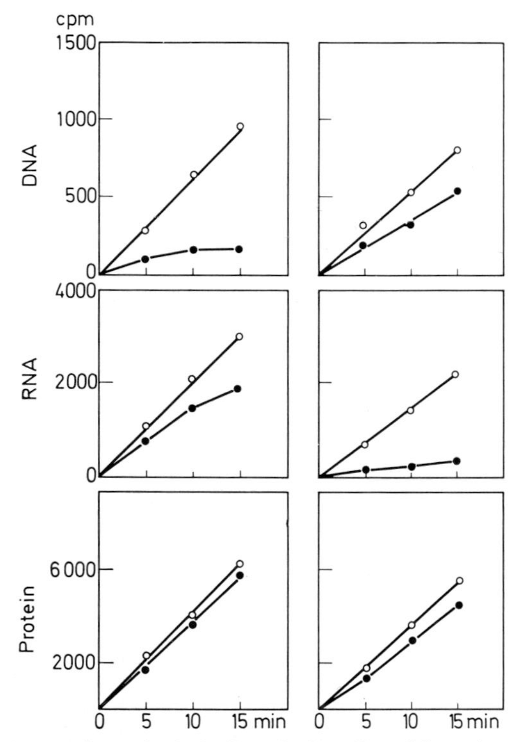

Fig. 12. Nucleic acid synthesis in B. subtilis affected by mitomycin C (left) and by the derivative missing one of the proposed alkylating sites, the aziridine ring (right). Controls: o——o

Fig. 14). The results of these experiments show that the synthesis of all types of RNA is inhibited to the same extent.

Inhibition of RNA synthesis by quinones including mitomycin derivatives is accompanied by a decrease in intracellular RNAase-activity (Fig. 15). Upon treatment of B. subtilis with mitomycin, the opposite effect was observed (Fig. 16). The activation of RNAase needs the presence of the aziridine ring system. We have found that the degradation of RNA and ribosomes is also dependent on this functional group in the molecule.

The mechanism by which the quinones (mitomycin derivatives, granaticin, and the synthetic aminoquinones) interfere with nucleic acid metabolism is not yet known. Since the aminonaphthoquinone antibiotic streptonigrin interacts with DNA, we

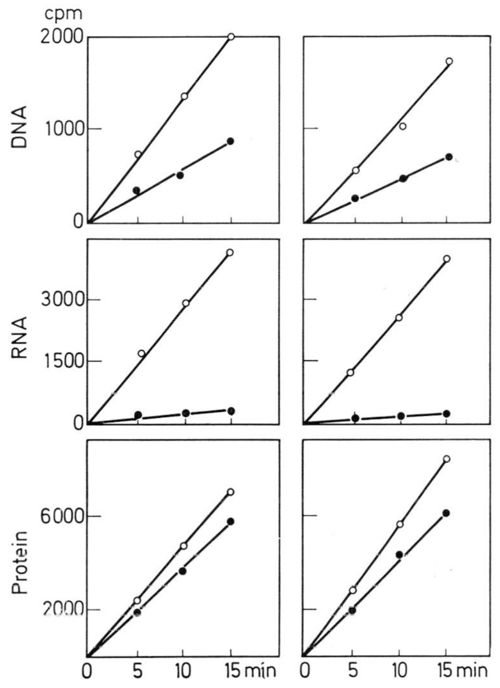

Fig. 13. Nucleic acid synthesis in B. subtilis affected by granaticin, $0.6 \cdot 10^{-3}$ μMoles/ml (left), and aminoquinone, $2.3 \cdot 10^{-3}$ μMoles/ml (right). Controls: o——o

have studied the physico-chemical properties and the transforming activity of DNA from quinone treated B. subtilis. No changes have been found until now. However, we cannot exclude the possibility that in quinone treated cells radicals are formed. The radicals might affect the pyrimidine bases of DNA in analogy to the X-ray induced damage of the pyrimidines. Damage of pyrimidine bases by X-rays is markedly depressed in the presence of cystein. The inhibitory effect of granaticin on growth and nucleic acid synthesis can also be reversed by cystein, not by reducing agents. A second possibility to explain the inhibitory effect of quinones on nucleic acid synthesis is that the quinones interfere with the phosphorylation of the precursors. A quite different mechanism might be responsible for the effect of quinones: during

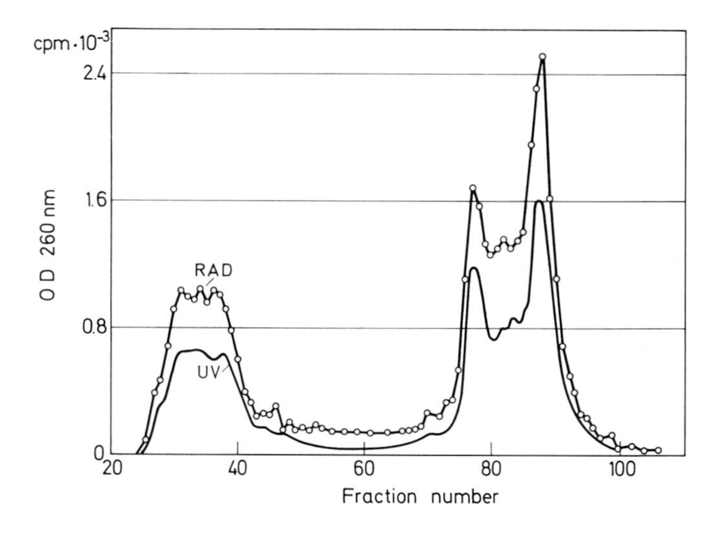

µg/ml	RNA	cpm / OD		%
Granaticin	4/5 S	16 S	23 S	Inhibition
0	1548	1607	1569	
0.1	1423	1278	1280	10 - 20
0.2	948	891	875	40-45
0.3	102	92	87	90-95

Fig. 14. The effect of granaticin on the synthesis of sRNA, 16 S rRNA and 23 S rRNA in B. subtilis

replication and transcription of DNA the two strands must be separated. As has been recently pointed out by CAIRNS [75], an oxygen and energy requiring as yet unknown process is involved in the replication of DNA, which can be inhibited by carbonmonoxide or cyanide. The quinones as well might influence this step of DNA replication and perhaps also transcription.

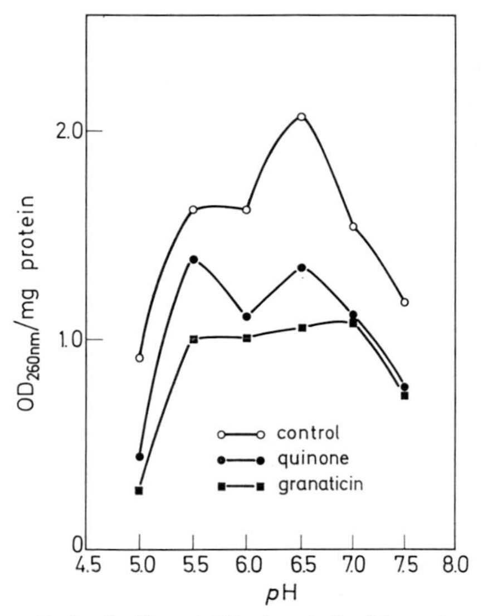

Fig. 15. RNAase-activity in B. subtilis treated with aminoquinone (2 μg/ml) or quinone antibiotic granaticin (3 μg/ml)

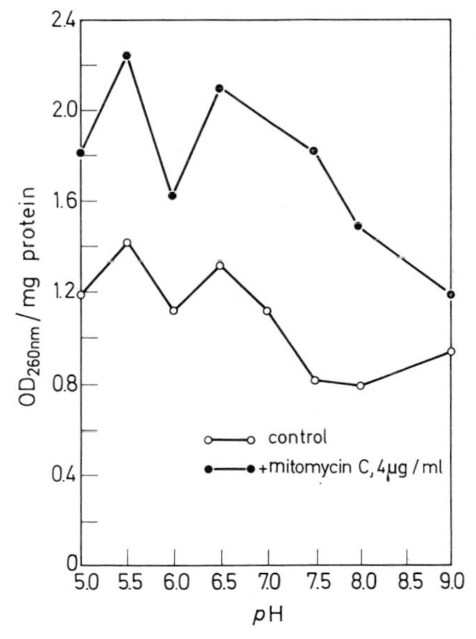

Fig. 16. RNAase-activity in B. subtilis treated with mitomycin

Conclusions

Inhibitors acting on DNA and DNA replication have been used to study a variety of biochemical processes, only few of which could be discussed here. We have attempted to select examples of more general interest.

1. The important discovery that DNA needs not be metabolically stable requires repair mechanisms in higher cells as well as in microorganisms. Mammalian cells are able to recover from treatment with alkylating agents [58]. Therefore, these substances provide useful tools to elucidate mechanisms of repair replication in higher organisms and to discover the enzymes which are involved.

2. Another point concerning the alkylating agents should be stressed. Tumors from different sources have been found to respond differently to alkylating agents or mitomycins. This can be explained by a difference in the ability of the tumor cell to repair damaged DNA.

3. The striking phenomenon that mitomycin can induce the synthesis of phage specific protein, and that the DNA of the host can be degraded and incorporated into phage-like particles provides an exciting new aspect on the possible origin of episomal DNA, including virus particles.

4. Further studies on the mechanism of action of mitomycin revealed that the inhibitory effect on nucleic acid synthesis must not be caused by alkylation and crosslinking of the DNA. The quinone ring in mitomycins might also play a role in the inhibitory effect on nucleic acid synthesis.

Several inhibitors, including quinones, are used as drugs. Recently, aminoquinones [76, 77] have been shown to be active against several experimental tumors and less toxic than ethyleneiminoquinones. Detailed studies on the molecular mode of action of these inhibitors will help to avoid their misuse in medicine as well as in biological research.

References

1. Michaelis, L.: Cold Spr. Harb. Symp. quant. Biol. **12**, 131 (1947).
2. Parker, F. S., and J. L. Irvin: J. biol. Chem. **199**, 897 (1952).
3. Watson, J. D., and F. H. C. Crick: Nature (Lond.) **171**, 377 (1953).
4. Lerman, L.: Proc. nat. Acad. Sci. (Wash.) **49**, 94 (1963).

5. PRITCHARD, N. J., A. BLAKE, and A. R. PEACOCKE: Nature (Lond.) **212**, 1360 (1966).
6. KIRK, J. M.: Biochim. biophys. Acta (Amst.) **42**, 167 (1960).
7. KAWAMATA, J., and M. IMANISHI: Nature (Lond.) **187**, 1112 (1960).
8. KERSTEN, W., H. KERSTEN, and H. M. RAUEN: Nature (Lond.) **187**, 60 (1960).
9. — Biochim. biophys. Acta (Amst.) **47**, 610 (1961).
10. REICH, E., and I. H. GOLDBERG: Review in: Progress in nucleic acid research III, p. 184. New York: Academic Press 1964.
11. KERSTEN, W., u. H. KERSTEN: 6. Konferenz der Gesellschaft für Biologische Chemie. Hoppe Seylers Z. physiol. Chem. **349**, 953 (1968).
12. BLAKE, A., and A. R. PEACOCKE: Biopolymers **6**, 1225 (1968).
13. HARTMANN, G., W. BEHR, K. A. BEISSNER, K. HONIKEL und A. SIPPEL: Angew. Chem. **18**, 710 (1968).
14. WARING, M.: Nature (Lond.) **219**, 1320 (1968).
15. GOTTLIEB, D., and P. D. SHAW: Antibiotics I, mechanisms of action. Berlin-Heidelberg-New York: Springer 1968.
16. CRICK, F. H. C., L. BARNETT, S. BRENNER, and R. J. WATTS-TOBIN: Nature (Lond.) **192**, 1227 (1961).
17. KERSTEN, W., H. KERSTEN, F. E. STEINER und B. EMMERICH: Hoppe-Seylers Z. physiol. Chem. **348**, 1415 (1967).
18. SCHOLTISSEK, CH.: Biochim. biophys. Acta (Amst.) **103**, 146 (1965).
19. KERSTEN, W., u. H. KERSTEN: Biochem. Z. **341**, 174 (1965).
20. HARTMANN, G., H. GOLLER, K. KOSCHEL, W. KERSTEN und H. KERSTEN: Biochem. Z. **341**, 126 (1964).
21. O'BRIEN, J. G., J. G. OLENICK, and F. E. HAHN: Proc. nat. Acad. Sci. (Wash.) **55**, 1511 (1966).
22. CIAK, J., and F. E. HAHN: Science **151**, 347 (1966).
23. WARING, M. I.: Biochim. biophys. Acta (Amst.) **87**, 358 (1964).
24. SENTENAC, A., A. RUET, et P. FROMAGEOT: Bull. Soc. Chim. biol. (Paris) **49**, 247 (1967).
25. BROOKES, P., and P. D. LAWLEY: Biochem. J. **80**, 496 (1962).
26. LORKIEWITZ, Z., and W. SZYBALSKI: J. Bact. **82**, 195 (1961).
27. IYER, V. N., and W. SZYBALSKI: Proc. nat. Acad. Sci. (Wash.) **50**, 355 (1963).
28. TANAKA, N., H. YAMAGUCHI, and H. UMEZAWA: Biochem. biophys. Res. Commun. **10**, 171 (1963).
29. FALASCHI, A., and A. KORNBERG: Fed. Proc. **23**, 940 (1964).
30. TERAWAKI, A., and J. GREENBERG: Biochim. biophys. Acta (Amst.) **119** (1966).
31. LEVINE, M., and M. BOTHWICK: Virology **21**, 568 (1963).
32. ROSENKRANZ, H. S., A. J. GARRO, J. A. LEVY, and S. CARR: Biochim. biophys. Acta (Amst.) **114**, 501 (1966).
33. GOSS, W., W. REITZ, and T. COOK: J. Bact. **89**, 1068 (1965).
34. PIETSCH, P., and H. GARRET: Nature (Lond.) **219**, 488 (1968).
35. —, and C. CORBERT: Nature (Lond.) **219**, 933 (1968).

36. SZYBALSKI, W., and V. N. IYER: In: Antibiotics I, mechanism of action, p. 211. GOTTLIEB, D., and P. SHAW, Eds. Berlin-Heidelberg-New York: Springer 1967.
37. LAWLEY, P. D., and P. BROOKES: J. molec. Biol. **25**, 143 (1967).
38. LIPPSETT, M., and A. WEISSBACH: Biochemistry **4**, 206 (1965).
39. WHITE, J. R., and H. L. WHITE: J. Flisha Mitshell Scient. Soc. **81**, 37 (1965).
40. SZYBALSKI, W.: J. Ark. med. Soc. **66**, 488 (1966).
41. BEUKERS, R., and W. BERENDS: Biochim. biophys. Acta (Amst.) **41**, 550 (1960).
42. WACKER, A.: Rev. Progr. nucl. acid res. mol. biol. **1**, 369 (1963).
43. KAPLAN, H.: Proc. nat. Acad. Sci. (Wash.) **55**, 1442 (1966).
44. MCGRATH, R., and R. WILLIAMS: Nature (Lond.) **212**, 534 (1966).
45. REITER, H., and B. STRAUSS: J. molec. Biol. **14**, 179 (1965).
46. HANAWALT, P., and R. HAYES: Biochem. biophys. Res. Commun. **19**, 462 (1965).
47. LAWLEY, P., and P. BROOKES: Nature (Lond.) **206**, 480 (1965).
48. SETLOW, R., and W. CARRIER: J. molec. Biol. **17**, 237 (1966).
49. BOYCE, R., and P. HOWARD-FLANDERS: Proc. nat. Acad. Sci. (Wash.) **51**, 293 (1964).
50. KOHN, K. W., N. H. STEIGBIGEL, and C. L. SPEARS: Proc. nat. Acad. Sci. (Wash.) **53**, 1154 (1965).
51. STRAUSS, B. S., and M. RUBBINS: Biochim. biophys. Acta (Amst.) **161**, 68 (1968).
52. PAPIRMEISTER, B., and C. L. DAVISON: Biochem. biophys. Res. Commun. **17**, 608 (1964).
53. KERSTEN, H.: Z. physiol. Chem. **329**, 31 (1962).
54. —, B. SCHNIEDERS, G. LEOPOLD, and W. KERSTEN: Biochim. biophys. Acta (Amst.) **108**, 619 (1965).
55. HOWARD-FLANDERS, P., W. D. RUPP, and B. M. WILKINS: In: Replication and recombination of the genetic material, p. 142. PEACOCKE, W. J., and R. D. BROCK, Eds., Canberra: Australian Acad. Science 1968.
56. — Ann. Rev. Biochem. **37**, 173 (1968).
57. HANAWALT, P. C.: In: Photophysiology, Vol. IV, 203. New York: Academic Press 1968.
58. STRAUSS, B. S.: Curr. Top. Microbiol. Immunol. **44**, 1 (1968).
59. SETLOW, R. B.: Progr. nucl. Acid Res. **8**, 257 (1968).
60. OTSUJI, N.: Biken's J. **5**, 9 (1962).
61. SEKIGUSHI, M., and Y. TAKAGI: Nature (Lond.) **183**, 1134 (1959).
62. BEN-PORAT, T., M. REISSIG, and A. S. KAPLAN: Nature (Lond.) **190**, 33 (1961).
63. MAGEE, W. E., and O. V. MILLER: Biochim. biophys. Acta (Amst.) **55**, 818 (1962).
64. MUNK, K., u. B. SAUER: Z. Naturforsch. **20 b**, 671 (1965).
65. COOPER, S., and N. D. ZINDER: Virology **18**, 405 (1962).

66. OKAMOTO, K., J. MUDD, J. MANGAN, W. M. HUANG, T. V. SUBBAIAH, and J. MARMUR: J. molec. Biol. **34**, 143 (1968).
67. — — — J. molec. Biol. **34**, 429 (1968).
68. SMITH-KIELAND, J.: Biochim. biophys. Acta (Amst.) **119**, 486 (1966).
69. KERSTEN, H., W. KERSTEN, G. LEOPOLD, and B. SCHNIEDERS: Biochim. biophys. Acta (Amst.) **80**, 521 (1964).
70. SUZUKI, H., and W. W. KILGOORE: Science **146**, 1585 (1964).
71. KERSTEN, W., and H. KERSTEN: FEBS Meeting, Oslo 1967, Abstract 285.
72. BUDDE, H.: Dissertation, Münster 1967.
73. UZU, K., M. SHIMUZU, S. WAKAKI, H. ENDO, and M. MATSUI: Intern. Congr. Biochem. Japan 1967.
74. KELLER-SCHIERLEIN, W., M. BUFFRANI u. S. BASCZA: Helv. chim. Acta **51**, 1257 (1968).
75. CAIRNS, J., and D. T. DENHARDT: J. molec. Biol. **36**, 335 (1968).
76. PETERSEN, S., W. GAUSS, H. KIEHNE u. L. JÜHLING: Z. Krebsforsch. **72**, 162 (1969).
77. GRUNDMANN, E., L. JÜHLING, J. PÜTTER u. H. J. SEIDEL: Z. Krebsforsch. **72**, 185 (1969).
78. KERSTEN, H., u. W. KERSTEN: Z. physiol. Chem. **334**, 141 (1963).

Structure and Function of DNA-dependent RNA-Polymerase

W. SEIFERT and W. ZILLIG

Max-Planck-Institut für Biochemie, München

With 5 Figures

RNA-Polymerase = enzyme of transcription in vivo:

The *transcription of the genetic information* of the DNA-base-sequences into RNA-structure is performed by the *DNA-dependent RNA-polymerase* [1, 2]. This enzyme has been highly purified from E. coli [3]. It catalyses the synthesis of RNA in vitro in the presence of a DNA-template and the 4 ribonucleoside-triphosphates. The requirements for the reaction are shown in the first figure (Fig. 1).

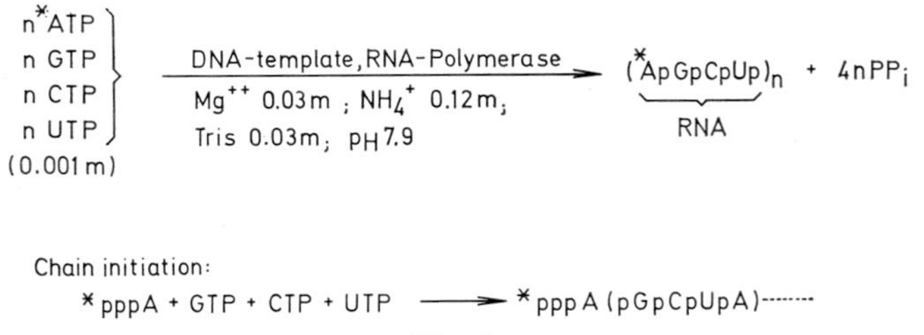

$$\left.\begin{array}{l} n\,{}^{*}ATP \\ n\ GTP \\ n\ CTP \\ n\ UTP \end{array}\right\} \xrightarrow[\substack{Mg^{++}\ 0.03\,m;\ NH_4^+\ 0.12\,m; \\ Tris\ 0.03\,m;\ pH\ 7.9}]{\text{DNA-template, RNA-Polymerase}} \underbrace{({}^{*}ApGpCpUp)_n}_{RNA} + 4n\,PP_i$$

(0.001 m)

Chain initiation:

$$^{*}pppA + GTP + CTP + UTP \longrightarrow {}^{*}pppA\,(pGpCpUpA)\cdots\cdots$$

Fig. 1

Pulse-label experiments have shown that the RNA-chains are growing 5′ to 3′ [4].

It should be emphasized that DNA-dependent RNA-polymerase is not an "ordinary enzyme" — in the sense that its catalytic action is not the most interesting problem, but rather its *specificity of binding to special sites on the DNA and of initiating RNA-synthesis* at the starting signal of an operon and terminating it at the end of this operon. This is shown in the Figs. 2 and 5.

At least for E. coli there is much evidence for a *single enzyme* which synthesizes all types of RNA (ribosomal-, transfer- and messenger-RNA) and for the identity of the purified RNA-polymerase with the *enzyme of the transcription process in vivo:*

The comparison of the RNA-products by DNA-RNA-hybridization experiments has shown that the *transcription of DNA is asymmetric* under proper conditions in vitro as it is in vivo: only one strand of native double-stranded DNA is transcribed [5].

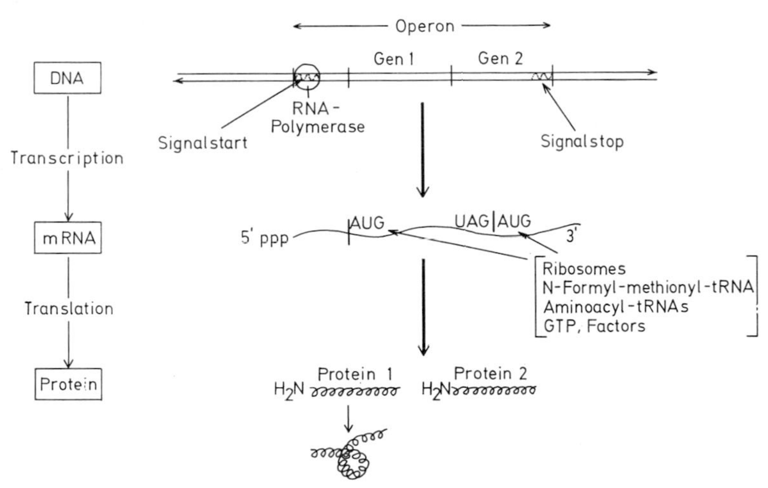

Fig. 2. Outline of DNA-dependent protein synthesis

The transcription is *highly specific,* since on T_4- and on λ-DNA only certain regions (the early genes) are copied by E. coli-polymerase in vitro as in vivo [6].

Another argument for *only one enzyme* comes from the use of *Rifamycin* which blocks bacterial RNA-synthesis in vivo (^{14}C-incorpor.) and is a strong inhibitor of RNA-polymerase in vitro. A rifamycin-resistant mutant has an altered RNA-polymerase [7].

On the other hand it is known [8] that the *synthesis of the different RNA's in the cell are under different control-mechanisms.* This phenomenon has to be explained not by the existence of different RNA-polymerases but by *factors* which change the function of the fundamental enzyme in a specific way or which block specific DNA-template regions as in the case of the repressor-control of messenger-RNA-synthesis.

We will first discuss the structure of the enzyme, then the different steps of its function and finally some problems of its regulation.

Structure of RNA-Polymerase

I. Purification

The enzyme can be purified from E. coli cell homogenates by centrifugation (because of its large molecular weight), DEAE-cellulose-chromatography, ammonium sulfate precipitation and suc-

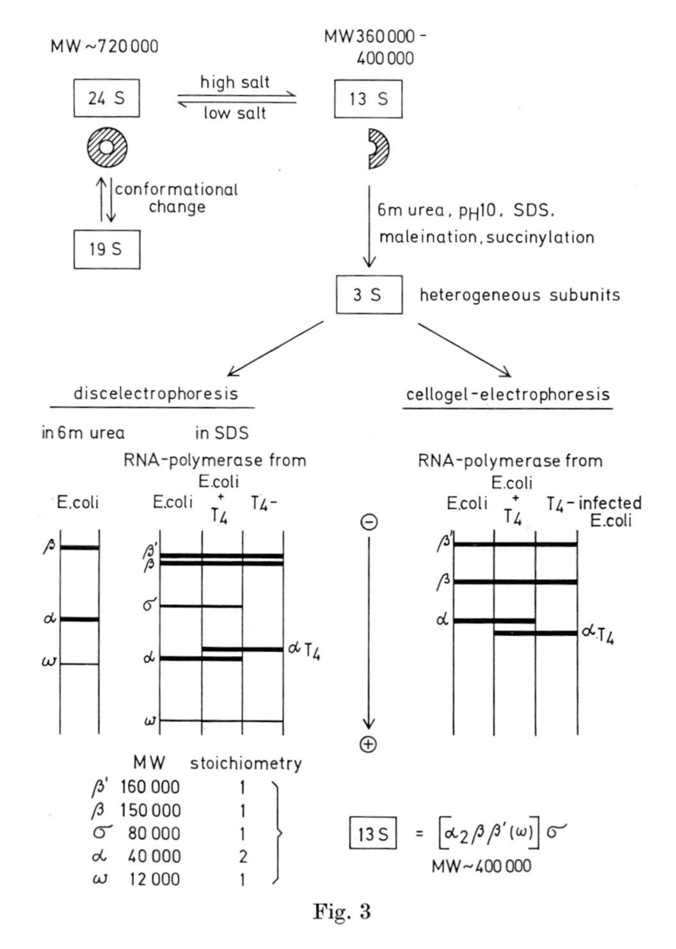

Fig. 3

rose gradient centrifugation at low salt (as 24S-particle) and at high salt (as 13S-particle) [3]. But we will not discuss the purification procedures in detail.

Purification can be followed by disc-electrophoresis: the highly purified enzyme shows only two main bands (α and β) in 6 m urea-(pH 10)-disc-electrophoresis.

The structural features of RNA-polymerase are outlined in the scheme on p. 34 (Fig. 3).

II. Subunits

24S- and 13S-form

The 13S-form of RNA-polymerase reversibly aggregates at low ionic strength to 24S and at very low ionic strength to a small amount of higher aggregates. Between 0.1 and 0.2 ionic strength (test conditions), 13S- and 24S-form are in a rapid equilibrium and can therefore not be separated by centrifugation [9]. NEUHOFF has separated in his micro-disc-electrophoresis technique three different enzymatically active forms of RNA-polymerase which he attributes to 24S-, 18S- and 13S-form [10].

Although binding to DNA and enzymatic activity is optimal at medium salt concentration, where both 13S- and 24S-form are existent, some evidence has been presented which appears to be in favor of the 13S-form as *active particle*. But this question is still open for discussion.

This problem might be solved by high resolution *electron-microscopy*. In the EM the RNA-polymerase shows a ringlike structure at low salt (24S), and it is tempting to think of the DNA-template as going through the hole of this ring — an idea which also appears thermodynamically reasonable. But EM-pictures of the DNA-bound enzyme do not show any details.

3S-Subunits

By using 6 m urea or pH 10 or after maleination and succinylation or treatment with detergent like SDS, the 13S-enzyme can be dissociated into different subunits which are separated by disc-electrophoresis on polyacrylamide gel, or by electrophoresis on cellogel [11].

Similar results were obtained by BURGESS in Watson's laboratory. He separated $\beta\beta'$ from α on urea-sephadex-columns and determined molecular weights and amino acid composition [12]. ZILLIG succeeded in separating β and β' and α on cellogel in preparative amounts so that amino acid composition, endgroup-analysis and fingerprints will now be performed.

III. Function of Subunits

A very important question besides the protein chemistry of the subunits is their different function in the complex reaction of RNA-polymerase, but little is known about this.

Only for the *σ-subunit* it seems rather clear by the work of BURGESS [12] that it is engaged in the initiation but not in the synthesis of RNA.

By chromatography on phosphocellulose he separated the σ-unit from the rest of the RNA-polymerase (which he calls PC-enzyme or minimal enzyme) and could stimulate RNA-synthesis on T_4-DNA by adding σ-factor to the minimal enzyme, which alone is rather inactive on this template. Moreover, he showed that in the complex with minimal enzyme, σ acts catalytically in the initiation of RNA-chains (pppA and pppG-termini) and is released from the enzyme-DNA-complex after use.

Thus the function of this subunit seems to be established. On the other hand, TOCCHINI-VALENTINI has shown that in a rifamycin-resistant RNA-polymerase it is the minimal enzyme ($\alpha_2\beta\beta'$) which is altered, and not the σ-subunit, — although rifamycin is known to block the initiation reaction of RNA-polymerase [7]. Therefore it may be sometimes difficult to attribute detailed steps of the RNA-synthesis-reaction to the separated subunits which in the active complex work in close interaction with each other.

The β-subunits might be involved in the binding to DNA [12]. The binding site for the four substrates has not been identified on the subunits. More work in this direction is necessary to establish the functional role of the different subunits.

In *T_4-infected E. coli* we have found an RNA-polymerase which lacks the σ-subunit and shows a modified α-subunit in the disc-electrophoresis and a modified β-subunit in the immunochemical analysis. The low activity of this enzyme on T_4-DNA compared to normal E. coli-polymerase may be due to one of these modifications [13].

We have shown that this *T_4-polymerase is blocked in the initiation reaction on T_4-DNA* [14] — this may be the consequence of the lost σ-subunit. On the other hand, and in contrast to the results of Bautz and Dunn [15], we could not stimulate this T_4-polymerase by addition of E. coli-σ-factor significantly, probably because the modified α-subunit does not allow the formation of a complex with normal σ [14].

The fact that the σ-band is not found on cellogel-electrophoreses and that an E. coli-polymerase antiserum which has been preabsorbed with the σ-free T_4-polymerase shows no reaction with the σ-containing E. coli-polymerase may give some evidence for the possibility that σ is not a different protein subunit but rather a dimer of α. This would agree with its molecular weight [16].

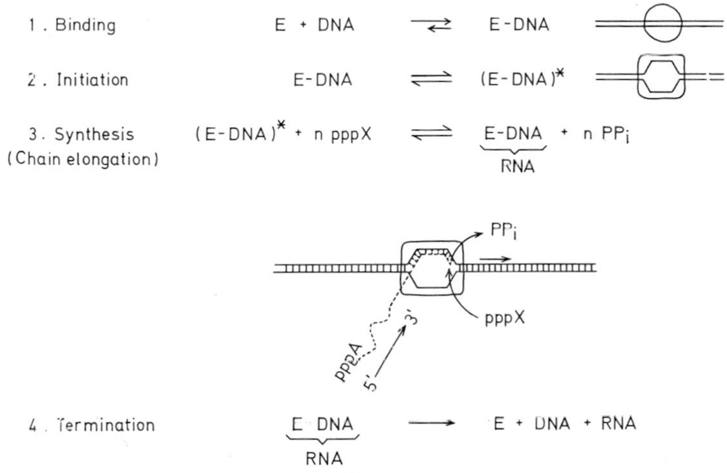

1. Binding $\quad E + DNA \rightleftharpoons E\text{-}DNA$

2. Initiation $\quad E\text{-}DNA \rightleftharpoons (E\text{-}DNA)^*$

3. Synthesis (Chain elongation) $\quad (E\text{-}DNA)^* + n\,pppX \rightleftharpoons \underbrace{E\text{-}DNA}_{RNA} + n\,PP_i$

PPi
pppX
pppA
3'
5'

4. Termination $\quad \underbrace{E\text{-}DNA}_{RNA} \longrightarrow E + DNA + RNA$

Fig. 4

Function of RNA-Polymerase

The different steps in the overall reaction of RNA-synthesis are shown schematically in Fig. 4.

I. Binding

The binding of the RNA-polymerase molecules to specific binding sites on the DNA-template is a rapid and reversible reaction. The number of binding sites and their specificity can be determined by different methods, for example by sucrose gradient centrifugation, or by a membrane filter technique in which the RNA-polymerase-DNA-complex sticks to the filter, or simply from DNA-saturation curves, which show great difference between different DNA's [17]. Thus the specificity and number of binding sites depends on the DNA-template.

Evidence that different RNA-polymerases bind to different specific binding sites on the same DNA is still lacking, except in the case of T_4-early-late-gene regulation.

On T_4-DNA we have counted about 100 binding sites for E. coli-polymerase (24S), that means 1 polymerase-molecule per 2000 nucleotide pairs, which would be in the order of the expected number of genes on the T_4-genome [16].

A possible source of error are strand breaks, free ends or denaturated single stranded regions where RNA-polymerase binds even better than to its specific binding sites on native DNA. Therefore the quality of the isolated DNA is crucial in such experiments.

The binding reaction is inhibited by competing polyanions as *heparin or transfer-RNA* which bind to the enzyme and also by *proflavin* which is known to intercalate in the DNA and which largely reduces the apparent number of binding sites [17].

The important problem of the *structure of these specific binding sites* on a certain DNA and their recognition by RNA-polymerase is not yet solved. It is even unknown if they are recognized by a specific secondary structure or by methylation signals or simply by their specific base sequence. The most direct approach should be the isolation of the start signals and the termination signals on the DNA as well-defined oligonucleotides.

New hybridization techniques combined with the use of deletion mutants might solve this problem, if a small DNA consisting of one or only some operons could be isolated.

Quite recently KAMEYAMA reported [18] the isolation and characterization of the DNA-regions bound to E. coli-polymerase by DNase digestion of an RNA-polymerase-DNA-complex. Although it is difficult to present unequivocal evidence that these bound oligonucleotides are really the specific binding regions and not unspecifically bound and protected pieces of the DNase digest, and although in view of the reversibility of the polymerase binding such a protection against DNase is hard to understand, some arguments are in favor of the interpretation of the authors.

There is accumulating evidence that the *promotor-region* — a genetic element besides the operator — corresponds to the *binding site or initiation site of RNA-polymerase.* Promotor mutants show a low level of RNA-synthesis and, as a consequence, low levels of all enzymes controlled by this operon [19].

II. Initiation

The next step — which topographically occurs probably at the same binding site — is the *initiation reaction*, in which the σ-subunit is engaged (possible by guiding the RNA-polymerase to the correct binding sites for initiation). This appears to be a rather complex reaction, which consists at least of two subsequent steps.

a) Lag-Phase

In the model for RNA-synthesis a local strand separation of the DNA appears necessary in order to fit the nucleoside triphosphates to their complementary bases on the codogenic strand. The *lag-phase of the RNA-synthesis* appears below 17 °C, is dependent on temperature and ionic strength, is independent of substrate- and enzyme-concentration and is not observed with single-stranded DNA as template. These facts were interpreted by WALTER et al. as a consequence of this local melting process [20].

Since this lag-phase disappears with E. coli-polymerase above 17 °C but with Bacillus stearothermophilus-polymerase [21] only above 35 °C and with another temperature coefficient for the length of the lag-phase, it is not simply a property of this DNA-region. This indicates that the enzyme is directly involved in this activation reaction, possibly by a conformational change.

b) Purine-Endgroup

A second event of initiation was analyzed by ANTHONY, WU, and GOLDTHWAIT [22]. They have shown that *the binding of the first purine nucleoside triphosphate* (pppA for calf-thymus-DNA and pppG for Micrococcus lysodeikticus-DNA) requires a higher concentration of substrate than the following polymerization reaction (for which the apparant K_m is 10 times less than for the ATP or GTP in the initiation reaction).

c) Number and Kinetics of Initiation

The kinetics of initiation and the number of initiation sites can be followed by simply adding only 3 labelled TPs (^3H or ^{32}P labelled including the initiating purine) to DNA and enzyme, which then can synthesize only short pieces of RNA and stays firmly bound to the DNA. The complex sticks to membrane filters and is counted. At 37 °C this initiation reaction takes about 2 min for E. coli polymerase [14]. Similar results were obtained with another technique involving the use of heparin, a polyanion which inhibits free and DNA-bound RNA-polymerase but not the synthesizing enzyme [16].

d) Inhibitors

One *heparin*-molecule binds to one 13S-enzyme-molecule, probably to the binding site for the DNA, and therefore blocks initiation. *Rifamycin* is another inhibitor for the initiation reaction, which acts very similar to heparin in spite of its quite different chemical structure.

III. Synthesis

RNA-chains are synthesized from 5′- to 3′-end. The transcription of the DNA is asymmetric. Strand *selection* probably occurs during initiation. Therefore the polymerase must recognize some polarity of the initiation site. This problem is of particular interest, since in the case of λ- and T_4-DNA there occurs a strand-switch in the time pattern of gene-activity on these DNA's. The early genes are copied from one strand, while the late genes are copied from the other strand of the double-stranded DNA [23]. Therefore, this strand switch may be important for the control of gene transcription.

The synthesis of RNA is accompanied by a *translocation* of the RNA-polymerase along the DNA-template, a process which is not at all understood in molecular terms.

Actinomycin, an inhibitor which binds to the guanosine-residues of the DNA, blocks the synthesis of RNA by inhibiting this translocation.

The model shows a hybrid DNA-RNA-region, which is suggested only by the work of HAYASHI [24].

^{32}P-exchange between pyrophosphate and nucleoside-triphosphate has been observed and may be explained by the following reaction scheme:

$$\begin{gathered}\text{pppA-RNA-(DNA-E)} + {}^*\text{pppX} \\ \downarrow \\ \text{pppA-RNA-(DNA-E)} \sim \text{pX} + {}^*\text{PP}_i \\ \downarrow \\ \text{pppA-RNA-pX-(DNA-E)}\end{gathered}$$

The first step is reversible, while the second step is irreversible.

IV. Termination

Nothing is known about the termination of the RNA-chains, which should occur at the end of each operon. In contrast to the initiation, there is even no genetic evidence for special termination signals on the DNA, which must exist, however, analogous to the termination signals on the messenger-RNA for protein synthesis.

In vitro, long RNA-chains are synthesized at higher salt, they are released and can serve as messengers for protein synthesis in a cell-free system.

V. Salt Influence

The influence of salt-concentration on RNA-synthesis in vitro has been analysed in detail in our laboratory [25]. At low salt, a plateau is reached after a reaction time of about 40 min at 37 °C. Bremer and Konrad [26] have shown that in this plateau the enzyme molecules are still fixed to the DNA and have not liberated their RNA-chains.

The arrest of the enzyme is due to an endproduct-inhibition by the synthesized RNA-chain [27] — probably at the strand-exchange-site in the active complex —, and may be overcome by an increase of the ionic strength. Polyamines like spermidine and divalent cations show the same effect [25].

The most interesting aspect of this phenomenon which is only observed with double-stranded DNA, is the possibility for regulating the rate of RNA-synthesis. It is not known whether this mechanism is used in vivo. It is more probable that *in vivo* ribosomes attached to the growing RNA-chains play this regulatory role.

REVEL and GROS [28] have shown that the *stimulation of RNA-synthesis by ribosomes* is mediated by a special *Factor C* for the attachment of the 30S-ribosomal subunit to the mRNA. This mechanism probably explains the coupling of translation with transcription in protein synthesis [29].

The rate of RNA-synthesis in vitro is under optimal conditions in the range of the in vivo synthesis, that means *20 to 50 nucleotides* are synthesized per chain per sec.

Regulation of Transcription

Different possibilities exist for the control of RNA synthesis in the living cell. We must differentiate between the regulation of the rates of the formation of different classes of RNA (mRNA, rRNA, tRNA) and the specific regulation of certain messenger-RNA species.

I. Negative Control by Repressors (Fig. 5)

The regulation of single messenger RNA's is mediated by specific *repressors*. The RNA-polymerase binds and initiates at the

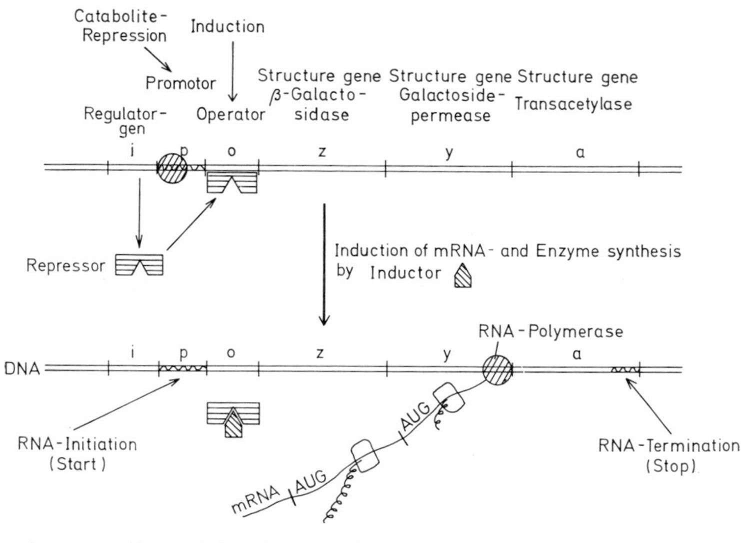

Fig. 5. Transcription of the Lac-Operon (E. coli)

promotor region of an operon (promotor-mutants show highly reduced levels of RNA synthesis), while the repressor binds to the *operator* region besides the promotor and therefore blocks the synthesis of RNA by the enzyme. Since the *lac-repressor* has been isolated, this mechanism can be studied in vitro [30].

II. Positive Control by Initiation Factors

A strong coupling between protein synthesis (aminoacid-requirement) and RNA-synthesis exists in stringent E. coli-strains, whereas in "*relaxed*" *strains* this interaction is released and in the absence of protein synthesis RNA-synthesis continues. It has been shown that this regulation concerns only the *stable RNA's* — that is ribosomal- and transfer-RNA —, while messenger RNA (as shown by hybridization for the tryptophane-synthetase-messenger) is not concerned [31]. This shows different control mechanisms.

Since there is no evidence for different E. coli-RNA-polymerases, and since in most polymerization reactions (compare: DNA-synthesis or protein synthesis) the *initiation reaction* is the crucial point and the rate-limiting step where regulation mechanisms might intervene, it is reasonable to suggest different initiation signals on the DNA for the different types of RNA and correspondingly different factors for initiation in the cell.

This kind of regulation may be important also in differentiation processes of higher cells where groups of genes must be activated or inactivated.

A model in this sense may be the *T_4-phage* where for the transcription of late genes not only newly synthesized progeny-DNA is necessary but also the *gene 55-product* [32] which might be a *new σ-factor* necessary for the modified T_4-polymerase to read the late genes. A similar example of positive control is found in the control mechanisms of *λ-phage* development.

III. Control by Modification of RNA-Polymerase

Another way of regulating RNA-synthesis is shown by the *modification of the E. coli-RNA-polymerase after T_4-phage infection.* We could demonstrate structural modifications of the different subunits [13], which inactivate the enzyme for the transcription of the early genes of T_4-DNA (which are copied by normal

E. coli-polymerase), but may be necessary to switch on the transcription of late genes.

This reaction is preceded by a very rapid process which needs no protein synthesis (chloramphenicol-experiments) but results in a specific change of template activity of the polymerase. The altered enzyme shows no chemical difference as compared to E. coli polymerase, but may be altered by a conformational change. This alteration of the polymerase might be responsible for the block of E. coli-gene-transcription after T_4-phage-infection [13].

These altered and modified RNA-polymerases in the T_4-infected E. coli-cell demonstrate another type of regulation which is not mediated by repressors as in the Jacob-Monod-model, but by structural changes of the transcribing enzyme itself.

Outlook

The outline of the transcription process and of the structure and function of RNA-polymerase is known, but we are far from understanding the molecular details of this complex process. New methods — especially physicochemical techniques — are necessary for the elucidation of the elementary steps.

I. Genetics

Another approach should come from the *genetics of the RNA-polymerase and of the initiation and termination signals on the DNA. Operator- and promotor-mutants* are already well-known for some operons. *Mutants of RNA-polymerase* have been isolated only recently by the use of streptomycin and rifamycin for selection. Khesin [33] isolated a temperature-sensitive polymerase and located it between the streptomycin-resistance-marker and the thymine-marker on the genetic map of E. coli.

Tocchini-Valentini has shown that the genetic marker for his rifamycin-resistant minimal-enzyme maps on the E. coli-genome close to the Arginine-H marker [7].

Therefore the genes for the α- and β-subunits (minimal enzyme) appear to be located at another place than possibly the gene for the heat-labile σ-subunit. Such mutants should prove very useful for the elucidation of the function of the different polymerase-subunits.

II. Comparison Between Different Species

Most studies on RNA-polymerase were done with the enzyme from E. coli. But in view of the template-specificity and the recognition of different initiation sites on the DNA the comparison of RNA-polymerases from other and higher organisms should be very interesting. Polymerases from the bluegreen-alga Anacystis [34] and from Bacillus stearothermophilus [21] showed very similar properties in structure and function as compared to the E. coli enzyme. Mammalian RNA-polymerase is of particular interest, but only recently a sufficient purification of free enzyme from the chromatin-complex was obtained [35].

The low activity of these mammalian enzymes (about 1000 fold lower than that of E. coli-enzyme) may be a property of the polymerase itself or may be due to the loss of an initiation factor during purification. Nothing is known until now about their subunit structure and their initiation sites on different DNA's.

RNA-polymerase is one of the most essential enzymes for all living cells and its functional aspects must have been conserved during evolution while other regulatory properties — as its sensitivity to special control mechanisms — may have changed. Therefore, detailed comparative analysis of enzymes from very different organisms is of great interest.

References

1. Volkin, E., and L. Astrachan: Virology **2**, 433 (1956).
Gros, F., and W. Gilbert: Nature (Lond.) **190**, 581 (1961).
Brenner, S., F. Jacob, and M. Meselson: Nature (Lond.) **190**, 576 (1961).
2. Weiss, S. B.: Proc. nuc. Acid. Res. **46**, 1020 (1960).
Furth, J. J., J. Hurwitz, and M. Goldman: Biochem. biophys. Res. Commun. **4**, 362 (1961).
3. Chamberlin, M., and P. Berg: Proc. nuc. Acid. Res. **48**, 81 (1962).
Fuchs, E., W. Zillig, P. H. Hofschneider, and A. Preuss: J. molec. Biol. **10**, 546 (1964).
Zillig, W., E. Fuchs, and R. L. Millette: Proc. nuc. Acid Res. **1**, 323 (1967).
4. Bremer, H., M. W. Konrad, K. Gaines, and G. S. Stent: J. molec. Biol. **13**, 540 (1965).
5. Hayashi, M., M. N. Hayashi, and S. Spiegelman: Proc. nuc. Acid. Res. **51**, 351 (1964).
Green, M.: Proc. nuc. Acid. Res. **52**, 1388 (1964).

6. Khesin, R. B.: Biokhimiya **27**, 1092 (1962).
Geiduschek, E. P., and L. Snyder: J. molec. Biol. **19**, 541 (1966).
Naono, S., and F. Gros: Cold Spr. Harb. Symp. **31**, 363 (1966).
Cohen, S. N., U. Maitra, and J. Hurwitz: J. molec. Biol. **26**, 19 (1967).
7. Tocchini-Valentini, G. P., P. Marino, and A. J. Colvill: Nature (Lond.) **220**, 275 (1968).
— (in press).
8. Maaløe, O., and N. O. Kjieldgaard: Control of macromolecular synthesis. New York: Benjamin 1966.
9. Priess, H., and W. Zillig: Biochim. biophys. Acta (Amst.) **140**, 540 (1967).
Zillig, W., E. Fuchs, G. Walter, R. L. Millette, and H. Priess: In: The bioch. of virus replic, p. 37. Oslo 1968.
10. Neuhoff, V., W.-B. Schill und H. Sternbach: Hoppe-Seylers Z. physiol. Chem. **349**, 1126 (1968).
— (in press).
11. Palm, P., E. Fuchs, and W. Zillig: (in press).
12. Burgess, R. R.: Pers. communications.
—, A. A. Travers, J. J. Dunn, and E. K. F. Bautz: Nature (Lond.) **221**, 43 (1969).
13. Walter, G., W. Seifert, and W. Zillig: Biochem. biophys. Res. Commun. **30**, 240 (1968).
Seifert, W., P. Qasba, P. Palm, M. Schachner, and W. Zillig: Europ. J. Biochem. **9**, 319 (1969).
14. Seifert, W.: Unpublished results.
15. Bautz, E. K. F., and J. J. Dunn: Biochem. biophys. Res. Commun. **34**, 230 (1969).
16. Zillig, W.: Unpublished results.
17. Richardson, J. P.: J. molec. Biol. **21**, 83 (1966).
Jones, O. W., and P. Berg: J. molec. Biol. **22**, 199 (1966).
18. Matsukage, A., S. Murakami, and T. Kameyama: Biochim. biophys. Acta (Amst.) **179**, 145 (1969).
19. Beckwith, J.: Meeting on molecular genetics. Köln 1969.
20. Walter, G., W. Zillig, P. Palm, and E. Fuchs: Europ. J. Biochem. **3**, 194 (1967).
21. Remold-O'Donnell, E., and W. Zillig: Europ. J. Biochem. **7**, 318 (1969).
22. Anthony, D. D., C. W. Wu, and D. A. Goldthwait: Biochemistry 8, 246 (1969).
23. Guha, A., and W. Szybalski: Virology **34**, 608 (1968).
24. Hayashi, M. N., and M. Hayashi: Proc. nat. Acad. Sci. (Wash.) **55**, 635 (1966).
25. Fuchs, E., R. L. Millette, W. Zillig, and G. Walter: Europ. J. Biochem. **3**, 189 (1967).
26. Bremer, H., and M. W. Konrad: Proc. nat. Acad. Sci. (Wash.) **51**, 801 (1964).
27. Krakow, J. S.: J. biol. Chem. **241**, 1830 (1966).

28. Revel, M., and F. Gros: Biochem. biophys. Res. Commun. **27**, 12 (1967).
29. Stent, G. S.: Science **144**, 816 (1964).
30. Müller-Hill, B., L. Crapo, and W. Gilbert: Proc. nat. Acad. Sci. (Wash.) **59**, 1259 (1968).
31. Forchhammer, J., and N. O. Kjieldgaard: J. molec. Biol. **37**, 245 (1968).
Edlin, G., G. S. Stent, and R. F. Baker: J. molec. Biol. **37**, 257 (1968).
Yanofski, C.: J. molec. Biol. **37**, 257 (1968).
32. Snyder, L., and E. P. Geiduschek: Proc. nat. Acad. Sci. (Wash.) **59**, 459 (1968).
33. Khesin, R. B.: Molec. gen. Genet. **103**, 194 (1968).
34. Helm, K. v. d., u. W. Zillig: Hoppe-Seylers Z. physiol. Chem. **348**, 902 (1967).
35. Mertelsmann, R., and H. Matthaei: Biochem. biophys. Res. Commun. **33**, 136 (1968).
Helm, K. v. d.: Pers. comm.
Sekeris, C. E.: Pers. comm.
36. Kerjean, P., J. Marchetti, et J. Szulmajster: Bull. Soc. Chim. biol. (Paris) **49**, 1139 (1967).

Inhibitors of the RNA Polymerase Reaction

U. Lill, R. Santo, A. Sippel, and G. Hartmann

Institut für Biochemie der Universität, Würzburg

With 4 Figures

Introduction

Recent experiments have shown that the DNA directed RNA polymerase is involved in the biosynthesis of all classes of cellular RNA [1—4]. A specific inhibition of this enzyme should reveal its importance for the operation of certain metabolic chains in the cell. Therefore it is not surprising that inhibitors of transcription have been used extensively in biological and biochemical research. Numerous efficient inhibitors are known. During the recent years the mode of action of many of the inhibitors has been elucidated. According to these studies the inhibitors may be divided into three classes (Fig. 1).

Compounds of one class act as substrate analogues or antimetabolites. Their chemical structures are closely related to those of ribonucleoside triphosphates, the substrates of RNA polymerase.

Other compounds exert their influence as inactivators of the template which directs the course of RNA synthesis.

Finally, some inhibitors act as specific poisons of the catalytic activity of the enzymic protein itself.

Since bivalent metal ions are required for the reaction, chelating agents also block RNA biosynthesis. In vivo, however, chelating agents cannot be used as specific inhibitors, since many cellular reactions are metal ion dependent and would be blocked simultaneously.

1. Substrate Analogues

A well known example of antimetabolites suppressing the RNA polymerase reaction is cordycepin triphosphate [5]. This nucleotide is used by RNA polymerase as analogue of ATP. It is incorporated into the growing RNA chain since it contains the nucleoside 5′-phosphate group activated by pyrophosphate and, in addition, the 2′-hydroxyl group, which is important for the recognition as substrate by the enzyme. On the other hand, cordycepin triphosphate lacks the nucleophilic 3′-hydroxyl group in the sugar moiety, which would be required for the condensation of the next

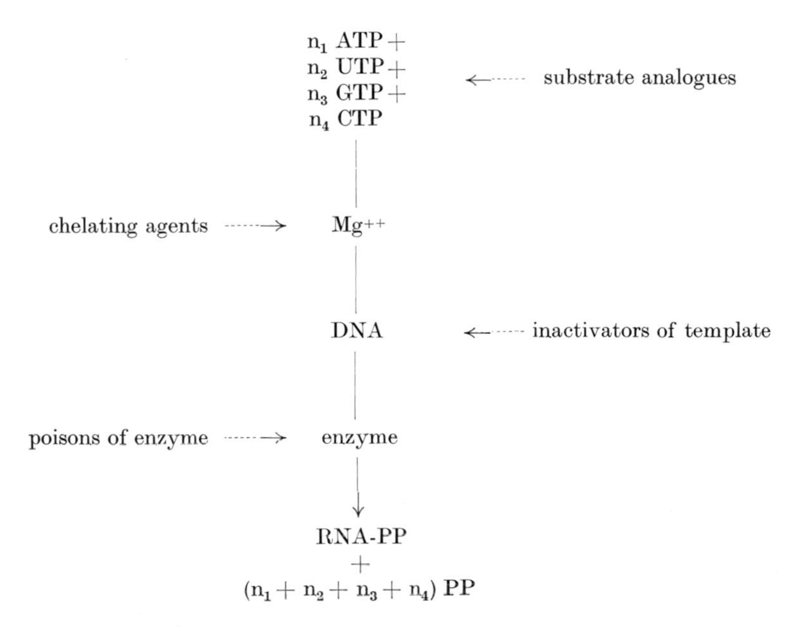

Fig. 1. Types of inhibitors of RNA polymerase

nucleotide. Consequently, RNA chain growth is immediately terminated after incorporation of the cordycepin nucleotide and cannot be continued [6, 7]. This inhibitory substrate analogue seems to be a very promising agent for the study of chain initiation and termination by RNA polymerase [8, 9]. The same mode of action has been found in vivo for the nucleoside cordycepin. After uptake by the cell the nucleoside is first phosphorylated to the corresponding triphosphate [10] and, subsequently, blocks the synthesis of cellular RNA [11].

In vivo, however, the specificity of inhibitory action on RNA biosynthesis of analogues of nucleotides is considerably impaired by their side effects on other nucleotide dependent reactions in the cell.

2. Inactivators of the Template

Compounds blocking the biological function of the template are much more specific in their inhibitory action, since the number

Table 1. *Inhibition of the RNA polymerase reaction by inactivators of the template*
The data are taken from [12], [13] and [14]

Inhibitor	Concentration required for 50% inhibition ($M \cdot 10^5$)
Synthetic materials:	
proflavin sulfate	6
ethidium bromide	0.6
Anthracylines:	
ruticulomycin A	0.5
nogalamycin	0.5
cinerubin A and B	1
daunomycin	3
isoquinocyclin	4
echinomycin	0.3
olivomycin	0.2
mithramycin	0.2
actinomycin	0.03
chromomycin A_3	0.03

of template dependent enzymic reactions in the cell is more limited. In addition to some synthetic compounds such as proflavin sulfate [12] or ethidium bromide [13], many antibiotics belong to this class of inhibitors (Table 1). All of them form rather strong complexes with nucleic acids.

The large group of anthracyclines and related antibiotics, however, are less specific in their reaction with the template than are the actinomycins and chromomycins. The latter require a certain chemical composition and secondary structure of the nucleic acid for association and inhibitory action [14].

The general mode of action of this class of inhibitors is based on their physical interaction with the template. Probably the complex of the inhibitor with the template blocks the movement of RNA polymerase along the DNA during the reaction. The enzyme is not able to overcome the barrier. Consequently, the process of polycondensation is interrupted (Fig. 2). MÜLLER and CROTHERS have pointed out that this kind of inhibitory action should not be permanent as long as the inhibitor is not covalently

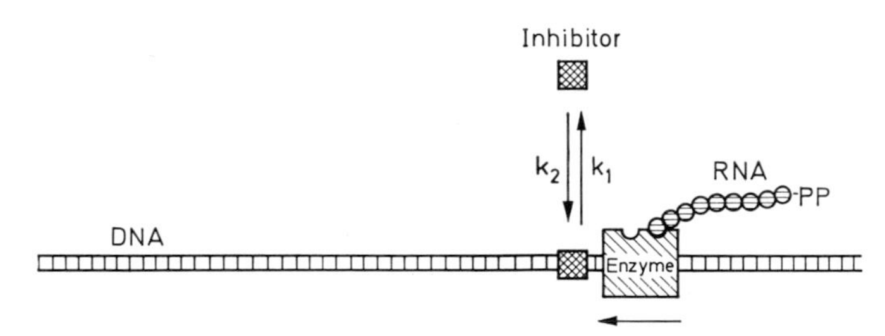

Fig. 2. Mode of action of an inactivator of the template

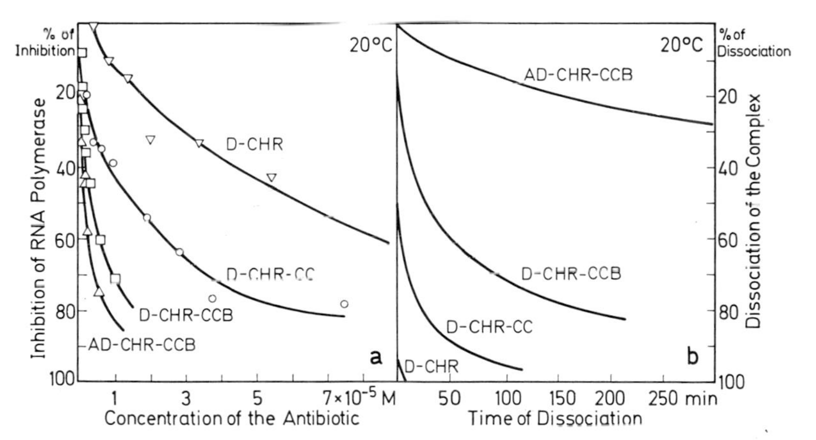

Fig. 3a and b. Dissociation rate of the complex of chromomycin with DNA and its inhibitory action. a The incubation mixture (total volume 0.25 ml) contained $5 \cdot 10^{-2}$ M Tris-HCl pH 7.9, $8 \cdot 10^{-3}$ M $MgCl_2$, $2 \cdot 10^{-3}$ M $MnCl_2$; $1.1 \cdot 10^{-3}$ M salmon sperm DNA, $6 \cdot 10^{-4}$ M of each GTP, CTP and UTP, $4 \cdot 10^{-4}$ M (^{14}C) ATP, 13 μg partially purified E. coli RNA polymerase; after 15 min incubation at 20° the radioactivity incorporated into the acid insoluble material was determined [incorporation without inhibitor = 0% inhibition: 1 nmole (^{14}C) AMP]. b These data are taken from [16]

bound to the template [15]. In the course of dynamic equilibrium the complex will dissociate repeatedly into free template and inhibitor. Hereupon catalysis of the polycondensation along the template is resumed by the enzyme. If this hypothesis is correct, then the slower the complex with the template dissociates, the more potent should the inhibitor be. This has been confirmed with chromomycin and its derivatives [16]. These antibiotics are composed of chromomycinone and two side chains containing varying numbers of sugar residues [17; see Appendix]. They all associate with DNA. The dissociation rate of the complexes increases in the order of decreasing size of the sugar side chains. For instance, the complex with chromomycin A_3, which contains five sugar residues, dissociates with the slowest rate, the complex with the compound D-CHR, which has lost all sugar residues except one, decomposes with the highest rate (Fig. 3b) [16]. In accordance with the hypothesis, chromomycin A_3 is the most active and the compound D-CHR the least active inhibitor of the RNA polymerase reaction (Fig. 3a).

3. Poisons of RNA Polymerase

The most specific attack on the RNA polymerase reaction can be achieved by poisoning the enzymic activity itself. In the laboratory of Zillig it has been observed that trace amounts of the blood anticoagulant heparin block the activity of RNA polymerase [18, 19]. Other template dependent reactions, such as DNA polymerase, are not considerably affected even by a concentration of $0.5 \cdot 10^{-5}$ M [20].

Very specific inhibitors of bacterial polymerases are antibiotics which belong to the class of rifamycins and streptovaricins [21—23]. By chemical modification of the naturally occurring rifamycin B, the Research Laboratories of Lepetit, Milan, and of Ciba, Basle, succeeded in obtaining much more potent derivatives [24, 25], such as rifampicin. DNA polymerase is not affected even by a concentration which is four orders of magnitude higher than that needed for a 50% inhibition of RNA polymerase. This behaviour is in complete contrast to that of antibiotics which interfere with the function of DNA as template [14]. Rifampicin acts very species-specific on DNA directed RNA polymerase isolated from different sources. Whereas bacterial RNA polymerase from E. coli [21, 26], M. luteus [27], B. subtilis [49] or B. stearothermophilus [28] are strongly inhibited, the same enzyme from rat liver [29] or Ehrlich ascites cells [30, 31] is not blocked at all. On the other hand, the activity of RNA polymerase from the bluegreen algae Anacystis nidulans is reduced to only 50% even by very high concentrations of rifampicin [54]. Doubtless, such species-specific inhibitors are very promising as tools in biological investigations [48—50].

Of great interest is the question why mammalian and bacterial RNA polymerases differ so much in their sensitivity towards rifampicin. The general properties of these enzymes are rather similar [32, 33]. On the other hand, even bacterial RNA polymerases frequently become resistant to rifamycins (and, simultaneously, against streptovaricins) by mutation of a genetic locus, as has been shown for enzyme preparations from mutants of E. coli [1, 2, 34—36, 53] and of M. luteus [27]. Very important for the interpretation of these results is the observation of WEHRLI, KNÜSEL, SCHMID and STAEHELIN, that rifampicin forms a strong complex with RNA polymerase from sensitive strains. There is no association with the enzyme from a rifampicin resistant strain [37]. These observations indicate an association of the antibiotic with specific sites of the enzyme. Obviously, substitution of single amino acids in the enzymic protein by genetic mutation leads to a loss of binding capacity for rifampicin. Simultaneously, the sensitivity of the enzyme for the inhibitor has disappeared. This leads to the conclusion that the binding of rifampicin to the protein has to be related to the inhibition of enzymic activity.

In 1967 we have observed that the enzymic activity of a complex of RNA polymerase with DNA and substrates is not blocked by addition of rifampicin [51]. Hence the question arises if the presence of substrate and template prevents the association of the inhibitor with the enzyme. NEUHOFF, SCHILL and STERNBACH have found by disc electrophoresis and diffusion technique, that rifampicin does not prevent the reaction of the enzyme with the template [38]. We have used gel filtration as described by WEHRLI et al. [37] to study this problem. Our investigations showed that the amount of rifampicin bound by the complex of enzyme with template and substrate is comparable to that bound by free enzyme (Table 2).

Apparently the binding of inhibitor and of template and substrate to RNA polymerase are largely independent of each other. The next question concerns the behaviour of the inhibiting action

Table 2. *Binding of rifampicin to RNA polymerase in the absence or presence of template and substrate*

These experiments were performed with slight modifications as described in [37]; 1 mg of partially purified E. coli RNA polymerase, 1 μmole salmon sperm DNA and 0.15 μmoles of each UTP, ATP and GTP were used

	Reaction of [^{14}C]-rifampicin with		
	Enzyme	Enzyme followed by addition of DNA and NuTP	Enzyme *in the presence* of DNA and NuTP
Rifampicin bound to RNA polymerase (nmoles/mg protein)	0.13	0.13	0.12
Enzymic activity of the protein after reaction with rifampicin	inactive	inactive	active

of rifampicin. Will we find non-competition with respect to template and substrate as has been observed for the binding? In that case the enzyme after reaction with the inhibitor should be inactive regardless of a prior incubation with template and substrate.

This has not been found. On the contrary, the complex of enzyme, template and substrate — although it binds almost as much inhibitor as free enzyme — retains a considerable enzymic activity. In a control experiment where free enzyme had reacted with the same amount of rifampicin almost all activity was abolished. These experiments clearly show that the association of the inhibitor with RNA polymerase does not cause inactivation in every case.

Several interpretations are possible for these results. We prefer as explanation of the inhibitory action of rifampicin its effect as a modifier of the protein. Under certain conditions the antibiotic may prevent by its attachment to the protein some conformational changes of the enzyme which are required for catalytic activity at the start of the reaction. If this hypothesis is correct, one should expect that factors which change the properties of the protein should strongly influence the inhibitory action of bound rifampicin.

It is well known that the reaction with the template alters the properties of the enzyme [39, 40]. This change occurs rather slowly at low temperatures and depends on the origin of the enzyme [18, 28]. Our hypothesis requires that the sensitivity of the enzyme for bound rifampicin is altered with a similar rate as the enzymic properties during the reaction with DNA and Mg^{++}. Indeed, this expected change in sensitivity has been observed (Fig. 4). Ribonucleoside triphosphates increase the magnitude of the effect, but do not change the rate of desensitization significantly (Fig. 4).

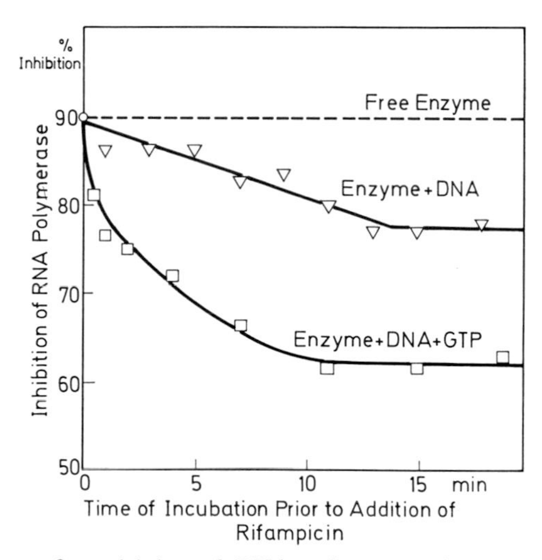

Fig. 4. Decrease of sensitivity of RNA polymerase for rifampicin during reaction with salmon sperm DNA. The incubation mixture (total volume before addition of inhibitor 0.15 to 0.17 ml) contained $3.6 \cdot 10^{-2}$ M Tris-HCl pH 7.8, $1.1 \cdot 10^{-2}$ M $MgCl_2$, $3 \cdot 10^{-3}$ M $MnCl_2$, 81 μg partially purified E. coli RNA polymerase; in the experiments with DNA: $2.8 \cdot 10^{-3}$ M salmon sperm DNA; in the experiment with DNA and GTP: $2.8 \cdot 10^{-3}$ M DNA and $1 \cdot 10^{-3}$ M GTP; this mixture was incubated at 17° for the time indicated on the abscissa; subsequently 0.4 μg rifampicin and 0.15 μmoles of each ATP, UTP, GTP (if not present in the incubation mixture) and 0.1 μmole (^{14}C) CTP were added (total volume after these additions 0.25 ml); after further incubation for 15 min at 27° the radioactivity incorporated into the acid insoluble material was determined [incorporation without rifampicin = 0% inhibition = 1 nmole (^{14}C) CMP]

High ionic strength alters the properties of the enzyme, such as molecular weight [41—43]. On the other hand, the interaction of the enzyme with rifampicin is not affected by high salt concentrations [37]. Nevertheless, the action of enzyme bound inhibitor should depend on the ionic strength according to our hypothesis. Indeed, the inhibitory action of rifampicin on the enzyme, which had previously reacted with template and substrate, is different at low and high salt concentrations. The inhibition is considerably increased in the presence of 0.4 M KCl (Table 3).

Although these observations are consistent with the notion that rifampicin acts as a modifier and interferes with alterations

Table 3. *Effect of ionic strength on the inhibition of RNA polymerase by rifampicin in the presence of DNA and substrate*

The incubation mixture contained 0.1 M Tris-HCl pH 7.9 (in the experiments with KCl: 0.1 M Tris HCl pH 7.9 containing 0.4 M KCl), $1.6 \cdot 10^{-2}$ M $MgCl_2$, $4 \cdot 10^{-3}$ M $MnCl_2$, $1.2 \cdot 10^{-3}$ M of each GTP, ATP and UTP, $2.3 \cdot 10^{-3}$ M salmon sperm DNA, 22 μg partially purified E. coli RNA polymerase and was incubated for 6 min at 37°; subsequently 0.5 μg rifampicin was added and the mixture incubated for 1 min at 37°; hereupon 0.1 μmoles (^{14}C) GTP and 50 μmoles KCl (if not yet present in the incubation mixture) were added (total volume after these additions 0.25 ml). After 10 min incubation at 37° the radioactivity incorporated into the acid insoluble material was determined

	Nucleotide incorporation (cpm)	
	− 0.4 M KCl	+ 0.4 M KCl
− Rifampicin	4806	5357
+ Rifampicin	2133	585
Percent inhibition	56%	89%

of the enzyme necessary for catalytic activity at the start of the reaction, the hypothesis is still far from being proved. It helps to understand the existence of various RNA polymerases with different sensitivity for the action of rifampicin. The same modifier may affect genetically different enzymes — even with exactly the same catalytic activity — to a different extent.

The explanation outlined here is reminiscent of that discussed for the mode of action of streptomycin. This antibiotic, by attaching to one of the ribosomal proteins of the 30 S ribosome [44], can cause misreading of mRNA during protein synthesis [45]. The inhibitory action of the bound streptomycin varies markedly with the Mg^{++} concentration [46]. It is reasonable to assume that certain functional activities of the ribosomal protein have been altered by the binding of the antibiotic. The effects produced are not necessarily inhibitory since ribosomes isolated from certain mutant strains require the attachment of streptomycin to become active [47]. Similar observations should be expected for RNA polymerase from rifampicin dependent bacterial strains.

Our own work described here has been generously supported by the Fonds der Chemischen Industrie and the Deutsche Forschungsgemeinschaft. Chromomycin A_3 and its derivatives were generously supplied by Takeda Chemical Industries, Ltd., Osaka, Japan. We are much indebted for a gift of rifampicin to Gruppo Lepetit, Milano, Italy.

References

1. Tocchini-Valentini, G., P. Marino, and A. Colvill: Nature (Lond.) **220**, 275 (1968).
2. Ezekiel, D., and J. Hutchins: Nature (Lond.) **220**, 276 (1968).
3. Lancini, G., R. Pallanza, and L. Silvestri: J. Bact. **97**, 761 (1969).
4. —, and G. Sartori: Experentia (Basel) **24**, 1105 (1968).
5. Guarino, A.: In: Gottlieb, D., and P. Shaw: Antibiotics, Vol. I, p. 468. Berlin-Heidelberg-New York: Springer 1967.
6. Shigeura, H., and G. Boxer: Biochem. biophys. Res. Commun. **17**, 758 (1964).
7. Klenow, H., and S. Frederiksen: Biochim. biophys. Acta (Amst.) **87**, 495 (1964).
8. Sentenac, A., E. Simon, and P. Fromageot: Biochim. biophys. Acta (Amst.) **161**, 299 (1968).
9. —, A. Ruet, and P. Fromageot: Europ. J. Biochem. **5**, 385 (1968).
10. Klenow, H.: Biochim. biophys. Acta (Amst.) **76**, 347 (1963).
11. Frederiksen, S., and H. Klenow: Biochem. biophys. Res. Commun. **17**, 165 (1964).
12. Hurwitz, J., J. Furth, M. Malamy, and M. Alexander: Proc. nat. Acad. Sci. (Wash.) **48**, 1222 (1962).
13. Waring, M.: Biochim. biophys. Acta (Amst.) **87**, 358 (1964).
14. Hartmann, G., W. Behr, K.-A. Beissner, K. Honikel und A. Sippel: Angew. Chem. **80**, 710 (1968); Angew. Chem. internat. Edit. **7**, 693 (1968).
15. Müller, W., and D. Crothers: J. molec. Biol. **35**, 251 (1968).
16. Behr, W., K. Honikel, and G. Hartmann: Europ. J. Biochem. **9**, 82, (1969).

17. BERLIN, Y., S. ESIPOV, M. KOLOSOV, and M. SHEMYAKIN: Tetrahedron Letters **1966**, 1643.
18. WALTER, G., W. ZILLIG, P. PALM, and E. FUCHS: Europ. J. Biochem. **3**, 194 (1967).
19. FUCHS, E., R. MILLETTE, W. ZILLIG, and G. WALTER: Europ. J. Biochem. **3**, 183 (1967).
20. HONIKEL, K., and G. HARTMANN: Unpublished results.
21. HARTMANN, G., K. HONIKEL, F. KNÜSEL, and J. NÜESCH: Biochim. biophys. Acta (Amst.) **145**, 843 (1967).
22. MIZUNO, S., H. YAMAZAKI, K. NITTA, and H. UMEZAWA: Biochem. biophysic. Res. Commun. **30**, 379 (1968).
23. WILHELM, J., N. OLEINICK, and J. CORCORAN: Biochim. biophys. Acta (Amst.) **166**, 268 (1968).
24. MAGGI, N., C. PASQUALUCCI, R. BALLOTTA, and P. SENSI: Chemotherapia (Basel) **11**, 285 (1966).
25. BICKEL, H., F. KNÜSEL, W. KUMP, and L. NEIPP: Antimicrobial Agents Chemotherapy **1966**, 352.
26. MIZUNO, S., H. YAMAZAKI, K. NITTA, and H. UMEZAWA: J. Antibiot. (Tokyo) Ser. A **21**, 66 (1968).
27. BOCK, L., and G. HARTMANN: Unpublished results; see BOCK, L., Diplomarbeit, Chemische Institute der Universität, Würzburg 1969.
28. REMOLD-O'DONNEL, E., and W. ZILLIG: Europ. J. Biochem. **7**, 318 (1969).
29. WEHRLI, W., J. NÜESCH, F. KNÜSEL, and M. STAEHELIN: Biochim. biophys. Acta (Amst.) **157**, 215 (1968).
30. UMEZAWA, H. S., H. YAMAZAKI, and K. NITTA: J. Antibiot. (Tokyo) Ser. A **21**, 234 (1968).
31. MIZUNO, S., H. YAMAZAKI, K. NITTA, and H. UMEZAWA: Biochim. biophys. Acta (Amst.) **157**, 322 (1968).
32. SEIFART, K., and C. SEKERIS: Europ. J. Biochem. **7**, 408 (1969).
33. CUNNINGHAM, D., S. CHO, and D. STEINER: Biochim. biophys. Acta (Amst.) **171**, 67 (1969).
34. WEHRLI, W., F. KNÜSEL, and M. STAEHELIN: Biochem. biophys. Res. Commun. **32**, 284 (1968).
35. BABINET, C., et H. CONDAMINE: C.R. Acad. Sci. (Paris) **267** D, 231 (1968).
36. NITTA, K., S. MIZUNO, H. YAMAZAKI, and H. UMEZAWA: J. Antibiot. (Tokyo) Ser. A **21**, 521 (1968).
37. WEHRLI, W., F. KNÜSEL, K. SCHMID, and M. STAEHELIN: Proc. nat. Acad. Sci. (Wash.) **61**, 667 (1968).
38. NEUHOFF, V., W.-B. SCHILL und H. STERNBACH: Hoppe-Seylers Z. physiol. Chem. **350**, 335 (1969).
39. KHESIN, R., O. ASTAUROVA, M. SHEMYAKIN, S. KAMZOLOVA, and V. MANYAKOV: Molekularnaja Biologia **1**, 736 (1967).
40. NOVAK, R., and P. DOTY: J. biol. Chem. **243**, 6068 (1968).
41. RICHARDSON, J.: J. molec. Biol. **21**, 83 (1966).
42. STEVENS, A., A. EMERY, and N. STERNBERGER: Biochem. biophysic. Res. Commun. **24**, 929 (1966).

43. Priess, H., and W. Zillig: Biochim. biophys. Acta (Amst.) **140**, 540 (1967).
44. Kaji, H., and Y. Tanaka: J. molec. Biol. **32**, 221 (1968).
45. Davies, J., D. Jones, and H. Khorana: J. molec. Biol. **18**, 48 (1966).
46. Luzzatto, L., D. Apirion, and D. Schlessinger: Proc. nat. Acad. Sci. (Wash.) **60**, 873 (1968).
47. Likover, T., and C. Kurland: J. molec. Biol. **25**, 497 (1967).
48. Fromageot, H., and N. Zinder: Proc. nat. Acad. Sci. (Wash.) **61**, 184 (1968).
49. Geiduschek, E., and J. Sklar: Nature (Lond.) **221**, 833 (1969).
50. Haselkorn, R., M. Vogel, and R. Brown: Nature (Lond.) **221**, 836 (1969).
51. Sippel, A., and G. Hartmann: Biochim. biophys. Acta (Amst.) **157**, 218 (1968).
52. Rinehart, K., jr., H. Mathur, K. Sasaki, P. Martin, and C. Coverdale: J. Amer. chem. Soc. **90**, 6241 (1968).
53. Yura, T., and K. Igarashi: Proc. nat. Acad. Sci. (Wash.) **61**, 1313 (1968).
54. von der Helm, K., and W. Zillig: Personal communication.

Interaction of RNA Polymerase with Rifamycin

M. Staehelin and W. Wehrli

Biological Laboratories of the Pharmaceutical Department of CIBA Limited, Basle, Switzerland

With 3 Figures

The rifamycins, together with the streptovaricins and tolypomycin form a novel class of antibiotics which have in common some structural features as well as the unique property of inhibiting specifically RNA polymerase of bacterial but not of mammalian origin. The chemical similarity between rifamycin [1], streptovaricins [2], and tolypomycin [3] lies in the fact that they are all ansa-compounds, i.e. compounds containing an aromatic ring system which is spanned by an aliphatic bridge. For this reason the name "ansamycins" has recently been proposed for these antibiotics [4].

Hartmann et al. [5] have first demonstrated that rifamycin SV inhibits RNA polymerase of *E. coli*. Using ^{14}C-rifampicin, a chemically altered rifamycin, we were able to show that rifampicin interacts very strongly with the enzyme [6]. The complex can be detected either by gel filtration (Fig. 1) or by density gradient centrifugation (Fig. 2). The extent of this interaction closely paralleled the inhibition of the enzymatic activity, i.e. 50% inhibition was reached at the same rifampicin concentration at which the binding of the antibiotic to the enzyme had reached 50% of the maximal value (Fig. 3). This strongly suggested that the interaction of rifamycin with the enzyme is responsible for the inhibition.

Recent studies [7] have shown that only one molecule of rifampicin is bound to the smaller active enzyme unit which exists at high ionic strength and has a sedimentation constant of 13 S and which is believed to be the monomer, whereas two molecules of rifampicin can be bound to the larger 24 S form which exists at

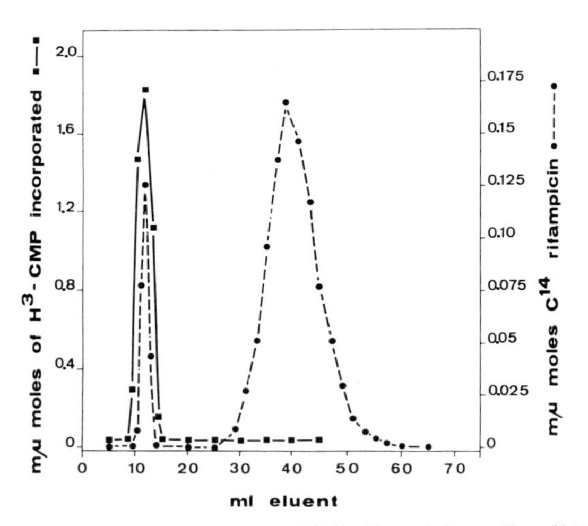

Fig. 1. Determination of the binding of ^{14}C-rifampicin to *E. coli* RNA polymerase by chromatography on Sephadex G 75 [6]. ■——■ RNA polymerase activity (mμmoles of ^{3}H-CMP incorporated per 0.1 ml of each 1 ml fraction). The recovery of polymerase activity was 30 to 40%. ●- - - -● Rifampicin (mμmoles per 1 ml fraction). Note that in the peak of free rifampicin only each second fraction is shown

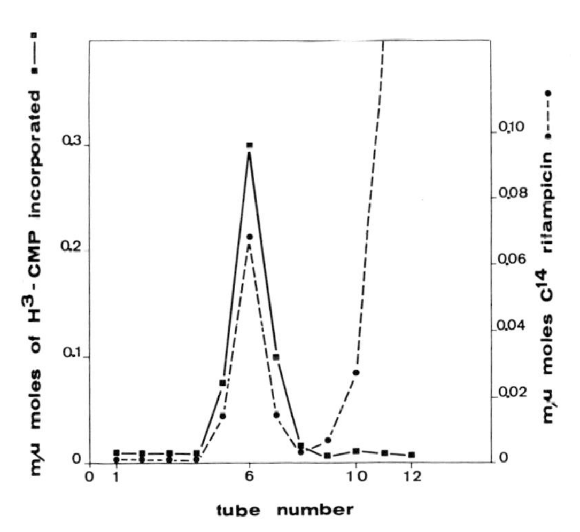

Fig. 2. Determination of the binding of ^{14}C-rifampicin to *E. coli* RNA polymerase on a sucrose density gradient [6]. ■——■ RNA polymerase activity (mμmoles of ^{3}H-CMP incorporated per 0.01 ml of each 0.4 ml fraction). ●- - - -● Rifampicin (mμmoles per 0.4 ml fraction)

low salt concentration and is presumably the dimer with a molecular weight of about 720000 daltons [8].

Once rifampicin is bound to the enzyme, it remains bound very strongly. ^{14}C-rifampicin complexed to *E. coli* RNA polymerase could not be removed by an excess of unlabelled rifampicin. The capacity to bind the antibiotic is directly related to the mechanism of enzyme inhibition. Mutant strains of *E. coli* and *Staph. aureus* have been isolated which were resistant to rifamycin. The isolated

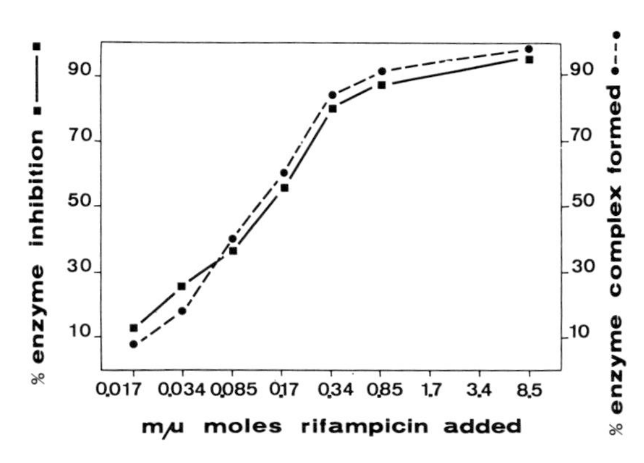

Fig. 3. Relationship between the extent of complex formation and the inhibition of RNA polymerase. 0.1 ml of partially purified normal *E. coli* RNA polymerase (0.24 mg protein) was mixed with the indicated amounts of rifampicin and incubated for 10 min at 37°. The complex was isolated on Sephadex G 75 columns and determined as described in Ref. [6]. The amount of complex formed after incubation for 30 min at 37°, using 17 mμmoles of rifampicin, was taken as 100%. 0.1 ml of each fraction was assayed for remaining polymerase activity

RNA polymerase from these strains was no more susceptible to the inhibitory action of rifampicin and also lost its capacity to bind ^{14}C-rifampicin.

The very strong binding of rifampicin offered an opportunity to study the binding of other rifamycin derivatives. Incubation of RNA polymerase with rifamycin B or SV, for instance, prior to the addition of ^{14}C-rifampicin completely prevented the binding of the labelled antibiotic. This technique thus made it possible to study the interaction of a variety of chemical derivatives of rifamycin with RNA polymerase. Recently, we have found that the aromatic ring system can be quite extensively substituted without any impairment of either the affinity of the binding to the enzyme or of enzyme inhibition. Modification of the aliphatic bridge, in contrast, led to a rapid loss of both activities. Interestingly, some derivatives were found which had only partial activity. Thus, the successive reduction of the double bonds in the bridge led to a progressive decrease of the antibiotic activity. But again there was no indication of any dissociation between the binding capacity and the enzyme inhibition.

In summary, rifamycin seems to be a unique tool for the study of RNA polymerase. It occupies two sites on the dimeric and one site on the monomeric form of the enzyme. These sites can be blocked in a more or less strong manner according to the rifamycin derivative used. The lack of rifampicin binding to the mutant strains indicates that this site of the molecule has been structurally altered by the mutation.

References

1. Oppolzer, W., V. Prelog und P. Sensi: Experientia (Basel) **20**, 336 (1964).
2. Rinehart, Jr., K. L., H. H. Mathur, K. Sasaki, P. K. Martin, and C. E. Coverdale: J. Amer. chem. Soc. **90**, 6241 (1968).
3. Kishi, T., M. Asai, M. Muroi, S. Harada, E. Mizuta, S. Terao, T. Miki, and K. Mizuno: Tetrahedron letters **1969**, 91.
4. Prelog, V.: Personal communication.
5. Hartmann, G., K. O. Honikel, F. Knüsel, and J. Nüesch: Biochim. biophys. Acta (Amst.) **145**, 843 (1967).
6. Wehrli, W., F. Knüsel, K. Schmid, and M. Staehelin: Proc. nat. Acad. Sci. (Wash.) **61**, 667 (1968).
7. —, and M. Staehelin: In preparation.
8. Priess, H., and W. Zillig: Biochim. biophys. Acta (Amst.) **140**, 540 (1967).

Effects of some RNA Polymerase Inhibitors on Binding and Chain Initiation

A. Sentenac and P. Fromageot

Service de Biochimie, Département de Biologie, Centre d'Etudes Nucléaires de Saclay, 91 Gif-sur-Yvette, France

With 7 Figures

The *in vitro* synthesis of RNA by DNA dependent RNA polymerase in the presence of a template can be divided into four successive steps: binding of the enzyme to the DNA, formation of the first phosphodiester bridge, or initiation, elongation by reiterative addition of nucleotides, and termination. It is remarkable that with purified DNA and RNA polymerase, two events have been found to exhibit a specificity: the binding of the polymerase to the template, and the initiation of chain. Thus, there must be signals, structural or in the sequence of the template, which account for these facts.

The purpose of the present report is to give some additional data on these two processes.

The specificity of binding of RNA polymerase reflects the fact that among all the RNA polymerase molecules which can bind to DNA at low salt concentration, only a few are able to catalyse RNA synthesis as shown by Pettijohn and Kamiya [1]. The sites of the DNA which allow the bound enzyme to express its activity are the specific sites. At this stage several questions arise: what distinguishes specific and unspecific sites, and what are the differences between free, bound and functional RNA polymerase? The use of RNA polymerase inhibitors may help to clarify these problems.

Study of DNA protection by RNA polymerase, alone or in presence of its substrates. Jones and Berg [2] have found by competition experiments that the strength of binding of RNA polymerase for the specific sites is greater than for the unspecific ones. Fig. 1 shows the kinetics of binding of RNA polymerase to both types of sites. These measurements are based on two facts: first, RNA polymerase bound to DNA is adsorbed by Millipore filters [2], even after hydrolysis of the free part of the template by DNase; second, the polymerase retained is associated with a segment of DNA [3, 4]. This segment of DNA is presumably the template area to which the polymerase is bound. Thus, by adding

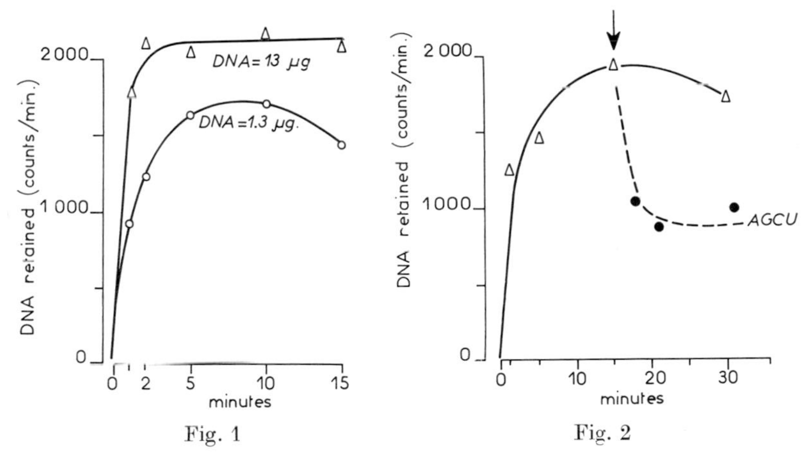

Fig. 1

Fig. 2

Fig. 1. Protection of DNA by RNA polymerase. Incubation mixture (1 ml) contains Tris pH 8:50 mM; $MgCl_2$:5 mM; $MnCl_2$:1 mM; β mercaptoethanol: 8 mM; [^{32}P] E. coli DNA (90000 cpm/μg) and 15 μg RNA polymerase. After various times at 37°, 150 μl aliquots are taken, DNase (10 μg/ml) added for 5 min at 37°, and the mixture processed by direct filtration [18]

Fig. 2. Protection of DNA by RNA polymerase during RNA synthesis. Incubation mixture (1.5 ml) as in Fig. 1 contains 28 μg [^{32}P] E. coli DNA and 25 μg RNA polymerase. After various times at 37°, 150 μl aliquots are taken and processed as in Fig. 1. At 15 min the four nucleotide triphosphates 0.1 mM are added to a part of the incubation mixture

DNase after various periods of time after mixing [^{32}P] *E. coli* DNA and RNA polymerase, and collecting the protected DNA, one can establish a kinetics of the binding process and estimate the amount of DNA nucleotides protected by one RNA polymerase molecule. It has been measured that one RNA polymerase molecule protects under the conditions used about 75 nucleotides against

DNase hydrolysis [4]. If one assumes that a specific site is located statistically every 1000 residues, one can calculate that RNA polymerase bound to such sites protects at the most 3.7% of the DNA. Fig. 1 shows that with an enzyme/DNA weight ratio of 1, maximum protection represents about 1% of total DNA, thus in the range of the specific binding, and is attained in 2 min. On the other hand, with an enzyme/DNA ratio of 10, maximum protection extends to 9%, in the range of unspecific binding, and is attained in 5 to 10 min. It therefore appears that the polymerase binds more rapidly to the specific than to the unspecific sites. As the extent of [^{32}P] DNA recovery does not decrease significantly if the DNase treatment is prolonged for 20 min at 37°, the reversibility of the binding [5] must be a slow process.

It is interesting to compare the extent of DNA protection resulting from RNA polymerase, simply bound or in the process of chain elongation. Fig. 2 shows that in the latter case the amount of DNase resistant DNA falls to half its value obtained with stationary enzyme. RNA polymerase catalysing a pyrophosphate exchange in the presence of the four nucleotides protects DNA as the simply bound enzyme. Moreover, inhibition of chain elongation by 3'dATP prevents the decrease in protection observed during active RNA synthesis. This suggests that the decrease in protection seen in Fig. 2 does not result from the functional state of the enzyme, but from its motion along the DNA.

Whereas free enzyme is not retained by Millipore filters [2] RNA polymerase-DNA complex treated by DNase is adsorbed. The retention could be due to the presence of a segment of denatured DNA at the binding site of the enzyme [2] or to a new property of the bound enzyme itself.

Effects of Congo Red, Salt, and Rifampicin on binding of RNA polymerase and chain initiation. KRAKOW [6] observed that Congo red inhibits DNA dependent RNA synthesis. Fig. 3 shows that Congo red prevents the binding of free polymerase to DNA; it also releases previously bound enzyme from its template, but in this case about twice as much dye is needed. However, when RNA polymerase has initiated a short oligoribonucleotide [7], it becomes resistant to the inhibitor. Thus, RNA polymerase, free, bound to DNA, or having made an oligonucleotide, has different susceptibilities to Congo red, an observation suggesting three possible states of the enzyme.

High salt concentration dissociates aggregated forms of RNA polymerase [8], prevents the binding of the enzyme to DNA and detaches bound enzyme [9], unspecific binding being more susceptible than the specific one [1]. After RNA chain initiation,

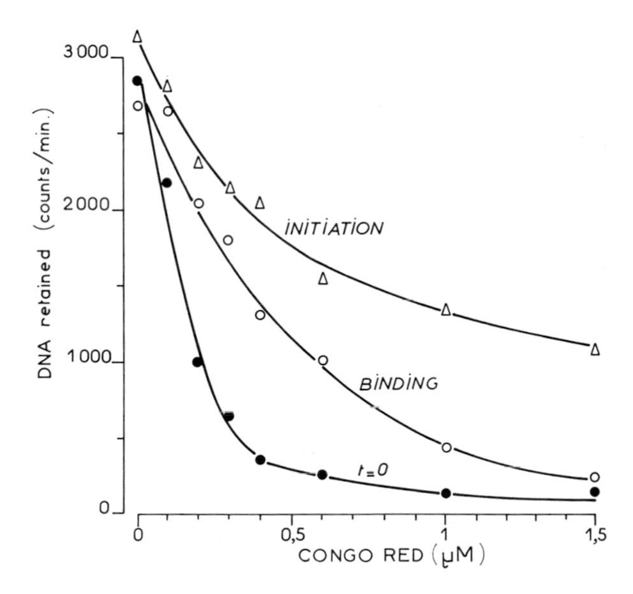

Fig. 3. Effect of Congo red on DNA protection. Incubation mixtures (0.5 ml) contain [^{32}P] E. coli DNA 2 μg, RNA polymerase 3 μg and the salts reported in Fig. 1. ●——● Congo red is added before RNA polymerase; incubation 10 min at 37° followed by 5 min incubation at 37° with DNase (10 μg/ml). ○——○ DNA, polymerase and salts are incubated 10 min at 37°; Congo red and DNase are then added and incubated 5 min at 37°. Δ——Δ DNA, polymerase, salt and 0.05 mM GTP, UTP, CTP and 3′dATP are first incubated 10 min at 37° before Congo red and DNase addition. All samples are processed by direct filtration [18]

RNA polymerase becomes resistant to high salt concentrations. Thus the effects of Congo red and salt on RNA polymerase binding reaction are very similar.

It is possible that heparin which inhibits in vitro RNA synthesis if added to the incubation medium before the start of the

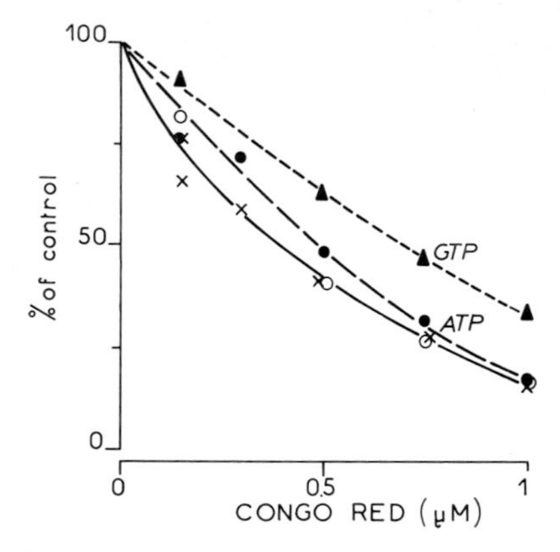

Fig. 4. Influence of Congo red on chain initiation by ATP and GTP. Incubation mixture contains calf thymus DNA 34 mμmoles; RNA polymerase 15 μg and salts as in Fig. 1; nucleoside triphosphate 20 μM, [^{3}H] UTP and [γ^{32}P] ATP or [γ^{32}P] GTP; incubation at 37° for 20 min. RNA is recovered by direct filtration [18]. ○——○ total RNA; ●- - - - -● ATP initiated chains; ▲- - - - -▲ GTP initiated chains

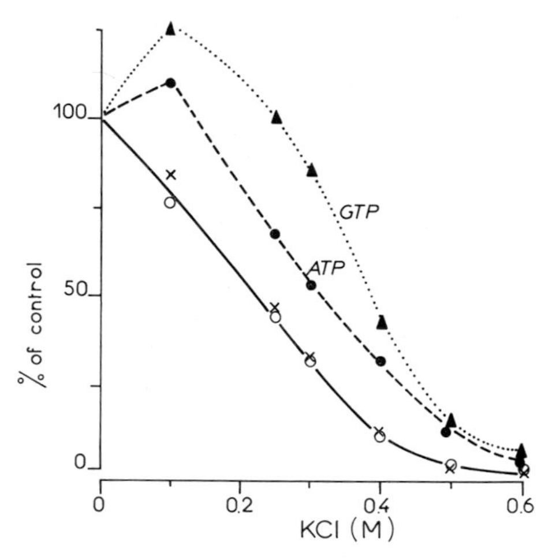

Fig. 5. Influence of KCl on chain initiation by ATP and GTP. Calf thymus DNA 34 mμmoles and RNA polymerase 15 μg are mixed at 0° before addition of salt and reaction is started by addition of nucleotides as in Fig. 4. RNA is recovered by direct filtration after 45 min of incubation at 37° [18]. ○——○ Total RNA; ●- - - - -● ATP initiated chains; ▲- - - - -▲ GTP initiated chains

reaction [10] acts like Congo red and interferes with the binding of RNA polymerase to its template.

Since Congo red and salt affect the binding of RNA polymerase to DNA, it was of interest to study whether chain initiation by ATP and GTP are inhibited in the same way. Figs. 4 and 5 give the results of such experiments and show that with both inhibitors ATP initiated chains are more inhibited than GTP initiated chains. MAITRA et al. [11] have already reported a differential effect of divalent ions on chain initiation by ATP and GTP. These results suggest different affinities of the polymerase for the ATP and GTP initiation sites.

Rifampicin binds specifically to bacterial RNA polymerase [12, 13] and inhibits strongly RNA synthesis but not chain elongation. Fig. 6 shows that rifampicin has no significant effect on the binding of the enzyme to DNA. The inhibitory role of rifampicin on RNA synthesis results from the inhibition of the initiation process, a conclusion also attained by UMEZAWA et al. [14]. It should be noticed that chain initiation by ATP and by GTP are inhibited to the same extent. This observation suggests a unique mechanism for both types of chain initiation.

Chromatography of RNA polymerase on phosphocellulose allowed BURGESS et al. [15] to dissociate the purified molecule into PC enzyme and an RNA synthesis stimulating factor σ. PC enzyme alone is able to synthesize very small amounts only of RNA in the presence of native T_4 phage DNA, and this capacity is greatly enhanced by addition of factor σ which acts as an initiation [16] factor. It was of interest to examine whether factor σ is the target of rifampicin. This is not the case as rifampicin inhibits RNA synthesis catalysed by PC enzyme alone on calf thymus DNA. Furthermore, factor σ can still associate with PC enzyme in the presence of rifampicin.

Influence of temperature on chain initiation. The existence of events preliminary to chain initiation can be detected by lowering the temperature. Fig. 7 shows that RNA polymerase at 0° initiates a few RNA chains only, in the presence of T_7, *Micrococcus lysodeikticus*, *Cytophaga johnsonii* DNA as template, and the total RNA made is very small or undetectable. After heat denaturation, however, the amount of chains initiated at 0° is definitely higher. The poor efficiency of RNA polymerase in chain initiation with native templates at 0° reflects therefore the need for a template and/or enzyme modification to allow initiation to proceed, modification(s) which are overcome or facilitated in the presence of denatured template or with T_4 DNA. In the presence of other salt concentrations, WALTER et al. [10] have also studied the effects of lowering temperature on RNA synthesis, and noticed lag times of variable duration, becoming longer as the temperature was decreased. These authors attributed this lag time to the process of DNA

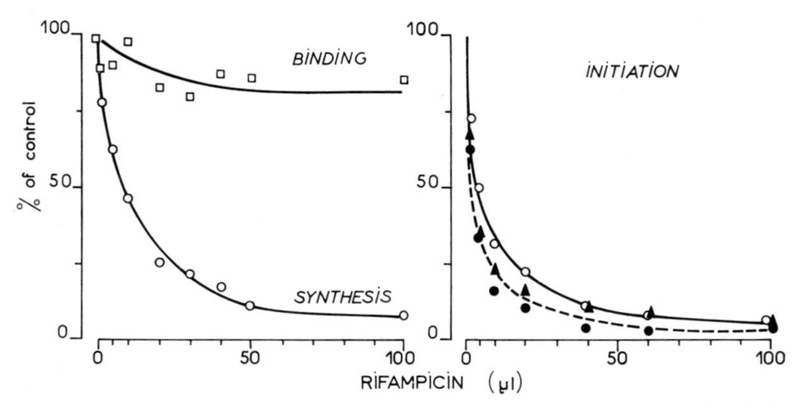

Fig. 6. Effect of Rifampicin on binding of RNA polymerase and chain initiation. The binding of RNA polymerase (3 µg) on [^{32}P] E. coli DNA (2 µg) is measured as in Fig. 1 after 10 min incubation at 37 °C. Rifampicin ($A_{333\ nm}$: 0.15) is added before RNA polymerase. □——□; RNA synthesis in the presence of Rifampicin is measured by [^{3}H] GMP incorporation in the presence of the same amount of RNA polymerase and cold E. coli DNA ○——○; Chain initiation and RNA synthesis are measured after incubation for 20 min at 37 °C of the mixture described in Fig. 4. Total volume 0.3 ml; E. coli DNA (15 µg); RNA polymerase: 6 µg. ○——○ [^{3}H] UMP incorporation; ●- - - - -● [γ^{32}P] ATP incorporation; ▲- - - - -▲ [γ^{32}P] GTP incorporation. The results are given as percent of the controls without Rifampicin

strands separation, as it was not observed in the presence of denatured DNA. However, it has been shown by KRAKOW [17] that the binding of RNA polymerase to denatured DNA but not to native DNA liberates a polymerase component called γ, very probably identical to the stimulating factor σ described by BURGESS et al. [15]. Therefore, differences existing in RNA chain initiation at low temperature on native and denatured templates

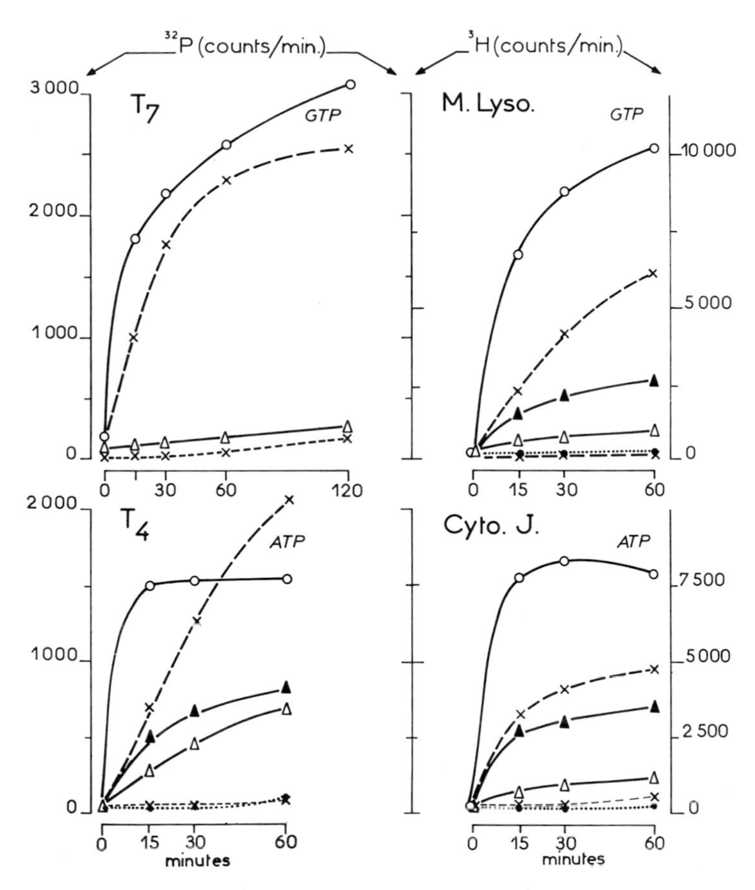

Fig. 7. Comparison of chain initiation at 0° with native and denatured DNA. Incubation mixtures (1 ml, except for T_7 assay 1.25 ml) contain salts and nucleotides of Fig. 4; 26 μg of RNA polymerase and different templates: T_7DNA (50% G-C) 36 mμmoles; T_4DNA (34% G-C) 58 mμmoles; Micrococcus lysodeikticus DNA (72% G-C) 69 mμmoles; Cytophaga Johnsonii (34% G-C) 65 mμmoles; [^{3}H] CTP, [γ^{32}P] ATP or [γ^{32}P] GTP as indicated in the figure. Incubations are carried out at 37° or 0° and 250 μl aliquots are taken at various times, and processed by direct filtration. ×- - - - - × [^{3}H] CMP incorporation at 37°, with native template; ○——○ γ^{32}P labelled nucleotide incorporated at 37° with native template; △——△ γ^{32}P labelled nucleotide incorporated at 0° with native template; ▲——▲ γ^{32}P labelled nucleotide incorporated at 0° with heat denatured template (10 min at 100°). [^{3}H] CMP incorporation at 0° with native or denatured templates is given by the lowest broken lines

cannot be attributed solely to differences in templates. Changes in RNA polymerase conformation have also to be considered.

Thus, the two specific steps of RNA synthesis, binding and initiation, can be differentiated by the use of RNA polymerase inhibitors. It appears as a general rule that RNA polymerase which has initiated synthesis becomes much more resistant to all inhibitors. The growing part of the RNA chain is probably bound to the enzyme and thus stabilizes the transcription complex on the template. Moreover, the variations in susceptibility towards the agents investigated, of RNA polymerase when from the free state this enzyme becomes bound and initiates RNA chains, reflect probably successive changes in protein structure. These changes in relation with the template and the presence of the initiation factor σ are likely to provide the stepwise control resulting in the transcription specificity.

References

1. Pettijohn, D., and T. Kamiya: J. molec. Biol. **29**, 275 (1967).
2. Jones, O. W., and P. Berg: J. molec. Biol. **22**, 199 (1966).
3. Novak, R. L.: Biochim. biophys. Acta (Amst.) **149**, 593 (1967).
4. Sentenac, A., A. Ruet, and P. Fromageot: FEBS Letters **2**, 53 (1968).
5. Stead, N. W., and O. W. Jones: J. molec. Biol. **26**, 131 (1967).
6. Krakow, J. S.: Biochim. biophys. Acta (Amst.) **95**, 532 (1965).
7. Sentenac, A., A. Ruet, and P. Fromageot: Europ. J. Biochem. **5**, 385 (1968).
8. Richardson, J. P.: Proc. nat. Acad. Sci. (Wash.) **55**, 1616 (1966).
9. — J. molec. Biol. **21**, 83 (1966).
10. Walter, G., W. Zillig, P. Palm, and E. Fuchs: Europ. J. Biochem. **3**, 194 (1967).
11. Maitra, U., Y. Nakata, and J. Hurwitz: J. biol. Chem. **242**, 4908 (1967).
12. Hartmann, G., K. Honickel, F. Knüsel, and J. Nuesch: Biochim. biophys. Acta (Amst.) **145**, 843 (1967).
13. Wehrli, W., J. Nuesch, F. Knüsel, and M. Staehelin: Biochim. biophys. Acta (Amst.) **157**, 215 (1968).
14. Umezawa, H., S. Mizuno, H. Tamazaki, and K. Nitta: J. Antibiot. Ser. A (Tokyo) **21**, 234 (1968).
15. Burgess, R. R., A. A. Travers, J. J. Dunn, and E. K. F. Bautz: Nature (Lond.) **221**, 43 (1969).
16. Darlix, J. L., A. Sentenac, A. Ruet, and P. Fromageot: Europ. J. Biochem. (in press).
17. Krakow, J. S.: Personal communication.
18. Sentenac, A., E. J. Simon, and P. Fromageot: Biochim. biophys. Acta (Amst.) **161**, 299 (1968).

Zur molekularen Wirkungsweise einiger matrizeninaktivierender Antibiotika

WERNER MÜLLER

Org.-chem. Institut der Universität Göttingen

Herr HARTMANN hat in seinem Vortrag einen generellen Mechanismus für die Wirkungsweise solcher Antibiotika erläutert, die man als Matrizeninaktivatoren bezeichnet. Nach diesem Mechanismus, der von CROTHERS, MATZURA und mir [1, 2] im Zusammenhang mit der Wirkungsweise der Actinomycine entwickelt wurde, hängt die Wirksamkeit der einzelnen Inaktivatoren bei gleicher Beladung der Matrize einerseits von der Geschwindigkeit des Polykondensationsprozesses und zum anderen von der Lebensdauer des Matrizen-Hemmstoffkomplexes in der von Herrn HARTMANN angedeuteten Weise ab.

Wir konnten seinerzeit diesen Wirkungsmechanismus für verschiedene natürliche, d. h. im Peptidteil variierte Actinomycine sowie einer Reihe synthetischer Derivate nachweisen, fanden aber auch, daß es einige Derivate mit abweichendem Verhalten gibt.

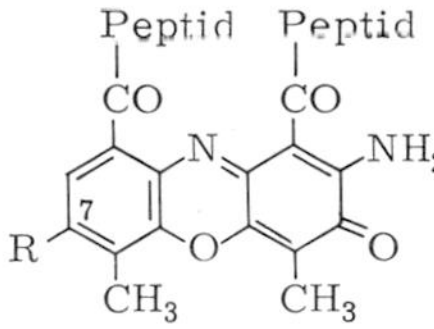

Peptid Peptid
CO CO
N NH_2
7
R O O
CH_3 CH_3

I a: R = H	II a: R = OCH_3
I b: R = NH_2	II b: R = $NHCOCH_3$
I c: R = NO_2	II c: R = $NHCOC(CH_3)_3$
I d: R = Br	
I e: R = H, H anstelle von CH_3	
I f: R = H, Cl anstelle von NH_2	

Während alle getesteten natürlichen und auch die meisten am Chromophor veränderten Actinomycine die erwartete Parallelität zwischen der Lebensdauer ihrer DNS-Komplexe und ihrer Hemmwirkung im RNA-Polymerasesystem zeigten, sind alle die Derivate, die Substituenten von einer bestimmten Größe ab in 7-Stellung des Chromophors tragen, weniger wirksam als die z. T. sehr hohen Lebenszeiten ihrer DNS-Komplexe erwarten lassen. Für I a—f trifft der diskutierte Mechanismus offenbar zu, für II a—c finden wir Abweichungen, die wir bisher nur so deuten können, daß wir annehmen, daß die Polymerase die Dissoziation der DNS-Komplexe über diese Substituenten zu beschleunigen vermag. Da diese Substituenten in dem von uns vorgeschlagenem Strukturmodell für den Actinomycin-DNS-Komplex als einzige Molekülteile des Actinomycins in die große Rille der Helix schauen, wäre eine solche Deutung einigermaßen plausibel.

Wir haben inzwischen auch zu klären versucht, ob dieser Wirkungsmechanismus für die Anthracyclin-Antibiotika [3] in Betracht kommt. Uns standen dafür einige Rhodomycine, das Pyrromycin und das Cinerubin A zur Verfügung, von denen wir im Zuge der Vorarbeiten für die kinetischen Messungen zunächst die DNS-Bindungskonstanten k_0 und die Anzahl der Bindungspunkte pro Basenpaar B_0 durch Spektraltitration bestimmen mußten. Die Ergebnisse sind in Tabelle 1 zusammengestellt:

Tabelle 1. *Stabilitätskonstanten k_0 (in L/Mol) und maximale Beladungswerte B_0 (in Anzahl Liganden pro Basenpaar) für die Bindung einiger Anthracycline an Kalbsthymus-DNS bei 22 °C in folgenden Medien*

Anthracyclin	BPES-Puffer[a]		RNS-Polymerase-Puffer[b]	
	k_0	B_0	k_0	B_4
β-Rhodomycin A	$8,6 \times 10^6$	0,17	$1,7 \times 10^6$	0,225
β-Isorhodomycin A	nicht meßbar		$7,7 \times 10^4$ (als Mg^{2+}-Komplex gebunden)	0,294
β-Rhodomycin B	$3,4 \times 10^5$	0,38	—	—
ε-Pyrromycin	$1,4 \times 10^6$	0,29	$4,9 \times 10^5$	0,17
Cinerubin A	$3,4 \times 10^6$	0,30	$5,0 \times 10^5$	0,185
Rhodomin	$3,5 \times 10^5$	0,48	$6,0 \times 10^4$	0,32

[a] BPES-Puffer: 0,18 m NaCl, 0,001 m EDTA, 0,01 m Na-Phosphat, pH 6,9.

[b] RNS-Polymerase-Puffer: 0,13 m NH_4Cl, 0.02 m $MgAc_2$, 0,05 m Tris, pH 7,7.

Die Komplexe mit denaturierter DNS ergaben — soweit wir sie gemessen haben — in Übereinstimmung mit den Hinweisen aus der Literatur praktisch die gleichen Bindungsparameter.

Inzwischen hat Dr. STERNBACH (MPI f. Experimentelle Medizin, Göttingen) freundlicherweise für uns die Hemmung der RNS-Polymerase bei steigenden Beladungen der DNS-Matrize durch β-Rhodomycin A bestimmt. Unter Zugrundelegung des oben diskutierten Mechanismus konnte man aus den Hemmwerten eine mittlere Lebensdauer des Komplexes von rd. 15 sec berechnen. Damit hätte man die Komplexdissoziation weitgehend im registrierenden Spektralphotometer verfolgen können. Die ersten Messungen zeigten jedoch, daß diese Zerfallsreaktion wesentlich rascher abläuft; die mittlere Lebenszeit des Komplexes dürfte 3 sec kaum überschreiten. Für das Cinerubin A, welches laut Literatur eine stärkere Hemmwirkung als die Rhodomycine ausübt, fanden wir eine ähnlich starke Abweichung. Wir müssen deshalb annehmen, daß der Mechanismus der Matrizeninaktivierung durch diese Stoffe etwas komplizierter ist als im Falle der Actinomycine und Chromomycine. Möglicherweise bilden die Anthracycline mit der Polymerase auf der DNS längerlebige Tripelkomplexe. Es bedarf noch weiterer Untersuchungen um die Frage beantworten zu können, in wieweit man mit dem oben diskutierten Mechanismus die Hemmung der DNA-Polymerase durch die Anthracycline erklären kann. Eine wesentliche Voraussetzung erscheint uns insofern erfüllt, als diese Stoffe mit denaturierter, d. h. überwiegend einsträngiger DNS die gleichen stabilen Komplexe wie mit natürlicher DNS bilden.

Literatur

1. MATZURA, H., u. W. MÜLLER: FEBS, Fourth Meeting Abstracts, Oslo 1967, Abstract Nr. 17, p. 5.
2. MÜLLER, W., u. D. CROTHERS: J. molec. Biol. **35**, 251 (1968).
3. BROCKMANN, H.: In: Fortschr. d. Chemie Organ. Naturstoffe, Bd. 21, S. 121. ZECHMEISTER, L., Ed. Wien: Springer 1963

Discussion

HELMREICH (Würzburg): Dr. STAEHELIN, since there are two binding sites for rifampicin on the polymeric form, and only one binding site on the monomeric form of DNA-dependent RNA polymerase, and since you observed a good correlation between inactivation and binding of the inhibitor to the enzyme, I wonder whether you cannot decide with the use of rifampicin what form is the active and what form is the inactive form of RNA polymerase.

Staehelin (Basle): Dr. Seifert has already indicated that the two forms exist at two different salt concentrations: At high salt there is a monomeric form, and at low salt there is a dimeric form. The binding of the rifampicin is tested at these two different salt concentrations. The activity, of course, is always assayed at the same intermediate salt concentration.

H. Kersten (Münster): Dr. Seifert, you mentioned that methyl groups in DNA might function as a signal for RNA polymerase. Did you try DNA isolated from starved cultures of the methionine-requiring strain of E. coli — which is methyl-deficient — as a template for the RNA polymerase? If so, could you find a difference in binding of RNA polymerase to DNA?

Seifert (Munich): We have not tried this interesting experiment. The possibility of methylation signals as initiation sites was pure speculation.

H. Kersten: Rifamycin is produced by microorganisms. Have the polymerases been isolated from the organism which produces rifamycin? Do you know whether this polymerase will or will not interact with rifamycin?

Staehelin: The organism which makes rifamycin is S. mediterraneus. We have isolated RNA polymerase from this organism and found that it is rifamycin-resistant.

W. Kersten (Erlangen): Does anyone know how many RNA nucleotides are bound per RNA polymerase to the DNA template? How long is the piece of RNA still attached to the DNA during RNA synthesis?

Seifert: The average length of the synthesized RNA chains is in the range of some thousand nucleotides. The RNA-DNA-hybrid region covered by the polymerase molecule is in the range of 30—50 nucleotides. The RNA polymerase has about 100 Å. Kameyama (Ref. [18] in Seifert and Zillig) claimed recently that he has isolated such initiation regions in the form of specific polynucleotides.

W. Kersten: Are these nucleotides identical with the clusters mentioned by the Szybalski group (Ref. [23] in Seifert and Zillig)?

Seifert: Szybalski claims pyrimidine clusters, and in the Kameyama paper the DNA regions were shown to have the same base ratio as normal DNA. These are differing results.

Scholtissek (Giessen): Dr. Seifert, concerning the E. coli RNA-polymerase, have you tried polyanions other than heparin as inhibitors? Are there any data available on the purified enzyme of animal cells? Polydextran sulfate did not inhibit the RNA polymerase in crude extracts of chick fibroblasts but in this case we might not have measured the initiation reaction.

Seifert: I am not informed on the inhibition of mammalian polymerases by polyanions.

As all other polyanions, dextran sulfate is an inhibitor of E. coli polymerase. This inhibition is rather unspecific. It is reasonable to suggest that the polyanion binds to the site to which one of the DNA strands binds. If you measure the activity of the RNA synthesizing complex in the crude extract without addition of exogenous DNA, initiation has already taken place. Therefore, polyanions will not inhibit in this case.

Jovin (Göttingen): Can one exclude that the antibiotic rifamycin is not bound in some covalent way to the enzyme, if the inhibition is irreversible? Is there no other transformation involved?

Helmreich: Concerning this same point: Has a structural change of the protein upon the binding of rifamycin been studied?

Hartmann: This has not yet been studied.

Staehelin: Dr. Neuhoff (6th FEBS-Meeting, Madrid, 1969, Abstract Nr. 699) reported that in the presence of rifampicin the migration of RNA polymerase in his microdiffusion technique is not altered. This may be an indication that no gross changes occur in the presence of the antibiotic.

Seifert: The T_4 polymerase is inhibited by rifamycin as is E. coli polymerase, whereas mammalian polymerases, as we have already heard, are not inhibited by rifamycin.

We would like to interpret the alteration of RNA polymerase after T_4 infection, as mentioned in the paper, as a conformational change of the enzyme.

An interesting result of Szulmajster (Ref. [36] in Seifert and Zillig) concerns the problem of differentiation. In B. subtilis spores, there is RNA polymerase differing from that in the vegetative cell. So it might really be that different RNA polymerases or changes in the transcribing enzyme are controlling differentiation.

Hölzel (Hamburg): I would like to comment shortly on Dr. Kerstens' paper that even a simple molecule such as p-benzoquinone can inhibit DNA

Table 1. *Percentage of ^{14}C-p-benzoquinone in various fractions of ascites tumor cells. (Incubation: 2 h, 10^{-4} M benzoquinone)*

Total ^{14}C-benzoquinone applied	Whole cells	Nuclei (washed 2 ×)	Histones (as h.-sulfate)	Acidic residual nucleoprotein (nucleic acids)	DNA	RNA
100	28	13	2.2	10.0	0.25	0.1

and RNA synthesis in mammalian cells. The 50% inhibition of DNA synthesis is seen at 10^{-4} M benzoquinone, the 50% inhibition dose of RNA synthesis is found at about 3×10^{-4} M.

However, the inhibition of the nucleic acid synthesis seems not to be due to a strong binding of the benzoquinone molecule to DNA (Table 1). After a 2 h incubation of ascites cells with ^{14}C-labelled benzoquinone only small amounts of the benzoquinone are found on isolated DNA and RNA. About 10% of the applied benzoquinone is found in the acidic residual nucleoprotein fraction; the labelled benzoquinone did not bind to the nucleic acids, and it was also shown that the isolated nucleic acids did not accept the benzoquinone.

I would like to point out that inhibitor molecules with a quinoid structure affecting nucleic acid synthesis can bind in some case more easily to the nuclear proteins than to the nucleic acids, especially DNA. (Refs.: Hölzel, F., H. Hebbeln, E. Höcke und H. Maass: Z. Krebsforsch. **70**, 74 (1967); Hölzel, F. H., E. Wulfmeyer, I. Schwencke und H. Maass: Z. Krebsforsch. **70**, 95 (1967); Hölzel, F. H.: Unpublished results.)

II. Protein Synthesis

Localization of Streptomycin-Resistance in the 30s Ribosome of E. coli. Mode of Action of Cycloheximide

PETER TRAUB

Department of Biology, University of California at San Diego, La Jolla, California 92037

With 1 Figure

Among the members of the family of antibiotics, a considerable number of compounds interfere with protein synthesis through their interaction with ribosomes [1, 2]. In several cases, their gross mode of action is fairly well understood today. However, due to our ignorance of the ribosomal structure the molecular mechanisms of their various effects on the proper functioning of ribosomes in protein synthesis are still far from being intelligible. It is the concern of this paper to review briefly our present knowledge of the biochemical properties of two antibiotics specifically affecting protein synthesis in bacterial and mammalian systems, respectively, and the determination of their loci of action on the corresponding ribosomes. Streptomycin, as the antibotic interfering with protein synthesis in bacteria, and cycloheximide, as the drug impairing protein synthesis in mammalian cells, respectively, are the compounds which will be described.

I. Streptomycin

For a better understanding of the experimental results summarized in this chapter a short description of the structure of bacterial ribosomes and a brief outline of their biological function might be quite useful. However, simply because of the limited space available, the reader must be referred to previous reviews which cover these subjects in a comprehensive way [3—6].

A. The Mode of Action of Streptomycin

It is a well established fact today that streptomycin inhibits protein synthesis and causes misreading of the genetic code in extracts from streptomycin-sensitive cells unless streptomycin-resistance has been introduced by mutation. The two effects are very likely separate and distinct expressions of the action of streptomycin. Until recently, it remained undecided which one is responsible for the antibacterial action of the drug. Yet, the fact that, in the presence of the antibiotic, extensive misreading can occur in certain bacterial mutants with the production of up to 80% of faulty protein without leading to cell death, is likely to exclude gross misreading as the primary cause of killing [7].

There is a considerable body of evidence which suggests that the arrest of cell growth is due to a specific effect of streptomycin on initiation of protein synthesis and thus to the blockage of the ribosome cycle at a specific point [8, 9]. It could be shown that after addition of streptomycin to a growing culture of E. coli, polyribosomes gradually decrease in size and number and that 70s monomers accumulate progressively. Each accumulated monomer bears a molecule of stabilized mRNA, indicating that the 70s monomers do not arise from random fragmentation of polyribosomes. The monomers turned out to be inactive in an in vitro protein synthesizing system. Moreover, under conditions that are optimal for polypeptide chain initiation, polypeptide synthesis directed by poly AUG is completely inhibited by streptomycin, a finding that is supported by the observation that the activity of ribosomes to bind formyl-methionyl-tRNA in response to R17 phage RNA is considerably reduced and that of alanyl-tRNA completely inhibited in the presence of the antibiotic. In consequence, the amount of formyl-methionyl-alanine, the starting dipeptide coded for by R17 RNA, formed in the presence of streptomycin, was also found to be sharply reduced. These experimental results led to the conclusion that the inhibitory effect of streptomycin on protein synthesis consists of blockage of polypeptide chain initiation by formation of abortive initiation complexes. While these "streptomycin monomers" are prevented from moving along the mRNA strand, those 70s monomers that are already engaged in chain elongation can complete their growing polypeptide chains.

However, the results from in vitro experiments led to a somewhat different conclusion. In an MS2 phage RNA directed in vitro system already engaged in polypeptide synthesis, streptomycin completely blocked further incorporation of radioactively labeled amino acids in less time than that required for the incorporation of two amino acids per active ribosome [10]. The instructive result of this experiment was that the sedimentation pattern of the polyribosomes was essentially unchanged after incorporation had come to a full stop. The fact that no polyribosome runoff could be detected favored the conjecture that streptomycin inhibits polypeptide chain elongation. In the presence of the antibiotic polyribosomes are initially stabilized, but then gradually degraded, apparently by disruption of the ribosome-mRNA-peptidyl tRNA complex rather than by scission of the mRNA.

Both interpretations of the action of streptomycin could be reduced to a common denominator if it is assumed that the antibiotic blocks a step common to both chain initiation and chain elongation, e.g. the translocation of formyl-methionyl-tRNA or of peptidyl-tRNA from the acceptor to the donor site of the ribosome.

The mechanism by which streptomycin produces misreading in vitro [11] is still a matter of conjecture. In the presence of the antibiotic the ribosome presumably undergoes a configurational change that interferes with the correct alignment of the codon-anticodon pairs between mRNA and tRNA. It is reasonable to assume that this configurational change leads to a destabilization of the normal codon-anticodon pair and to the interaction of the mRNA codon also with different but related anticodons of other tRNA molecules. Both the regular and the anomalous anticodons compete for the same codon on the template. However, only pyrimidine bases of mRNA seem to be amenable to misreading, whereas purine bases appear to be inert [12].

Another feature of the action of streptomycin is phenotypic suppression [13, 14], that is, the ability of streptomycin to suppress missense or nonsense mutations in conditionally streptomycin-dependent cells. This property is not confined to streptomycin-resistant cells only, since in the presence of sublethal amounts of the antibiotic also missense and nonsense mutations in streptomycin-sensitive cells are amenable to phenotypic suppression [15].

Moreover, streptomycin was found to enhance the efficiency of genetic suppressors of amber and missense mutations [16].

B. The Locus of Action of Streptomycin

The determination of the locus of action of streptomycin was accomplished by the assignment of the streptomycin-resistant mutation to one of the cellular constituents involved in protein synthesis. Hybridization experiments, employing various elements of the protein synthesizing machinery from streptomycin-resistant and streptomycin-sensitive cells, turned out to be the appropriate means for this purpose.

By reassociation of the complete amino acid incorporating system from ribosomes and ribosome-free cell extracts from resistant and sensitive strains, it could be shown that the antibiotic acts at some step subsequent to amino acid activation and that sensitivity or resistance is a property of the ribosome [17, 18]. Subunit localization studies using ribosomal subunits from resistant and sensitive cells finally resulted in the assignment of streptomycin-resistance or sensitivity to the 30s ribosome [19].

Although the structurally altered component of the streptomycin-resistant ribosome was thought to be a protein [20, 21], no difference between the polyacrylamide gel electrophoresis or phosphocellulose chromatography profiles of 30s ribosomal protein from resistant and sensitive cells could be detected. At this stage, the partial reconstitution of ribosomes from their partially dissociated components [22, 23] made possible a refined localization of the action of streptomycin. The partial reconstitution system is based on the discovery that isolated ribosomal subunits from E. coli lose a distinct group of proteins when subjected to CsCl density-gradient equilibrium centrifugation at high Mg^{++}-ion concentration [22—24]. The resulting core particles and their corresponding split proteins are completely inactive when tested separately, in the presence of the appropriate native ribosomal subunits, for several of the known ribosomal functions [22, 23, 25, 26]. The activity, however, can be restored almost completely when the dissociated components are reassociated under defined conditions.

The availability of 23s core particles and of split proteins SP30 from resistant and sensitive 30s ribosomes permitted, beside the reconstitution of the original resistant and sensitive particles, the synthesis of two new hybrid particles [27, 28]. The analysis of their polypeptide synthesizing activities in response to polyuridylic acid and in the absence and presence of streptomycin revealed that those particles which contain 23s core particles from sensitive 30s ribosomes are sensitive to streptomycin, whereas

Table 1. *Sensitivity to streptomycin of reconstituted 30s ribosomes*

Reconstituted 30s		Native 30s	Sm	Radioactivity (cts/min)	% Inhibition
23s	SP30				
–	–	s	–	2999	45.5
–	–	s	+	1636	
–	–	r	–	3000	
–	–	r	+	3130	0 (–4.3)
s	s	–	–	3277	
s	s	–	+	1770	46
s	r	–	–	3432	
s	r	–	+	2022	41
r	s	–	–	3404	
r	s	–	+	3456	0 (–1.5)
r	r	–	–	3229	
r	r	–	+	3513	0 (–8.8)

The letters r or s indicate that the components are derived from streptomycin-resistant or streptomycin-sensitive cells, respectively. The reconstituted particles and native undissociated ribosomes were assayed for their activity in polyuridylic acid-directed incorporation of phenylalanine in the presence of 50s ribosomes from streptomycin-sensitive cells and in the absence and presence of streptomycin [27].

those derived from 23s core particles from resistant 30s ribosomes are not inhibited by the antibiotic (Table 1). The origin of the split protein SP30 does not show any correlation with the response of the reconstituted particles to streptomycin. Similar results were obtained when the properties of the various synthetic particles were studied with respect to translational errors in the reading of the genetic code [28]. The effect of misreading is confined to those particles that have been reconstituted from 23s core particles derived from sensitive 30 s ribosomes, regardless of the origin of the split protein.

Thus, the partial reconstitution of 30s ribosomes excluded already 7 to 8 of the 20 different 30s ribosomal proteins from consideration as possible candidates determining streptomycin-resistance or sensitivity. Yet, it left open the question whether the streptomycin mutation involves 16s RNA or one of the core

Table 2. *Sensitivity to streptomycin of reconstituted 30s ribosomes*

Reconstituted "30s"			Control	Incorporation activity (counts/min)		Inhibition
16s RNA	CP30	SP30	30s	− Sm	+ Sm	by Sm (%)
			s	11063	7042	36
			r	13174	12995	1.4
s	s	s		10498	6979	34
s	s	r		11904	7889	34
s	r	s		9898	9471	4.3
s	r	r		12037	11921	1.0
r	s	s		11112	7208	37
r	s	r		13098	8486	35
r	r	s		10695	10615	0.6
r	r	r		12491	12579	0 (−0.7)

The letters r or s indicate that the components are derived from streptomycin-resistant or streptomycin-sensitive cells, respectively. The reconstituted and native control particles were tested for their activity to synthesize polyphenylalanine in response to polyuridylic acid and in the presence of 50s ribosomes from streptomycin-sensitive cells [30].

proteins. This problem could be solved in a direct chemical way by the application of the total reconstitution technique that permits the synthesis of physically and functionally intact 30s ribosomes from free 16s RNA and free 30s ribosomal proteins [29]. In Table 2 are summarized the polyphenylalanine synthesizing activities of various meaningful combinations of 16s RNA, core protein CP30, and split protein SP30 from resistant and sensitive 30s ribosomes, in the absence and in the presence of streptomycin. As arises clearly from these data, only those particles are sensitive to streptomycin that contain the core protein from sensitive 30s ribosomes, whereas particles that are derived from core protein from resistant 30s ribosomes are not inhibited by the antibiotic. The results convincingly rule out 16s RNA and the split protein SP30 as the ribosomal component determining streptomycin resistance or sensitivity [30]. It must be concluded that one of the core proteins is the ribosomal component specifying the behavior of the 30s ribosome towards streptomycin [30].

The further assignment of the mutationally induced structural alteration of the 30s ribosome to a distinct ribosomal protein was accomplished by chromatographic separation of protein from streptomycin-resistant and streptomycin-sensitive 30s ribosomes into its individual components on phosphocellulose and by the performance of hybridization experiments of the above type [31]. The protein determining the response of 30s ribosomes to streptomycin was pinpointed as a component of the more basic one of two groups of 30s ribosomal proteins that can be demonstrated by polyacrylamide gel electrophoresis. It proved not to be identical with the "K" protein of E. coli K12 strains whose genetic locus, by means of conjugation and transduction experiments, was shown to be either identical with, or extremely close to, the streptomycin locus [20]. This result is in accordance with evidence from genetic experiments which have revealed that the streptomycin locus and the locus governing the "K" protein occupy different positions on the genome [32]. Employing the same technique of total reconstitution, the mutation leading to streptomycin-dependence could be demonstrated to reside in the same cistron as that defining streptomycin resistance. That is, the streptomycin-resistance and the streptomycin-dependence mutation affect the same ribosomal protein [33].

The final goal of this localization project will consist of the assignment of the mutationally induced amino acid exchanges in the altered ribosomal protein to the corresponding functional modifications of the ribosome. Hopefully, it will contribute to a more detailed understanding of the mode of action of streptomycin, which in turn might permit a deeper insight into the correlation of the structure of the ribosome with its function in protein synthesis.

From the observation that streptomycin-resistant 30s ribosomes, in contrast to sensitive ones, cannot bind the antibiotic

[34], it appears very likely that all effects induced by streptomycin on sensitive 30s ribosomes are due to the association of the drug with the ribosomal particles. One molecule of streptomycin per 30s ribosome seems to be sufficient to exert the inhibitory effect on the various ribosomal functions [34]. The results of reconstitution experiments, employing the techniques of partial and total reconstitution of physically and functionally intact 30s ribosomes from their dissociated structural constituents, indicate a clear dependence of the drug binding reaction on the completeness of the 30s ribosomal subunit [35]. Neither 16s RNA or 23s core particles, nor free ribosomal proteins from streptomycin-sensitive 30s ribosomes alone, are able to bind the antibiotic in a stable way. It could be demonstrated that core protein CP30 from streptomycin-sensitive 30s ribosomes is the determining factor [35], a result that is in accordance with the previously obtained result that the response of the 30s ribosome to streptomycin is governed by the core protein [30].

The binding of the drug is substantially enhanced in the presence of uridine- or cytidine-containing polynucleotides [34]. Adenine- and guanine-containing polynucleotides do not stimulate the binding reaction [34]. This might well be correlated with the known inertness of adenine and guanine to streptomycin induced misreading [12]. Furthermore, the temperature dependence of the binding of dihydrostreptomycin to sensitive 30s ribosomal particles [34] suggests an energy requiring configurational change of the primary complex between the antibiotic and the 30s ribosome which leads to the stabilization of the interaction between the two components. In this respect, it is noteworthy that bound streptomycin cannot be removed from the ribosome easily by washing and that it increases the resistance of streptomycin-sensitive ribosomes to thermal denaturation [36].

Single step mutation to streptomycin-resistance eliminates the binding site for streptomycin on the 30s ribosome [34]. This finding is inconsistent with the experimental fact that streptomycin-resistant cells in many cases are phenotypically suppressible by the antibiotic, implying its interaction with the template-ribosome complex [13, 14]. It should be mentioned, however, that there might well exist streptomycin binding sites on the ribosome whose weak interaction with the antibiotic cannot be detected under the experimental conditions of the analytical method employed. The detection of two molecules of streptomycin per 30s ribosomal particle at higher temperature of the incubation mixture points in this direction [34]. This weak interaction might be sufficiently strong to warrant phenotypic suppression of missense and nonsense mutations in streptomycin-resistant cells.

II. Cycloheximide

A. Structure and Function of Mammalian Ribosomes

In contrast to our substantial knowledge compiled on bacterial ribosomes, our knowledge of ribosomes from mammalian cells is still in its embryonic stage. While in the case of bacterial ribosomes research was concentrated especially on E. coli ribosomes, efforts to analyse the structure of animal ribosomes were somewhat divergent due to the investigation of ribosomal particles from a plentitude of differentiated tissues, the number of which is largely increased by the existence of an abundance of different species. Moreover, comparison of the chemical composition of ribosomes from different sources is difficult because of the employment of different methodology. Thus, it is not surprising to find that results originating from different laboratories sometimes deviate considerably from each other. Nevertheless, it is possible to present a rough outline of the chemical composition of mammalian ribosomes and a short description of their physical properties and of their function in protein synthesis, what might be useful for the interpretation of the mode of action of cycloheximide. Generally, it can be stated that the universality of the mechanism of protein synthesis implies similar architecture for both bacterial and animal ribosomes. Thus, in first approximation, the structure of mammalian ribosomes may be regarded as very similar to that of bacterial ribosomes. A comprehensive review of the chemical and physical properties of animal ribosomes was published several years ago [37].

Ribosomes from higher organisms consist, like those from bacteria, of two subunits which associate reversibly during protein synthesis. They are somewhat larger than bacterial ribosomes, the monomers having a sedimentation coefficient of 80s and the subunits having sedimentation values of 40s and 60s. Until recently it was impossible to dissociate 80s monomers into their subunits without destroying their protein synthesizing capacity. Dissociation could be achieved only by complete removal of Mg^{++}-ions in the presence of chelating agents, such as EDTA or pyrophosphate. Under these conditions, however, the ribosomal subunits undergo irreversible configurational changes which are expressed in smaller sedimentation coefficients (approximately 30s and 50s) and in the irreversibility of the dissociation process. This, in turn, leads to their functional inactivation [38, 39]. A remarkable progress consisted of the discovery that 80s ribosomes can be separated into their 40s and 60s subunits in solution of moderate salt concentration, in the absence or in the presence of Mg^{++}-ions, at low or at high temperature, respectively [40, 41]. The separation is presumed to result from the displacement of divalent Mg^{++}-ions which form ionic links between the subunits. However, the results do not exclude the possibility that hydrogen bonds are involved as the forces holding the two ribosomal subunits together in the 80s monomer. In fact, the two subunits can also be separated by exposing 80s monomers to 2 M urea in solution of low Mg^{++}-ion concentration [42]. Still another method employs separation of the two subunits by chromatography of 80s monomers on DEAE-cellulose [43]. These conditions do not impair the ability of the ribosomal subunits to reassociate with the formation of functionally active 80s monomers. With respect to the stoichiometry of the dissociation process, the 80s monomers were found to separate into equal amounts of both subunits, their particle weights being two thirds and one third of that of the monomers [38, 41]. The particle weight of the 80s ribosome was determined to be approximately 4×10^6, that of 40s and 60s subunits to be approximately 1.2×10^6 and 2.8×10^6, respectively [37].

The RNA content of ribosomes from different sources varies between 40 and 60% [37]. It is possible that these differences, at least partially, are due to varying degrees of contamination by extraneous proteins and also to the employment of different standard materials for the protein assays [44]. Occasionally, a slightly higher protein content was reported for the small subunit compared to that of the large one [44]. Each 40s subunit contains one molecule of 18s RNA with an approximate molecular weight of 0.6 to 0.7×10^6, whereas each 60s ribosomal subunit contains one molecule of each 28s RNA and 5s RNA with molecular weights of approximately 1.6 to 1.9×10^6, respectively [37,45]. The differences in the molecular weights of ribosomal RNA of different preparations may be attributed to the fact that different RNA molecules of the same size form random coils of varying degrees of compactness at a given salt concentration. All three ribosomal RNA species originally were thought to be represented by continuous polynucleotide chains, with double helical segments alternating with single stranded regions [46]. Recently, however, it was shown that upon denaturation 28s RNA from HeLa cells gives rise to a small molecule about 150 nucleotides in length and with a molecular weight of about 4×10^4 [47]. This polynucleotide with a sedimentation coefficient of 7s exists in an amount equivalent in number of molecules to that of 28s RNA.

The double helical content of unfractionated reticulocyte ribosomal RNA was estimated as 60% and the average length of the hair pin loops determined to be 10 to 20 residues with an upper limit of 35 residues [48]. Highly significant differences in the frequency of almost all sequences released by RNA digestion of ribosomal RNA from HeLa cells were demonstrated to occur between the two ribosomal RNA species [49, 50]. They are in agreement with results from DNA-RNA hybridization experiments which suggest that 18s RNA and 28s RNA are transcribed from different regions of the genome [51]. This is also consistent with the observation of significant differences in the base composition of the two ribosomal RNA species [52]. Compared with bacterial ribosomal RNAs, those of animal origin show a less pronounced asymmetrical base composition [37]. Ribosomal RNA from HeLa cells contains in appreciable amounts nucleotides methylated in the bases or in the ribose moieties [53, 54] and pseudouridylic acid [50]. The latter is distributed specifically along the polynucleotide chains of ribosomal RNA, suggesting the conversion of uridylic acid into pseudouridylic acid through an enzymic mechanism operating at specific sites determined by the primary or secondary structure of the ribosomal RNA [50].

Little is known about the protein from mammalian ribosomes. This is due in part to its marked tendency to form insoluble aggregates in solution of low ionic strength or in the absence of denaturing reagents. In general, ribosomal protein from animal ribosomes shows a similar chemical composition as that from bacterial ribosomes and exhibits, therefore, similar properties. This refers to its amino acid composition [55, 56] which is distinguished by a high content of basic and dicarboxylic amino acids, by an above-average amount of amino acids with hydrophobic side chains and by a low content of aromatic and sulfur-containing amino acids. The distribution of terminal amino acids is nonrandom, with proline, alanine, glycine and serine comprising 80% of the N-terminal positions [57].

Moreover, the protein of ribosomes from various sources turned out to be heterogeneous as revealed by starch and polyacrylamide gel electrophoresis [58—67]. The electrophoresis profiles of the protein moieties of both ribosomal subunits differ strikingly from each other [58, 62, 64—66]. Their summation results in the protein band pattern of undissociated 80s ribosomes [65] which give rise to about 25 to 30 recognizable electrophoretic bands in polyacrylamide gels. The band patterns of proteins isolated from the small subunits generally are less complex than those isolated from their complementary large subunits. In several cases the results from gel electrophoretic comparison of the protein composition of both ribosomal subunits suggest that in eukaryotic cells most of the ribosomal proteins may be shared in common by the large and small subunits [62, 66]. While ribosomal proteins isolated from different tissues of the same animal appear almost indistinguishable from each other upon polyacrylamide gel electrophoresis [60, 66], those derived from the same tissue of animals of various genera yield clearly different electrophoretic patterns [60, 62, 63, 66] although they show basic similarities. By contrast, the electrophoresis profile of ribosomal protein from E. coli is completely different from that of ribosomal protein from mammalian cells [60].

So far only few attempts have been undertaken to separate ribosomal protein of mammalian ribosomes into its molecular components and to characterize them physically and chemically [58, 61]. Fractionation of ribosomal protein from rat liver ribosomes resulted in the isolation of several more or less pure protein species whose molecular weights were determined or estimated to be between 10000 and 30000 [58]. The average molecular weight of the total protein from rat liver ribosomes was found to be 26000 [58] which is in good agreement with that of protein from bovine liver ribosomes which was determined to be 25000 [68].

However, in view of the fact that the average molecular weight of total protein from E. coli 70s ribosomes deviates considerably from the average of the molecular weights of the total proteins from the two ribosomal subunits towards a higher value [69], it appears likely that the molecular weight found for protein of liver ribosomes is put too high. First estimations of the distribution of individual ribosomal proteins on mammalian ribosomes indicated that they are represented by more than one copy per ribosomal particle [58].

With respect to the spatial arrangement of ribosomal proteins in rat liver ribosomes, the exposure of intact ribosomes to various proteolytic enzymes indicated that, in general, only a limited part of the protease-sensitive proteins are accessible to the enzymes, whereas in the free state they are readily degraded [67]. The results of these experiments were interpreted to the effect that only minor sections of the polypeptide chains are exposed on the ribosomal surface, while large, electrophoretically well defined parts of the molecules are embedded in the interior of the ribosome. The protein fragments formed were, in general, not dissociated from the ribosome as long as they remained electrophoretically recognizable. It is noteworthy that the mRNA dependent polypeptide synthesizing activity of protease-treated ribosomes first increased before it was reduced gradually by the action of the proteolytic enzymes. Apparently the intactness of the shielded portions of the polypeptide chains is of greater importance for the proper functioning of the ribosome in polypeptide synthesis than that of the exposed loops. The behavior of the individual ribosomal proteins towards digestion by proteolytic enzymes was markedly influenced by Mg^{++}-ion dependent configurational changes of the ribosomal structure which were induced by the addition of EDTA or of pyrophosphate or by variation of the ionic strength. This indicates that the resistance of ribosomal proteins in the intact ribosome to proteases is not due to steric hindrance of the enzyme action by ribosomal RNA [70].

The occurrence of distinct quaternary structures also in mammalian ribosomes was demonstrated by dissociation of a defined group of proteins from the ribosomes in solution of high salt concentration [71, 72]. In one case, the reattachment of the split proteins to the functionally inactive protein-deficient ribonucleoprotein particles restored partially the polypeptide synthesizing activity [71].

In general, the striking similarity of the physical and chemical properties of the molecular constituents of ribosomes from bacterial and mammalian cells suggests that these particles have very similar structures. In comparison to bacterial ribosomes, those of mammalian origin possess a larger particle weight, larger dimensions, contain relatively more RNA and proteins, and are distinguished by a more complex physical and chemical behavior.

Although the mechanism of protein synthesis in mammalian cells is fairly well understood, the detailed investigation of the various substrate binding reactions employing isolated ribosomal subunits was considerably delayed by the persisting failure to dissociate 80s ribosomes into their subunits without destroying their functional activity. Recently, however, dissociation of reticulocyte 80s monomers into their subunits at high KCl concentration yielded ribosomal subunits that retained their capacity to synthesize hemoglobin and polyphenylalanine. Similar to bacterial ribosomes, the small subunit was found to bind mRNA, whereas no binding of aminoacyl-tRNA to either subunit was observed [73]. Yet, the large subunit appeared to be the site to which the nascent peptide chain is bound [73]. First evidence for aminoacyl- and peptidyl-tRNA binding sites on reticulocyte ribosomes previously came from binding studies using 80s monomers and poly U as mRNA in solution of physiological Mg^{++} to K^{+} ratio [74]. It could be shown that in the presence of the two enzymic transfer factors TF-1 and TF-2 and of GTP the 80s monomer can bind two molecules of aminoacyl-tRNA [74—77], and that the presence of these cofactors is also obligatory for the formation of peptide bonds. The formation of phenylalanine-puromycin proved to be a convenient system to study various aspects of binding of aminoacyl-tRNA to ribosomes and of peptide bond formation [77].

Subsequent experiments, employing rat liver ribosomes, revealed that during peptide chain elongation the aminoacyl-tRNA binding reaction requires transferase TF-1 and GTP [78]. This step does not involve hydrolysis of the nucleotide. The reaction of endogenous peptidyl-tRNA with the bound aminoacyl-tRNA was found to be catalysed by peptidyltransferase which is an integral part of the ribosome. After peptide bond formation the new peptidyl-tRNA, one amino acid longer, occupies the acceptor site of the ribosome and therefore blocks the binding of another molecule of aminoacyl-tRNA. Only after translocation of the peptidyl-tRNA from the acceptor to the donor site, a GTP requiring reaction catalysed by transferase TF-2, can the incoming aminoacyl-tRNA molecule associate with the mRNA-peptidyl tRNA-ribosome complex and can peptide bond formation take place. Thus,

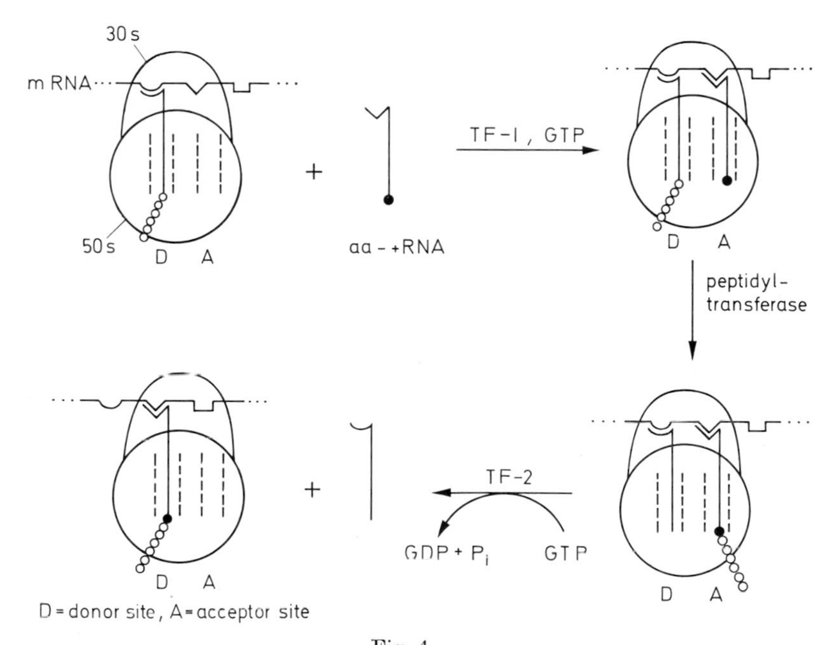

Fig. 1

these results suggest, in analogy to the E. coli protein synthesizing system, that transferase TF-1 is the aminoacyl-tRNA binding factor, that peptidyltransferase is a ribosomal activity, that transferase TF-2 is involved in translocation and that the binding of aminoacyl-tRNA and the translocation require GTP [78]. The reactions occurring in the course of polypeptide chain elongation, that is binding of aminoacyl-tRNA, peptide bond formation, and translocation of peptidyl-tRNA, are depicted in the scheme above.

B. Mode and Locus of Action of Cycloheximide

Cycloheximide is a potent inhibitor of protein synthesis in mammalian cells [79]. Using cell-free systems of various sources, the antibiotic was shown to exert its effect on protein synthesis after amino acid activation or transfer of activated amino acids to tRNA [80—84]. The following step of transfer of amino acids from aminoacyl-tRNA into protein turned out to be the reaction sensitive to cycloheximide [80, 81, 85—87]. However, breakdown of polyribosomes to monomers, which normally occurs during protein synthesis in vitro, was found not to be the cause of inhibition of protein synthesis, ruling out premature detachment of ribosomes from mRNA or fragmentation of mRNA [82—84, 88, 89]. The implication of this finding is that the movement of ribosomes relative to mRNA is slowed down drastically or even prevented in the presence of the antibiotic [87]. This could be shown clearly in the presence of sodium fluoride which is known to prevent polypeptide chain initiation but to allow readout of the information contained in polyribosome-incorporated mRNA, resulting in an apparent breakdown of polyribosomes to single ribosomes [90]. This sodium fluoride-dependent conversion of polyribosomes into monomers is inhibited by cycloheximide [90, 91]. "Freezing" of polyribosomes occurs without loss of the growing peptide chains bound to the polyribosomes [82—84, 88, 89]. Beside its effect on polypeptide chain elongation, cycloheximide also interferes severely with chain initiation [89, 90], as revealed by inhibition of polyribosome formation in reticulocytes that first have been treated with sodium fluoride to break down preexisting polyribosomes and then washed free of sodium fluoride. Under these conditions and in the absence of cycloheximide, reassembly of polyribosomes is observed [89]. An important step forward in the elucidation of the action of cycloheximide was brought about by the detection that the site of action of the antibiotic is apparently located in the ribosome-free supernatant [88, 89]. This finding suggested the interference of cycloheximide with the action of supernatant factors involved in polypeptide synthesis. As possible candidates the two transferases, TF-1 and TF-2, had to be taken into consideration [74—78]. And indeed, the observation that the effect of cycloheximide on polypeptide chain elongation could be partially reversed by the addition of large amounts of glutathione to the incubation medium [92, 93] suggested a close relationship between the action of the inhibitor and the sulfhydryl-dependent enzyme transferase TF-2 [94]. Further pursuit of this observation revealed the specific hydrolysis of GTP by transferase TF-2 as the reaction inhibited by cycloheximide [93]. The inhibition of incorporation of amino-acids from aminoacyl-tRNA into polypeptides by the antibiotic was paralleled by the inhibition of release of inorganic phosphate from GTP. These results show that one site of action of cycloheximide involves a sulfhydryl-sensitive enzyme which probably is identical with transferase TF-2. Since, however, the enzymatic hydrolysis of GTP during peptide bond formation is dependent on previous enzymatic steps in protein synthesis occurring on the ribosome, the possibility of other protein factors as the target of cycloheximide cannot be excluded from consideration.

The functional expression of the inhibitory effect of cycloheximide on transferase TF-2, of course, can be observed only in the presence of 80s ribosomes which, in aggregation with peptidyl-tRNA occupying the acceptor site, are the substrate for the enzyme. It is conceivable, therefore, that the 80s ribosome may influence the interaction between translocase and the antibiotic in a positive way. This is actually indicated by the existence of cycloheximide-resistant species of Saccharomyces which either are insensitive per se to high levels of the antibiotic or which are obtained from normally sensitive organisms by gene mutation [95—98]. It could be shown that the ribosomes are the cellular constituents which impart cycloheximide resistance to these species. The existence of such insensitive ribosomes implies that they tolerate or reverse the inactivation of translocase by the antibiotic, and from the protecting effect of glutathione it is tempting to assume that a sulfhydryl group at a strategic site of the resistant ribosome is involved in this toleration or reversion. Resistance and sensitivity to cycloheximide were shown to be properties associated with the 60s ribosomal subunit [96], as revealed by hybridization experiments employing ribosomal subunits from both cycloheximide-sensitive and cycloheximide-resistant species. This implies that transferase TF-2 fulfills its function on the large ribosomal subunit, in accordance with the conception of the large subunit as the particle harboring the acceptor and the donor site.

An interesting effect of cycloheximide was observed when it

was realized that the antibiotic is only active in protein synthesizing systems containing 80s ribosomes [80, 99] and that systems containing 70s ribosomes are indifferent to the action of cycloheximide [80, 99]. This differentiating effect of the antibiotic might well be related to the fact that ribosomes and supernatant factors can be crossed widely only between different systems having the same size ribosomes, but not between systems with 70s and 80s ribosomes. It found its nice application in the distinction between mitochondrial and extramitochondrial protein synthesis. It is now well established that mitochondria contain 70s ribosomes in contrast to cytoplasm which contains 80s ribosomes. In vivo and in vitro experiments have shown that cycloheximide specifically inhibits extramitochondrial protein synthesis but leaves mitochondrial protein synthesis unaffected [100—104].

References

1. Weisblum, B., and J. Davies: Bact. Rev. **32**, 493 (1968).
2. The Antibiotics, vol. 1. Gottlieb, D., and P. D. Shaw, Eds. Berlin-Heidelberg-New York: Springer 1967.
3. Attardi, G.: Ann. Rev. Microbiol. **21**, 383 (1967).
4. Ochoa, S.: Naturwissenschaften **55**, 505 (1968).
5. Matthaei, H., G. Sander, D. Swan, T. Kreuzer, H. Caffier und A. Parmeggiani: Naturwissenschaften **55**, 281 (1968).
6. Traub, P.: Curr. Top. Microbiol. Immunol. (in preparation).
7. Gorini, L., and E. Kataja: Proc. nat. Acad. Sci. (Wash.) **51**, 995 (1964).
8. Schlessinger, D., G. Mangiarotti, and D. Apirion: Proc. nat. Acad. Sci. (Wash.) **58**, 1782 (1967).
9. Luzzatto, L., D. Apirion, and D. Schlessinger: Proc. nat. Acad. Sci. (Wash.) **60**, 873 (1968).
10. Modolell, J., and B. D. Davis: Proc. nat. Acad. Sci. (Wash.) **61**, 1279 (1968).
11. Davies, J. E., W. Gilbert, and L. Gorini: Proc. nat. Acad. Sci. (Wash.) **51**, 883 (1964).
12. — Cold Spr. Harb. Symp. quant. Biol. **31**, 665 (1966).
13. Gorini, L., and E. Kataja: Proc. nat. Acad. Sci. (Wash.) **51**, 487 (1964).
14. Whitfield, H. J., R. G. Martin, and B. N. Ames: J. molec. Biol. **21**, 335 (1966).
15. Gorini, L., and E. Kataja: Biochem. biophys. Res. Commun. **18**, 656 (1965).
16. —, and J. E. Davies: Curr. Top. Microbiol. Immunol. **44**, 100 (1968).
17. Flaks, J. G., E. C. Cox, M. L. Witting, and J. R. White: Biochem. biophys. Res. Commun. **7**, 390 (1962).
18. Speyer, J. F., P. Lengyel, and C. Basilio: Proc. nat. Acad. Sci. (Wash.) **48**, 684 (1962).

19. Cox, E. C., J. R. White, and J. G. Flaks: Proc. nat. Acad. Sci. (Wash.) **51**, 703 (1964).
20. Leboy, P. S., E. C. Cox, and J. G. Flaks: Proc. nat. Acad. Sci. (Wash.) **52**, 1367 (1964).
21. Silengo, L., D. Schlessinger, G. Mangiarotti, and D. Apirion: Mutation Res. **4**, 701 (1967).
22. Hosokawa, K., R. Fujimura, and M. Nomura: Proc. nat. Acad. Sci. (Wash.) **55**, 198 (1966).
23. Staehelin, T., and M. Meselson: J. molec. Biol. **16**, 245 (1966).
24. Meselson, M., M. Nomura, S. Brenner, C. Davern, and D. Schlessinger: J. molec. Biol. **9**, **696** (1964).
25. Traub, P., and M. Nomura: J. molec. Biol. **34**, 575 (1968).
26. Raskas, H. J., and T. Staehelin: J. molec. Biol. **23**, 89 (1967).
27. Traub, P., K. Hosokawa, and M. Nomura: J. molec. Biol. **19**, 211 (1966).
28. Staehelin, T., and M. Meselson: J. molec. Biol. **19**, 207 (1966).
29. Traub, P., and M. Nomura: Proc. nat. Acad. Sci. (Wash.) **59**, **777** (1968).
30. — — Science **160**, 198 (1968).
31. Ozaki, M., S. Mizushima, and M. Nomura: Nature (Lond.) (1969) (in press).
32. Mayuga, C., D. Meier, and T. Wang: Biochem. biophys. Res. Commun. **33**, 203 (1968).
33. Kurland, C. G.: Personal communication.
34. Kaji, H., and Y. Tanaka: J. molec. Biol. **32**, 221 (1968).
35. Tanaka, Y., and H. Kaji: Biochem. biophys. Res. Commun. **32**, 313 (1968).
36. Wolfe, A. D., and F. E. Hahn: Biochem. biophys. Res. Commun. **31**, 945 (1968).
37. Petermann, M. L.: The physical and chemical properties of ribosomes. Amsterdam: Elsevier 1964.
38. Tashiro, Y., and P. Siekevitz: J. molec. Biol. **11**, 149 (1965).
39. —, and T. Morimoto: Biochim. biophys. Acta (Amst.) **123**, 523 (1966).
40. Yang, P. C., K. Hamada, and R. Schweet: Arch. Biochem. **125**, 506 (1968).
41. Martin, T. E., and I. G. Wool: Proc. nat. Acad. Sci. (Wash.) **60**, 569 (1968).
42. Petermann, M. L., and A. Pavlovec: Fed. Proc. **28**, 725 (1969).
43. Dickman, S. R., and E. Bruenger: Fed. Proc. **28**, 726 (1969).
44. Keller, P. J., E. Cohen, and J. A. Hollinshead Beeley: J. biol. Chem. **243**, 1271 (1968).
45. Forget, B. G., and S. M. Weissman: Science **158**, 1695 (1967).
46. Cox, R. A., H. J. Gould, and K. Kanagalingam: Biochem. J. **106**, 733 (1968).
47. Pene, J. J., E. Knight, and J. E. Darnell: J. molec. Biol. **33**, 609 (1968).
48. Cox, R. A., and K. Kanagalingam: Biochem. J. **103**, 431 (1967).
49. Roberts, W. K., and L. D'Ari: Biochemistry **7**, 592 (1968).
50. Amaldi, F., and G. Attardi: J. molec. Biol. **33**, 737 (1968).

51. Attardi, G., P. C. Huang, and S. Kabat: Proc. nat. Acad. Sci. (Wash.) **54**, 185 (1965).
52. Zimmermann, E. F., M. Heeter, and J. E. Darnell: Virology **19**, 400 (1963).
53. —, and B. W. Holler: J. molec. Biol. **23**, 149 (1967).
54. Brown, G. M., and G. Attardi: Biochem. biophys. Res. Commun. **20**, 298 (1965).
55. Ts'o, P. O. P., J. Bonner, and H. Dintzis: Arch. Biochem. **76**, 225 (1958).
56. Crampton, C. F., and M. L. Petermann: J. biol. Chem. **234**, 2642 (1959).
57. Cohn, P., and P. Simson: Biochem. J. **88**, 206 (1963).
58. Hamilton, M. G., and M. E. Ruth: Biochemistry **6**, 2585 (1967).
59. MacQuillen, A. M., and S. T. Bayley: Canad. J. Biochem. **44**, 1221 (1966).
60. Low, R. B., and I. G. Wool: Science **155**, 330 (1966).
61. Welfle, H., u. H. Bielka: Z. Naturforsch. **23**, 690 (1968).
62. Keller, P. J., E. Cohen, and J. A. Hollinshead Beeley: J. biol. Chem. **243**, 1271 (1968).
63. Buj, A. T., et G. Shapira: C. R. Acad. Sci. (Paris), Sér. D **264**, 2417 (1967).
64. Work, T. S.: J. molec. Biol. **10**, 544 (1964).
65. Kedes, H. L., R. J. Koegel, and E. L. Kuff: J. molec. Biol. **22**, 359 (1966).
66. Girolamo, M., and P. Cammarano: Biochim. biophys. Acta (Amst.) **168**, 181 (1968).
67. Östner, U., and T. Hultin: Biochim. biophys. Acta (Amst.) **154**, 376 (1968).
68. Curry, J. B., and R. T. Hersh: Biochem. biophys. Res. Commun. **6**, 415 (1962).
69. Moore, P. B., R. R. Traut, H. Noller, P. Pearson, and H. Delius: J. molec. Biol. **31**, 441 (1968).
70. Hultin, T., and U. Östner: Biochim. biophys. Acta (Amst.) **160**, 229 (1968).
71. Lerman, M. J.: Molec. Biol. **2**, 171 (1968), translated from Molekulyarnaya Biologiya.
72. Petermann, M. L., A. M. Rebond, and M. G. Hamilton: Fed. Proc. **26**, 285 (1967).
73. Hamada, K., P. Yang, R. Heintz, and R. Schweet: Arch. Biochem. **125**, 598 (1968).
74. Schweet, R. S., R. Arlinghaus, R. Heintz, and J. Shaeffer: Ann. Symp. on Fundamental Cancer Res., Univ. Texas, M. D. Anderson, and Tumor Institute **19**, 47 (1965).
75. Arlinghaus, R., J. Shaeffer, and R. S. Schweet: Proc. nat. Acad. Sci. (Wash.) **51**, 1291 (1964).
76. Heintz, R., H. McAllister, and R. S. Schweet: Cold Spr. Harb. Symp. quant. Biol. **31**, 633 (1966).
77. Heintz, R. L., M. L. Salas, and R. S. Schweet: Arch. Biochem. **125**, 488 (1968).

78. Skogerson, L., and K. Moldave: Arch. Biochem. **125**, 497 (1968).
79. Sisler, H. D., and M. R. Siegel: In: The antibiotics, Vol. 1, p. 283. Gottlieb, D., and P. D. Shaw, Eds. Berlin-Heidelberg-New York: Springer 1967.
80. Ennis, H. L., and M. Lubin: Science **146**, 1474 (1964).
81. Bennett, jr., L. L., V. L. Ward, and R. W. Brockman: Biochim. biophys. Acta (Amst.) **103**, 478 (1965).
82. Wettstein, F. O., H. Noll, and S. Penman: Biochim. biophys. Acta (Amst.) **87**, 525 (1964).
83. Williamson, A. R., and R. Schweet: J. molec. Biol. **11**, 358 (1965).
84. Colombo, B., L. Felicetti, and C. Baglioni: Biochem. biophys. Res. Commun. **18**, 389 (1965).
85. Siegel, M. R., and H. D. Sisler: Nature (Lond.) **200**, 675 (1963).
86. — — Biochim. biophys. Acta (Amst.) **87**, 83 (1964).
87. Trakatellis, A. C., M. Montjar, and A. E. Axelrod: Biochemistry **4**, 2065 (1965).
88. Colombo, B., L. Felicetti, and C. Baglioni: Biochim. biophys. Acta (Amst.) **119**, 109 (1966).
89. Felicetti, L., B. Colombo, and C. Baglioni: Biochim. biophys. Acta (Amst.) **119**, 120 (1966).
90. Lin, S.-Y., R. D. Mosteller, and B. Hardesty: J. molec. Biol. **21**, 51 (1966).
91. Godchaux, W., S. D. Adamson, and E. Herbert: J. molec. Biol. **27**, 57 (1967).
92. Baliga, B. S., A. W. Pronczuk, and H. N. Munro: Fed. Proc. **27**, 766 (1968).
93. Munro, H. N., B. S. Baliga, and A. W. Pronczuk: Nature (Lond.) **219**, 944 (1968).
94. Sutter, R. P., and K. Moldave: J. biol. Chem. **241**, 1698 (1966).
95. Cooper, D., D. V. Banthorpe, and D. Wilkie: J. molec. Biol. **26**, 347 (1967).
96. Rao, S. S., and A. P. Grollman: Biochem. biophys. Res. Commun. **29**, 696 (1967).
97. Siegel, M. R., and H. D. Sisler: Biochim. biophys. Acta (Amst.) **103**, 558 (1965).
98. Wilkie, D., and B. K. Lee: Genet. Res. **6**, 130 (1965).
99. Vazquez, D., and R. E. Monro: Biochim. biophys. Acta (Amst.) **142**, 155 (1967).
100. Beattie, D. S., R. E. Basford, and S. B. Koritz: Biochemistry **6**, 3099 (1967).
101. Sebald, W., Th. Bücher, B. Olbrich, and F. Kaudewitz: FEBS Letters **1**, 235 (1968).
102. Lamb, A. J., G. D. Clark-Walker, and A. W. Linnane: Biochim. biophys. Acta (Amst.) **161**, 415 (1968).
103. Beattie, D. S.: J. biol. Chem. **243**, 4027 (1968).
104. Sebald, W., Th. Hofstötter, D. Hacker, and Th. Bücher: FEBS Letters **2**, 177 (1969).

Inhibitors as Tools in Elucidating Ribosomal Function

D. VAZQUEZ, T. STAEHELIN*, M. L. CELMA, E. BATTANER, R. FERNÁNDEZ-MUÑOZ, and R. E. MONRO

Instituto de Biología Celular, Velazquez 144, Madrid-6, Spain

With 3 Figures

The way in which ribosomes are organized in *Escherichia coli* according to the translocation model [1—4 and refs. therein) to explain the overall reactions taking place in the biosynthesis of protein by *E. coli* ribosomes is shown in Fig. 1. It is well established that the direction of reading of mRNA is from the 5′ end to the 3′ end [5, 6]. The synthesis of bacterial protein is initiated with formyl-methionine [7, 8]. All the evidence so far suggests that the anticodon region of tRNA is recognized and its interaction with mRNA specifically stabilized by the 30 S subunit. Other portions of the tRNA and in particular the amino acid- or f-Met-bearing moiety interact with the 50 S subunit. According to the one entry site theory of the translocation model, now the most accepted one, the f-Met-$tRNA_f$ binds initially at the "A" site and is then translocated to the "P" site (Fig. 1a) leaving the "A" site open for the AA_1-$tRNA_1$ to enter (Fig. 1b) [4B, 9, 10]. According to the two entry sites variant of the translocation model, the chain is initiated by direct entry of f-Met-$tRNA_f$ at the "P" site, whereas during chain growth aminoacyl-tRNA binds at the "A" site [11—13]. The specificity for the initiating role of f-Met-$tRNA_f$ and its binding to the "P" site is due to the α-NH_2 of the methionine being blocked by formylation, and to the unique structure of the $tRNA_f$.

Once the f-Met-$tRNA_f$ is in the "P" site and the AA_1-$tRNA_1$ is bound to the "A" site, peptide bond formation takes place (Fig. 1c) catalyzed by the peptidyl transferase which is an integral part of

* Department of Zoology, University of Michigan, Ann Arbor.

the 50 S ribosome subunit [14—18 A]. Peptide bond formation takes place by transfer of the f-Met moiety in such a way that the -COOH group of methionine is linked to the $-NH_2$ group of the amino acid of the AA_1-$tRNA_1$ bound at the "A" site [19]. The

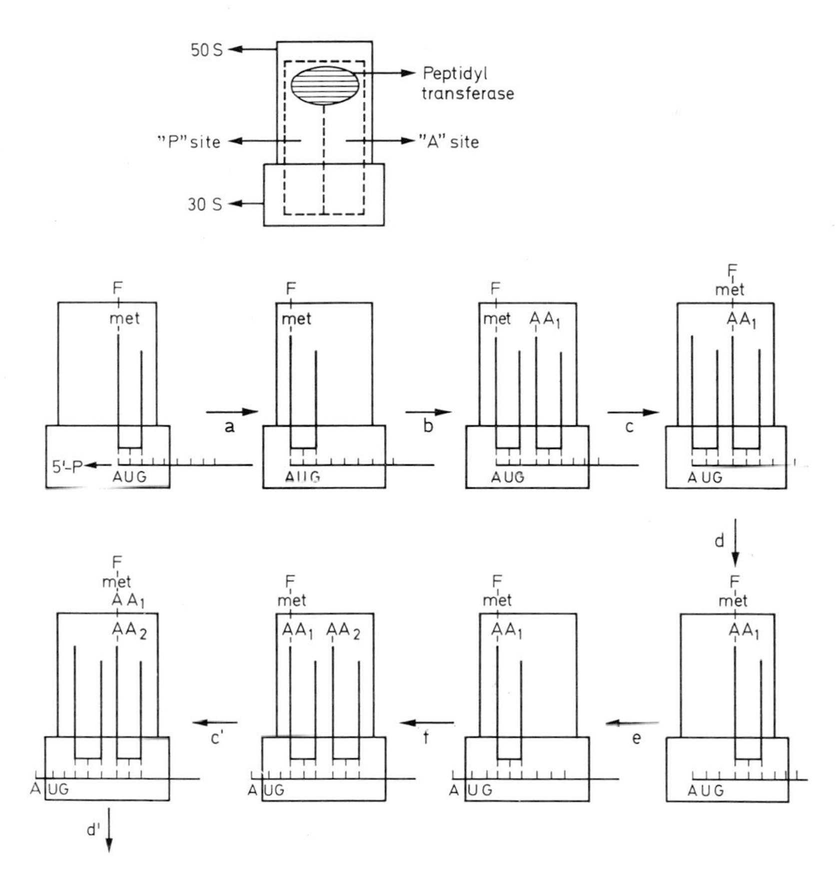

Fig. 1

stripped $tRNA_f$ is then released from the "P" site (Fig. 1d), and the f-Met-AA_1-$tRNA_1$ at the "A" site is moved to the "P" site (Fig. 1e) [1, 2, 14, 3, 4]. Movement of the mRNA is coupled to movement of the f-Met-AA_1-$tRNA_1$. This step is not well understood, but there are some indications that GTP and a translocase are involved in it [2—4 B, 4 C, 13]. When the translocase moves f-Met-AA_1-tRNA$_1$ from the "A" site to the "P" site, the triplet coding for AA_1-tRNA$_1$ also moves in the same way (Fig. 1e). The site "A" is then free, and AA_2-tRNA$_2$ comes into this position (Fig. 1f). The ribosomal peptidyl transferase will then transfer the f-Met-AA_1 from tRNA$_1$ at the "P" site to the α-amino-group of AA_2-tRNA$_2$ at the "A" site, thus forming f-Met-AA_1-AA_2-tRNA$_2$ (Fig. 1c′) (repetition of step 1c).

Table 1

	70 S type ribosomes	80 S type ribosomes
Organism or organelle	Bacteria Blue-green algae Chloroplasts Mitochondria	Mammalian cytoplasm Green algae cytoplasm Yeast cytoplasm Fungi cytoplasm Protozoa cytoplasm Higher plants cytoplasm
Composition: Protein	40%	60%
RNA	60%	40%
Subunits	50 S and 30 S	60 S and 40 S
Ribosomal RNA	5 S, 23 S, and 16 S	5 S, 25 S, and 16 S plant ribosomes 5 S, 29 S, and 18 S animal ribosomes

By this mechanism the growing polypeptide chain remains bound to the ribosome through the tRNA carrying the last amino acid incorporated into the chain. To finish protein synthesis, a chain-terminating codon (non-sense codon) is read [20, 21], the last peptidyl-tRNA bond is cleaved in a reaction requiring a supernatant factor [22], and the formyl group of the f-Met-end is removed by the action of a supernatant enzyme [23].

Basically, the same mechanism for protein synthesis as in *E. coli* is found in organisms other than bacteria. However, it is well known that ribosomes can be broadly classified according to their size into 70 S and 80 S. In the cytoplasm of cells from mammals, higher plants, fungi, yeasts, and protozoa, the ribosomes are of sedimentation coefficient 80 S, whereas in bacteria, blue-green algae, chloroplasts and possibly mitochondria [24, 25] the ribosomes are of the 70 S type. 70 S ribosomes differ from 80 S not only in their sedimentation coefficient but also in chemical composition, molecular weight of their RNA, response to ionic environment and to treatment with protein synthesis inhibitors (Tables 1 and 5) [25—28]. On the basis of differences in their rRNA, 80 S ribosomes can be divided into plant ribosomes (having 25 S and 16 S rRNA) and animal ribosomes (having 29 S and 18 S rRNA) [29].

Parallel to the differences in their ribosomes, there are also differences in the mechanism of protein synthesis by prokaryotic and eukaryotic organisms. f-Met-$tRNA_f$ is required for initiation of synthesis in *E. coli*, and there is evidence suggesting that it is also present in organelles like chloroplasts and mitochondria [30, 31] but it has never been found in protein synthesizing systems having 80 S ribosomes. To differences between 70 S and 80 S ribosomes, corresponding differences can be found in initiation factors and supernatant enzymes since there is evidence that ribosomes and supernatant can be crossed between widely different systems having the same size ribosomes but not between systems with 70 S and 80 S ribosomes [28, 32—36]. However, it appears that the basic mechanism for protein synthesis in systems having the 70 S and 80 S types of ribosomes is very similar.

A number of enzymes are directly involved in the steps shown in Fig. 1. Most of these enzymes are present in the supernatant fraction when the ribosomes are pelleted and washed. The specific aminoacyl-tRNA synthetases, the formylating enzyme and the enzymes required to cleave the last peptidyl-tRNA bond and release the completed polypeptide chain, and the de-formylase are all supernatant enzymes. The supernatant factors Ts, Tu and G (required for binding of aminoacyl-tRNA and translocation) [37—39] may also be enzymes, and all of them are found in the supernatant fraction. The initiation factors F_1, F_2 and F_3 are loosely associated with the ribosomes [40]. On the other hand, accumulative experimental evidence has shown that the enzyme, peptidyl transferase, involved in peptide bond formation in protein synthesis is an integral part of the ribosome [14—18]. Since it was originally thought that the peptide bond-forming reaction involved GTP, the hypothetical enzyme was termed *peptide synthetase*, by analogy with certain other nucleoside triphosphate-requiring enzymes. However, the demonstration that GTP is not directly involved shows that the enzyme does not belong to the class of enzymes termed synthetases. Since the reaction is believed to take place by simple transfer of a peptidyl group from tRNA to aminoacyl-tRNA (Fig. 1c), it may be classified along with other group transfer reactions (not involving nucleoside triphosphates), which are catalysed by the group of enzymes known generically as transferases. For this reason the operational name *peptidyl transferase* was proposed [14].

Table 2. *Binding of ^{14}C-chloramphenicol to different ribosomes*

Ribosomes from:	Ribosome type S	Binding of ^{14}C-chloramphenicol
Staphylococcus aureus	70	+
Bacillus megaterium	70	+
Escherichia coli	70	+
Pseudomonas striata	70	+
Anabaena cylindrica	70	+
Anacystis montana	70	+
Crithidia oncopelti cytoplasm	80	–
Saccharomyces fragilis cytoplasm	80	–
Tetrahymena pyriformis cytoplasm	80	–
Cytoplasm of rat liver cells	80	–
Cytoplasm of *Pisum sativum* cells	80	–
Chloroplast of *Pisum sativum* cells	70	+
Euglena gracilis cytoplasm	80	–
Chloroplast of *Euglena gracilis*	70	+

Results taken from Refs. [26, 41, 42].

Inhibitors of Protein Synthesis at the Ribosome Level

Since there are at least two classes of ribosomes, the antibiotics acting on them can be classified according to their specificity towards the ribosomes. Studies on binding of ^{14}C-chloramphenicol showed that the antibiotic binds specifically to 70 S ribosomes from a number of bacteria, blue-green algae and chloroplasts but not to 80 S ribosomes from protozoa, yeasts, higher plants and mammals [26, 41, 42] (Table 2). Factors required for binding of chloramphenicol are shown in Table 3. The effect of other protein synthesis inhibitors on the binding of chloramphenicol to ribosomes

Table 3. *Characteristics of ¹⁴C-chloramphenicol binding to ribosomes*

Experimental conditions	Binding of ^{14}C-chloramphenicol
Bacterial ribosomes in standard buffer	+
K^+ omitted	–
Mg^{++} omitted	–
K^+ replaced by NH_4^+	+
K^+ replaced by Na^+	–
Ribosomes replaced by 50 S subunits	+
Ribosomes replaced by 30 S subunits	–

The standard buffer was Tris/HCl pH 7.4 containing 10^{-2} M Mg^{++} and 0.2 M K^+. Data taken from Refs. [54, 55].

Table 4. *Binding of ^{14}C-chloramphenicol to E. coli and B. megaterium ribosomes. Effect of protein synthesis inhibitors*

Inhibitory	Non inhibitory
Chloramphenicol group	Streptogramin B group
Chloramphenicol	Streptogramin B
D-AMP-3	Viridogrisein
D-Thiocymetin	Staphylomycin S
D-Win 5094	Tetracycline group
Macrolides group	Tetracycline
Angolamycin	Chlortetracycline
Carbomycin	Oxytetracycline
Erythromycin	Streptomycin group
Lancamycin	Streptomycin
Methymycin	Neomycin
Oleandomycin	Kanamycin
Spiramycin	Puromycin
Streptogramin A group	Amicetin
Streptogramin A	Sparsomycin
Ostreogrycin G	Gougerotin
Lincomycin group	Fusidic acid
Lincomycin	Edeine
Celesticetin	Poly-dextran-sulphate
	GMP-PCP

In all these experiments the concentration of ^{14}C-chloramphenicol was 1 μM and the concentration of the other inhibitors 90 μM [28, 55]. All the antibiotics included as non-inhibitory of ^{14}C-chloramphenicol binding inhibit less than 25% under these conditions but some of them at higher concentrations do completely inhibit ^{14}C-chloramphenicol binding, as we have found with puromycin (unpublished results) and other workers have shown with different antibiotics and ribosomes (see Ref. [44]).

Table 5. *Inhibitors of protein synthesis*

Affecting 70 S ribosomes	Affecting 70 S and 80 S ribosomes
Chloramphenicol group	Puromycin
Chloramphenicol	Gougerotin
D-AMP-3	Poly-dextran-sulphate
D-Thiomycetin	Amicetin
D-Win-5094	Sparsomycin
Macrolides group	Edeine
Angolamycin	Pactamycin
Carbomycin	Fusidic acid
Erythromycin	Tetracycline group
Lancamycin	Tetracycline
Methymycin	Oxytetracycline
Oleandomycin	Chlortetracycline
Spiramycin	
Streptogramin A group	Affecting 80 S ribosomes
Streptogramin A	
Ostreogrycin G	Cycloheximide group
Streptogramin B group	Cycloheximide (Actidione)
Streptogramin B	Actiphenol
Viridogrisein	Streptovitacin A
Staphylomycin S	Streptimidone
Lincomycin group	Tenuazonic acid
Lincomycin	Anisomycin
Celesticetin	
Streptomycin group	
Streptomycin	
Neomycin	
Kanamycin	
Paromomycin	
Gentamycin	
Hygromycin B	
Viomycin	
Spectinomycin group	

Data taken from Ref. [28].

is shown in Table 4. The specific action of chloramphenicol has repeatedly been observed by a number of workers showing the inhibitory effect of the antibiotic on cell-free systems with 70 S ribosomes and the lack of effect in cell-free systems with 80 S ribosomes [27, 43; reviews]. In the same way studies on (a) binding of radioactive antibiotics, (b) competition with this binding by other antibiotics, and (c) studies on the effect of antibiotics on protein synthesis led to the classification of antibiotics acting on the ribosome according to their inhibitory spectrum [28; review] (Table 5).

Ribosome Subunit of Antibiotic Action

We can summarize the available methods to locate the ribosome subunit of action of antibiotics as follows: (1) binding of radioactive antibiotics or competition with this binding; (2) reconstitution of hybrid ribosomes from ribosome subunits derived from antibiotic-sensitive and -resistant cells, followed by studies on sensitivity of these reconstituted ribosomes to the required antibiotic; (3) studies on protein synthesizing activity of ribosomes reconstituted from ribosome subunits pretreated independently with the required antibiotic, followed by subsequent removal of the unbound inhibitor by gel filtration before the reconstitution experiments; and (4) effects of antibiotics on a function specifically associated with a ribosome subunit and which can be studied in the absence of the other subunit.

We know at least three functions which can be carried out by 30 S subunits in the absence of 50 S subunits: (a) binding of mRNA, (b) formation of the complex *AA*-tRNA-mRNA-30 S subunit, and (c) formation of the complex f-Met-tRNA-AUG-30 S subunit. In the same way we know that peptide bond formation is catalyzed specifically only by 50 S subunits and can be studied in the absence of 30 S subunits [15, 56]. By using these methods it was possible to elucidate the subunit of action of a number of antibiotics on 70 S ribosomes as shown in Table 6 in which references pertinent to the subject are also shown. Antibiotic inhibitors of the bacterial ribosome have recently been reviewed [44].

As regards 80 S ribosomes, there are very few reports concerning the ribosomal subunit upon which the antibiotics act. This is partly due to the difficulty in obtaining from 80 S ribosomes 60 S and 40 S subunits able to reconstitute the protein synthesizing system. Also some of the best known antibiotics are not active on 80 S ribosomes. However, recent evidence indicates that the 60 S and 40 S ribosomal subunits of protozoa and yeast have functions analogous to the 50 S and 30 S subunits of 70 S ribosomes [68, 69]. Peptide bond formation takes place on the 60 S subunit, while

Table 6. *Inhibitors of protein synthesis by 70 S ribosomes. Site of action*

30 S subunit	50 S subunit
Tetracycline group [9, 28, 45—47]	Chloramphenicol group [28, 54—56]
Tetracycline	Chloramphenicol
Oxytetracycline	D-Win-5094
Chlortetracycline	D-Thiomycetin
Streptomycin group [48—52]	D-AMP-3
Streptomycin	Macrolides group [28, 55—58, 65, 66, 68]
Neomycin	Angolamycin
Kanamycin	Carbomycin
Paramomycin	Erythromycin
Gentamycin	Lancamycin
Hygromycin B	Methymycin
Viomycin	Oleandomycin
Edeine [28]	Spiramycin
Poly-dextran-sulphate [28, 53]	Streptogramin A group [28, 54, 56, 59, 65]
Spectinomycin [77, 78]	Streptogramin A
	Ostreogrycin G
	Lincomycin group [28, 34, 54, 56, 60]
	Lincomycin
	Celesticetin
	Puromycin group [2, 15, 18A]
	Puromycin and analogues
	Amicetin [28, 44, 56, 62]
	Sparsomycin [56, 63, 64]
	Gougerotin [56, 57]
	Streptogramin B group [59, 66]
	Streptogramin B
	Viridogrisein
	Staphylomycin S

Numbers in brackets correspond to references relevant to the subunit on which the antibiotics act (see also ref. [72]). Certain antibiotics appear to bind to both subunits. In this Table we indicate only the subunit in which binding of these antibiotics appears to be more relevant to their mode of action.

mRNA-directed aminoacyl-tRNA binding takes place on the 40 S subunit. We can summarize what is known about the subunit of action of antibiotics as shown in Table 7.

Table 7. *Inhibitors of protein synthesis by 80 S ribosomes. Site of action*

40 S subunit	60 S subunit
Poly-dextran-sulphate	Puromycin
Edeine	Gougerotin
Tetracycline group	Amicetin
Tetracycline	Sparsomycin
Oxytetracycline	Anisomycin
Chlortetracycline	Tenuazonic acid
	Cycloheximide group
	Cycloheximide (Actidione)
	Actiphenol
	Streptovitacin A
	Streptimidone

Localization and Role of Peptidyl Transferase

Peptide bond formation is only one step in the complex sequence of reactions involved in protein synthesis. It is possible, however, to resolve the reaction by using some well defined experimental systems.

The antibiotic puromycin has been a very useful tool for the study of peptide bond formation. This antibiotic is known to be an analogue of the aminoacyl-adenosine moiety of *AA*-tRNA. This is precisely the part of the *AA*-tRNA which is involved in peptidyl transfer, and puromycin can replace *AA*-tRNA as a substrate for the reaction. However, puromycin lacks that part of the molecule responsible for interaction with template and the 30 S ribosome subunit. Because of this, the use of puromycin provides a simplified method for study of peptide bond formation. In this system the α-NH_2 group of puromycin becomes linked to the C-terminal end of an f-Met- or peptidyl-group. The product of the puromycin reaction (f-Met-puromycin or peptidyl-puromycin) is unable to take part in the next step of protein synthesis. However, all the evidence indicates that formation of a peptide bond between puromycin and a f-Met or peptidyl-group takes place by the same mechanism as peptide bond formation in protein synthesis. Consequently, studies on the puromycin reaction enable us to know details of the role of peptidyl-transferase in protein synthesis.

The puromycin reaction has been characterized by incubation of washed, polyphenylalanine-charged ribosomes with puromycin. The reaction is unaffected by washing of the ribosomes, and it is completely dependent on divalent and monovalent cations. The reaction is located on the 50 S ribosome subunit and does not require GTP, supernatant factors, or initiation factors. Moreover, the reaction is not inhibited by inhibitors of the supernatant enzymes (e.g. sulphydryl inhibitors) or by 5′-guanylyl methylene-diphosphonate (GMP-PCP) [70 A], known to inhibit protein synthesis by interfering with the function of GTP [2, 14, 18]. All these experimental data suggest that: (1) the mechanism of the puromycin reaction is similar and has similar requirements to peptide bond formation in protein synthesis, (2) the enzyme (peptidyl transferase) responsible for peptide bond formation is different from the known supernatant enzymes and has different requirements, and (3) peptidyl transferase is associated with ribosomes and is an integral part of the 50 S ribosome subunit.

Further support for the above suggestions has been obtained by using some other experimental systems. f-Met-$tRNA_f$ can be bound to the ribosomes in the presence of AUG or phage RNA as mRNA. In the same way polylysyl-tRNA binds to ribosomes in the presence of poly A. If ribosomes with f-Met-$tRNA_f$ or polylysyl-tRNA bound, are treated with puromycin under suitable ionic conditions, a peptide bond is formed and f-Met-puromycin or polylysyl-puromycin is obtained, respectively [17, 12, 70 B]. The requirements for these reactions are the same as for the above puromycin reaction with polyphenylalanine-charged ribosomes, and again no supernatant enzymes are required for the reaction, confirming that the peptidyl transferase is located on the ribosome.

Another system has been described to study peptide bond formation. In this system oligolysyl-tRNA and lysyl-tRNA are bound to ribosomes at the „P" and the „A" sites, respectively [16]. When these bindings take place, a peptide bond is formed (catalysed by the peptidyl transferase of the ribosome) by transfer of the polylysyl-residue to the α-NH_2 of the lysyl-tRNA. This system has the same requirements as those shown above and does not require supernatant enzymes, showing again that peptidyl transferase is an integral part of the ribosome.

Peptide bond formation between f-Met and puromycin can be studied in a still more simplified system, described as the "fragment reaction". The terminal fragments CAACCA-, AACCA-, ACCA- and CCA-Met-f, from f-Met-tRNA can be prepared by enzymic digestion followed by electrophoretic purification. Each of these f-Met-oligonucleotides (but not CA- or A-Met-f) undergoes a ribosome-catalysed reaction with puromycin to give f-Met-

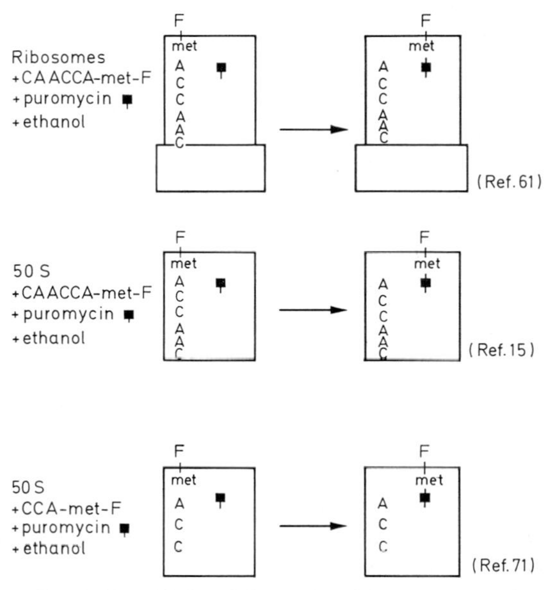

Fig. 2. Peptide bond formation. Fragment reaction

puromycin during a 20 min incubation at 0°. The reaction requires 50 S subunits, monovalent and divalent cations, and alcohol. Neither mRNA nor 30 S subunits are required (Fig. 2). Alcohol (methanol or ethanol) is effective in promoting the reaction in the concentration range from about 20 to 70% (v/v). It is possible that the presence of alcohol influences the conformation of the 50 S subunit and exposes the pertinent part of the "P" site at the catalytic centre for interaction with the fragment. Other explanations are also possible [15, 61, 71].

The advantage of the fragment reaction is that it is limited to a part of the 50 S subunit in the immediate vicinity of the catalytic centre since both the substrates (f-Met-oligonucleotide and puromycin replacing f-Met-tRNA and *AA*-tRNA, respectively) are of relatively small size. In this manner it can be expected that interactions which normally take place between tRNA and other parts of the ribosome are lacking in the fragment reaction. By using this system it was clearly established that neither GTP, nor the supernatant factors G and T, nor the initiation factors, are required for peptide formation. It was finally categorically concluded that the peptidyl transferase is an integral part of the 50 S subunit and that

Table 8. *Characteristics of the "fragment reaction"*

Experimental conditions	Synthesis of formyl-methionyl-puromycin or acetyl-leucyl-puromycin
Standard system	+
K^+ omitted	–
Mg^{++} omitted	–
Ribosomes omitted	–
CAACCA-Met-f replaced by CACCA-Leu-Ac	+
CAACCA-Met-f replaced by CACCA-Leu	–
Ribosomes replaced by 50 S or 60 S subunits	+
Ribosomes replaced by 30 S or 40 S subunits	–
+ GMP-PCP	+
+ PCBMS	+
Ethanol omitted	–

The standard system has a buffer Tris/HCl pH 7.4 containing 2×10^{-2} M Mg^{++}, 0.4 M K^+, ribosomes, and CAACCA-Met-f to which ethanol (0.5 volume) is added to start the reaction [15, 56, 61].

suitable monovalent and divalent cations are required for peptide bond formation (Table 8) [15, 18 A, B].

Although the reaction is known as the "fragment reaction" because fragments from f-Met-tRNA were used in the initial experiments, it was later found that the reaction also works with intact f-Met-tRNA, with N′-acetyl-*AA*-tRNA and with N′-acetyl-*AA*-oligonucleotides (obtained from N′-acetyl-*AA*-tRNA). When the entire tRNA structure is used (attached to the acylated aminoacyl moiety), the initial rate is 2 to 3 times as fast as with the corresponding fragments. The rate is also affected by the nature of the amino acid residue and by the incubation conditions. Substrates are inactive unless the α-NH_2 group is formylated or acetylated (or, presumably, is acylated with a second aminoacyl or peptidyl group) [71].

Confirmatory studies on the ribosome-integrated peptidyl transferase have been carried out with 70 S ribosomes not only from *E. coli* but also from other bacteria and blue-green algae, and with 80 S ribosomes from protozoa (*Crithidia oncopelti*) [68] and yeast (*Saccharomyces cerevisiae*) [69]. It appears probable from these studies that integration of the peptide bond-forming enzyme into the ribosome structure is common to eukaryotic as well as prokaryotic systems for protein synthesis. In either protozoa or yeast ribosomes peptidyl transferase is located in the 60 S ribosome subunit [68, 69].

Peptidyl transferase inhibitors. As the fragment reaction is probably confined to the immediate vicinity of the peptidyl transferase of either 50 S or 60 S ribosome subunits, this assay provides a means to determine whether inhibitors act specifically on peptidyl transfer. The fact that an antibiotic acts on the 50 S or the 60 S ribosome subunit does not necessarily imply that it acts on peptide bond formation. However, inhibition of the fragment reaction by an antibiotic may be taken as evidence for the action of this antibiotic on the larger ribosome subunit, blocking peptide bond formation.

Incubations for assay of the fragment reaction have been carried out in presence and absence of inhibitors under standard conditions using ribosomes from *E. coli* with CAACCA-Met-f or CACCA-Leu-Ac as a substrate. The results obtained show that the fragment reaction by bacterial ribosomes or their 50 S subunits is strongly inhibited by chloramphenicol and active analogues, certain macrolides, lincomycin, celesticetin, streptogramin A, amicetin, gougerotin and sparsomycin (Table 9) [56]. On the basis of the concentrations giving 50% inhibition, the antibiotics might be ranked in the following order of activities: (streptogramin A, lincomycin, carbomycin) > (spiramycin III, chloramphenicol) > (D-win 5094, celesticetin, amicetin, gougerotin, sparsomycin). (This ranking is meaningless in the case of sparsomycin, because the extent of inhibition varies greatly with pre-incubation conditions [see below]). The observed failure of tetracycline, edeine and poly-dextran-sulphate to inhibit the fragment reaction is consistent with evidence that they interfere with 30 S subunit function, and the inactivity found of the unnatural chloramphenicol isomers parallels their failure to inhibit protein synthesis [56]. Inactivity of streptogramin B-type antibiotics, fusidic acid (unpublished observation) and GMP-PCP shows that they do not act on peptidyl transfer.

Table 9. *Fragment reaction. Effects of protein synthesis inhibitors*

Inhibitors of 70 S ribosomes or 50 S subunits	Inhibitors of yeast ribosomes or 60 S subunits
Inhibitory	Inhibitory
Chloramphenicol	Anisomycin
D-Thiocymetin	Gougerotin
D-AMP-3	Sparsomycin
D-Win-5094	Amicetin
Carbomycin	
Spiramycin III	No effect
Streptogramin A	Fusidic acid
Lincomycin	Pactamycin
Celesticetin	Tetracycline
Gougerotin	Edeine
Sparsomycin	Poly-Dextran-Sulphate
Amicetin	Specific inhibitors of 70 S ribosomes
No effect	
Tetracycline	
Edeine	
Poly-Dextran-Sulphate	
Viridogrisin	
Anisomycin	
Fusidic acid	
Pactamycin	

The finding that gougerotin, sparsomycin and amicetin inhibit the fragment reaction, even though they do not affect chloramphenicol-binding, suggests that peptidyl transferase can be inhibited by action upon at least two distinct sites.

The fragment reaction using 80 S ribosomes from yeast was unaffected by chloramphenicol, lincomycin, streptogramin A, and the macrolides. This observation is in agreement with the known specificity of these antibiotics for inhibition of protein synthesis in 70 S systems. On the other hand, anisomycin, gougerotin, sparsomycin, and to a lesser extent amicetin, inhibit the fragment reaction by yeast ribosomes and their 60 S subunits (Table 9) [69]. We only found a slight inhibition by tenuazonic acid and cycloheximide of the fragment reaction by yeast ribosomes (a maximum of 30% inhibition at 10^{-3} M concentration of these inhibitors) whereas other workers have found that these antibiotics are good inhibitors of the fragment reaction by 80 S ribosomes from protozoa (*Crithidia oncopelti*) [68]. It is not at present possible to find an explanation for these apparently conflicting results.

The Sparsomycin "Reaction"

Sparsomycin induces formation of an inert substrate-ribosome complex in the fragment system. Under the standard conditions

Table 10. *Characteristics of the "sparsomycin reaction"*

Experimental conditions	Sparsomycin-stimulated binding of the fragment
Standard system	+
K^+ omitted	–
Mg^{++} omitted	–
Ribosomes omitted	–
Ribosomes replaced by 50 S or 60 S subunits	+
Ribosomes replaced by 30 S or 40 S subunits	–
CACCA-Leu-Ac replaced by CCA-Leu-Ac or CCA-Met-f	+

The standard system contains in a buffer Tris/HCl pH 7.4, 2×10^{-2} M Mg^{++}, 0.4 M K^+, ribosomes CACCA-Leu-Ac and sparsomycin. The reaction is started by addition of ethanol (0.5 volume) [64].

of the fragment reaction (with ethanol but not methanol), ribosomes are quantitatively precipitated, whereas small oligonucleotides of up to about 5 residues are soluble. So, specific binding of radioactively-labelled oligonucleotide derivatives to ribosomes was estimated by determination of radioactivity in suspension before and after sedimentation of the ribosome precipitate by low speed centrifugation. In this reaction puromycin was not added.

Binding is hardly detectable under the standard conditions of the reaction. However, if sparsomycin is added, there is interaction of suitable oligonucleotide derivatives with the 70 S ribosome or the 50 S subunit, but not with the 30 S subunit (Table 10) [64]. Requirements for this "sparsomycin reaction" are very similar to those for the fragment reaction. The substrates CCA-Met-f, UACCA-Leu-Ac, CACCA-Met-f and CCA-Met-f are active but not non-acylated CCA. The complex formed can be disintegrated by dissolving the ribosome precipitate in buffer without alcohol. If the ribosomes are then sedimented, all the radioactivity remains in the supernatant. This material so eluted

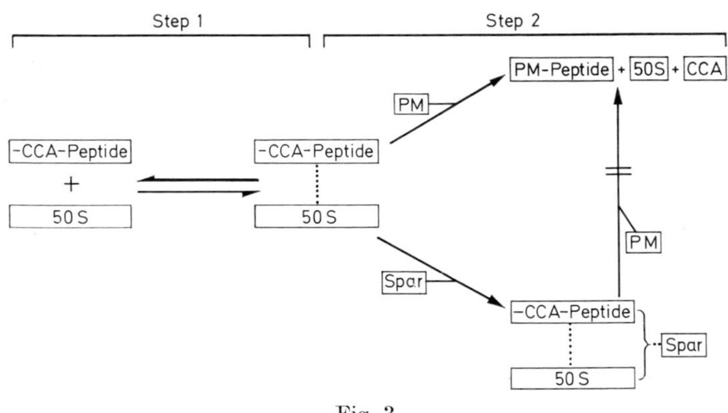

Fig. 3

was characterized by paper ionophoresis, and it was found that disintegration of the sparsomycin-induced complex releases the initial substrate in an unmodified form. It is reasonable to conclude that sparsomycin action does not involve covalent changes.

It was also shown that the complex formed in the presence of sparsomycin is unreactive towards puromycin (Fig. 3). Using 70 S ribosomes or 50 S subunits, the sparsomycin reaction is completely blocked by a number of antibiotics which inhibit peptide bond formation and binding of chloramphenicol to 50 S subunits (chloramphenicol, carbomycin, spiramycin III, streptogramin A and lincomycin), and is inhibited to a lesser extent by other antibiotics which inhibit peptide bond formation but not binding of chloramphenicol (gougerotin and amicetin) (Table 11) [64].

With 80 S ribosomes (or 60 S subunits) from yeast the sparsomycin reaction is inhibited by anisomycin and gougerotin and to a lesser extent by amicetin.

The standard concentration of ethanol in the fragment system discussed above was 33% (v/v). At a higher concentration of ethanol (50%), amicetin and gougerotin, in the absence of sparsomycin, induce formation of a substrate-ribosome complex, apparently similar to that formed with sparsomycin [74]. It is possible that the mode of action of gougerotin and amicetin are

Table 11. *Sparsomycin reaction. Effects of protein synthesis inhibitors*

Sparsomycin reaction with:

70 S ribosomes or 50 S subunits	80 S ribosomes or 60 S subunits
Inhibitory	Inhibitory
Chloramphenicol	Anisomycin
Carbomycin	Gougerotin
Spiramycin	Amicetin
Streptogramin A	
Lincomycin	No effect
Amicetin	Fusidic acid
Gougerotin	Pactamycin
	Tetracycline
No effect	Edeine
Tetracycline	Poly-dextran-sulphate
Edeine	Specific inhibitors of 70 S ribosomes
Poly-dextran-sulphate	
Viridogrisein	
Anisomycin	
Fusidic acid	
Pactamycin	

related to that of sparsomycin and that they compete for the same site, but that the inert complexes formed in their presence are less stable than with sparsomycin, and that a higher ethanol concentration is therefore required for stabilization [cf. binding of fragment in absence of antibiotics (see below)].

By addition of sparsomycin and puromycin to the system at different times it was observed that sparsomycin competes with puromycin for reaction with the bound peptidyl donor substrate but leaves open the question of whether the two antibiotics act at the same site as has already been proposed [63] or at a different site.

The hypothetical scheme shown in Fig. 3 provides some possible explanations for the similarities of the "fragment" and sparsomycin reactions. In the first step (Fig. 3) a CCA-"peptidyl" group binds at the "P" site on the 50 S subunit, in the vicinity of the peptidyl transferase catalytic centre. It is probable that this step requires Mg^{++} and K^{+} and is promoted by alcohol. In the second step (Fig. 3), the bound fragment either reacts with puromycin or interacts with sparsomycin to give peptidylpuromycin or the sparsomycin complex, respectively. Both reactions are essentially irreversible under our conditions, and the products are non-interconvertible. Inhibition by chloramphenicol and antibiotic inhibitors of chloramphenicol-binding could take place by interference either with step I or with some other less clearly defined step common to both puromycin and sparsomycin action. Puromycin and sparsomycin might interact with the ribosome either after binding of the CCA-peptidyl group (as shown in Fig. 3) or before this binding. Sparsomycin, gougerotin, and amicetin may act at a common ribosome site. This site appears to be present on ribosomes of both the 70 S and 80 S type, as these antibiotics are active on both types of ribosomes. In contrast, anisomycin acts at a different site, present only on 80 S ribosomes, and chloramphenicol acts at a site present only on 70 S ribosomes.

Binding of CACCA-Leu-Ac to Ribosomes

As indicated above, specific binding of CACCA-(^{3}H)-Leu-Ac to ribosomes was not detected in our assay under the standard conditions of the "fragment reaction" (with 33% ethanol) unless sparsomycin was added. However, as we know that the reaction of fragment with puromycin has a higher initial rate when started with more ethanol, it was thought that the function of the alcohol might be to promote specific interaction between substrate and 50 S subunit. In fact it was found that addition of 50% ethanol led to specific binding of CACCA-(^{3}H)-Leu-Ac to 70 S and 80 S ribosomes and to their 50 S and 60 S subunits but not to the 30 S and 40 S subunits. The requirements for this binding are similar to those for the "fragment reaction" and the "sparsomycin reaction". The effect of a number of peptide bond formation inhibitors was studied and the results are shown in Table 12 [74]. It was found that streptogramin A, spiramycin III, lincomycin, and carbomycin inhibit the binding by 50 S subunits, suggesting that they block interaction of the terminal part of the peptidyl-tRNA at the "P" site on the peptidyl transferase of the 50 S subunit. In a similar manner, anisomycin inhibits binding of CACCA-Leu-Ac to 60 S subunits, suggesting that it acts in a similar manner on the 60 S ribosome subunit of 80 S ribosomes.

Table 12. *Inhibitors of CACCA-Leu-Ac binding to ribosomes*

70 S ribosomes or 50 S subunits	80 S ribosomes or 60 S subunits
Streptogramin A Spiramycin III Carbomycin Lincomycin	Anisomycin

Localization of the Site of Action of Certain Antibiotics

The assays which we have developed to investigate the catalytic activity of 50 S subunits and the action of chloramphenicol, lincomycin, and sparsomycin, are particularly well suited for correlation with structural studies. The assays can be carried out with isolated 50 S subunits (in contrast to other assays of 50 S activity), and the substrates are relatively small molecules. The assays should therefore be specific to particular active centres on the subunit.

Further refinement of the assays was necessary before they could be successfully applied in the present project. A rapid method was developed for estimation of chloramphenicol and lincomycin binding, which could distinguish between maximum number of binding sites available and affinity for the sites. A method was also developed for estimation of the number of sites available for the sparsomycin-induced binding of CACCA-Leu-Ac. Both assays require only small amounts of ribosomes. It was then confirmed that there is one binding site for chloramphenicol and lincomycin per 50 S subunit, and it was shown that there is one site per subunit for sparsomycin-induced fragment binding.

Isopycnic centrifugation of 50 S subunits in CsCl solutions [ref. 73 and refs. therein] at various Mg^{++} concentrations leads to the formation of a series (α, β, γ) of discrete cores, which are of increasing density, and therefore equilibrate at different positions in the CsCl gradient. The core fractions can thus be obtained pure. The cores contain intact 23 S and 5 S RNA, but lack increasing numbers of the 30 odd proteins which go to make up the 50 S subunit. Disc ionophoresis in polyacrylamide gels shows that a distinct set of proteins is lost at each step. The β-cores lack all of the acidic proteins (about 4) and at least one of the basic proteins. The γ-cores lack, in addition, approximately 4 or 5 more of the basic proteins [75].

Table 13

	β-cores	γ-cores	Split protein
(a) Chloramphenicol binding	+ +	–	–
(b) Lincomycin binding	+ +	–	–
(c) Sparsomycin "reaction"	+ +	–	–
(d) Puromycin reaction	+ +	–	–

"a" to "c" were measured in terms of maximal number of binding sites available (there was approximately one site per 50 S subunit in each of these three assays). "d" was measured in terms of initial rate of reaction of CACCA-Leu-Ac with puromycin, at standard ribosome concentration.

β- and γ-core preparations were tested for activity in four different assays. Results, summarized in Table 13 [76], show that the β-cores possessed good activity for the binding of chloramphenicol and lincomycin, and for the sparsomycin-induced binding of CACCA-Leu-Ac. They were also active in catalysing the fragment reaction. In contrast, the γ-cores were devoid of activity in all of these assays. The split protein fractions obtained in preparation of the cores were also devoid of activity. Efforts to reconstitute the activity of the γ-cores by re-addition of split proteins have, so far, been only marginally successful and it appears that 50 S subunits are more intractable to re-constitution than 30 S subunits [52].

Our results are consistent with the hypothesis that the activities which we have studied all involve a common active centre on the 50 S subunit, and provide a step towards identification of the ribosomal components at this centre. The components are clearly present in β-cores, thus eliminating a number of acidic and basic proteins as possible candidates. The $\beta \rightarrow \gamma$ split protein fraction appears to be vital for integrity of the active centre, but it is not possible from the present results to decide whether the actual components of the active centre are in this fraction or in the γ-core fraction, since both fractions were inactive.

Acknowledgements

This work was supported by grants from the National Institutes of Health (AI 08598-01) and Sociedad Española de Industrias Químicas y Farmaceúticas, División Farmaceútica Lepetit. One of us (R. R. Monro) was a senior Fellow of the European Molecular Biology Organization and three of us (M. L. Celma, E. Battaner and R. Fernández Munoz) were Fellows of "Fondo Nacional para el Desarrollo de la Investigación Científica".

References

1. Watson, J. D.: Bull. Soc. Chim. biol. (Paris) **46**, 1399 (1964).
2. Traut, R. R., and R. E. Monro: J. molec. Biol. **10**, 63 (1964).
3. Nishizuka, Y., and F. Lipmann: Arch. Biochem. **116**, 344 (1966).
4A. Bretscher, M. S.: Nature (Lond.) **218**, 675 (1968).
4B. Erbe, R. W., M. M. Nau, and P. Leder: J. molec. Biol. **38**, 441 (1968).
4C. Pestka, S.: Proc. nat. Acad. Sci. (Wash.) **61**, 726 (1968).
5. Salas, M., M. Smith, W. M. Stanley, A. J. Wahba, and S. Ochoa: J. biol. Chem. **240**, 3988 (1965).
6. Thach, R. E., M. A. Cerere, T. A. Sundararajan, and P. Doty: Proc. nat. Acad. Sci. (Wash.) **54**, 1167 (1965).
7. Adams, J. M., and M. R. Capecchi: Proc. nat. Acad. Sci. (Wash.) **55**, 147 (1966).
8. Clark, B. F. C., and K. A. Marcker: J. molec. Biol. **17**, 394 (1966).
9. Mukundan, M. A., J. W. B. Hershey, K. F. Dewey, and R. E. Thach: Nature (Lond.) **217**, 1013 (1968).
10. Sarkar, S., and R. E. Thach: Proc. nat. Acad. Sci. (Wash.) **60**, 1479 (1968).
11. Clark, B. F. C., and K. A. Marcker: Nature (Lond.) **211**, 378 (1966).
12. Bretscher, M. S., and K. A. Marcker: Nature (Lond.) **211**, 380 (1966).
13. Anderson, J. S., J. E. Dahlberg, M. S. Bretscher, M. Revel, and B. F. C. Clark: Nature (Lond.) **216**, 1072 (1967).
14. Monro, R. E., B. E. Maden, and R. R. Traut: In Symp. Fed. Eur. Biochem. Soc., p. 179 (April 1966) Shugar, D., Ed. London: Academic Press 1967.
15. — J. molec. Biol. **26**, 147 (1967).
16. Gottesman, M. E.: J. biol. Chem. **242**, 5564 (1967).
17. Rychlik, I.: Biochem. biophys. Acta (Amst.) **114**, 425 (1966).
18A. Maden, B. E. H., R. R. Traut, and R. E. Monro: J. molec. Biol. **35**, 333 (1968).
18B. —, and R. E. Monro: Europ. J. Biochem. **6**, 309 (1968).

19. NATHANS, D., and F. LIPMANN: Proc. nat. Acad. Sci. (Wash.) **47**, 497 (1961).
20. WEIGERT, M. G., and A. GAREN: Nature (Lond.) **206**, 992 (1965).
21. BRENNER, S., A. O. W. STRETTON, and S. KAPLAN: Nature (Lond.) **206**, 994 (1965).
22A. CAPECCHI, M. R.: Proc. nat. Acad. Sci. (Wash.) **58**, 1144 (1967).
22B. SCOLNICK, E., R. TOMPKINS, T. CASKEY, and M. NIRENBERG: Proc. nat. Acad. Sci. (Wash.) **61**, 768 (1968).
23. GUSSIN, G. N., M. R. CAPECCHI, J. M. ADAMS, J. E. ARGETSINGER, J. TOOZE, K. WEBER, and J. D. WATSON: Cold. Spr. Harb. Symp. quant. Biol. **31**, 257 (1966).
24A. KÜNTZEL, H., and H. NOLL: Nature (Lond.) **215**, 1340 (1967).
24B. RIFKIN, M. R., D. D. WOOD, and D. J. L. LUCK: Proc. nat. Acad. Sci. (Wash.) **58**, 1025 (1967).
25. PETERMANN, M. L.: The physical and chemical properties of ribosomes. Amsterdam: Elsevier 1964.
26. VAZQUEZ, D.: Nature (Lond.) **203**, 257 (1964).
27. — Symp. Soc. Gen. Microbiol. **16**, 169 (1966).
28. —, and R. E. MONRO: Biochim. biophys. Acta (Amst.) **142**, 155 (1967).
29. STUTZ, E., and H. NOLL: Proc. nat. Acad. Sci. (Wash.) **57**, 774 (1967).
30. SCHWARTZ, J. H., R. MEYER, J. M. EISENSTADT, and G. BRAWERMANN: J. molec. Biol. **25**, 571 (1967).
31. SMITH, A. E., and K. A. MARCKER: J. molec. Biol. **38**, 241 (1968).
32. RENDI, R., and S. OCHOA: Science **133**, 1357 (1961).
33. SO, A. G., and E. W. DAVIE: Biochemistry **2**, 132 (1963).
34. CHANG, F. M., C. J. SIH, and B. WEISBLUM: Proc. nat. Acad. Sci. (Wash.) **55**, 431 (1966).
35. HEREDIA, C. F., and H. O. HALVORSON: Biochemistry **5**, 946 (1966).
36. PARISI, B., G. MILANESI, J. VAN ETTEN, A. PERANI, and O. CIFERRI: J. molec. Biol. **28**, 295 (1967).
37. NISHIZUKA, Y., and F. LIPMANN: Proc. nat. Acad. Sci. (Wash.) **55**, 212 (1966).
38. LUCAS-LENARD, J., and F. LIPMANN: Proc. nat. Acad. Sci. (Wash.) **55**, 1562 (1966).
39. GORDON, J.: Proc. nat. Acad. Sci. (Wash.) **59**, 179 (1968).
40. WAHBA, A. J., M. SALAS, and W. M. STANLEY: Cold. Spr. Harb. Symp. quant. Biol. **31**, 103 (1966).
41. ANDERSON, L. A., and R. M. SMILLIE: Biochem. biophys. Res. Commun. **23**, 535 (1966).
42. RODRIGUEZ-LOPEZ, M., and D. VAZQUEZ: Life Sci. **7**, 327 (1968).
43. HAHN, F. E.: In: Antibiotics: I. Mechanism of action. GOTTLIEB, D., and P. D. SHAW, Eds. Berlin-Heidelberg-New York: Springer 1967.
44. WEISBLUM, B., and J. DAVIES: Bact. Rev. **32**, 493 (1968).
45. SUZUKA, I., H. KAJI, and H. KAJI: Proc. nat. Acad. Sci. (Wash.) **55**, 1483 (1966).
46. CONNAMACHER, R. H., and H. G. MANDEL: Biochem. biophys. Res. Commun. **20**, 98 (1965).
47. DAY, L. E.: J. Bact. **91**, 1917 (1966).

48. Cox, E. C., J. R. White, and J. G. Flaks: Proc. nat. Acad. Sci. (Wash.) **51**, 703 (1964).
49. Davies, J.: Proc. nat. Acad. Sci. (Wash.) **51**, 659 (1964).
50. Kaji, H., and Y. Tanaka: J. molec. Biol. **32**, 221 (1968).
51. Staehelin, T., and M. Meselson: J. molec. Biol. **19**, 207 (1966).
52. Traub, P., and M. Nomura: Proc. nat. Acad. Sci. (Wash.) **59**, 777 (1968).
53. Miyazawa, F., O. R. Olijnyk, C. J. Tilley, and T. Tamaoki: Biochim. biophys. Acta (Amst.) **145**, 96 (1967).
54. Vazquez, D.: Biochem. biophys. Res. Commun. **15**, 464 (1964).
55. — Biochim. biophys. Acta (Amst.) **114**, 277 (1966).
56. Monro, R. E., and D. Vazquez: J. molec. Biol. **28**, 161 (1967).
57. Taubman, S. B., N. R. Jones, F. E. Young, and J. W. Corcoran: Biochim. biophys. Acta (Amst.) **123**, 438 (1966).
58. Cundlife, E., and K. McQuillen: J. molec. Biol. **30**, 137 (1967).
59. Ennis, H. L.: Molec. Pharmacol. **2**, 444 (1966).
60. Chang, F. M., and B. Weisblum: Biochemistry **6**, 836 (1967).
61. Monro, R. E., and K. A. Marcker: J. molec. Biol. **25**, 347 (1967).
62. Block, A., and C. Coutsogeorgopoulos: Biochemistry **6**, 3345 (1966).
63. Goldberg, I. H., and K. Mitsugi: Biochemistry **6**, 383 (1967).
64. Monro, R. E., M. L. Celma, and D. Vazquez: Nature (Lond.) (in press).
65. Vazquez, D.: Life Sci. **6**, 381 (1967).
66. — Life Sci. **6**, 845 (1967).
67. Clark, jr., J. M., and A. Y. Chang: J. biol. Chem. **240**, 4734 (1955).
68. Cross, G. A. M.: Personal communication.
69. Battaner, E., R. E. Monro, and D. Vazquez: (Unpublished results).
70A. Hershey, J. W. B., and R. E. Monro: J. molec. Biol. **18**, 68 (1966).
70B. Zamir, A., P. Leder, D. Elson: Proc. nat. Acad. Sci. (Wash.) **56**, 1795 (1966).
71. Monro, R. E., J., Černá, and K. A. Marcker: Proc. nat. Acad. Sci. (Wash.) **61**, 1042 (1968).
72. Vazquez, D., u. R. E. Monro: Abh. dtsch. Akad. Wissenschaften Berlin, Kl. Medizin, p. 569 (1968).
73. Staehelin, T., H. Raskas, and M. Meselson: In: Organizational biosynthesis, p. 443. Bryson, V., Ed. New York: Academic Press 1967.
74. Celma, M. L., R. E. Monro, and D. Vazquez: (Unpublished results).
75. Staehelin, T.: (Unpublished observations).
76. Monro, R. E., D. Vazquez, M. L. Celma, and T. Staehelin: (Unpublished observations).
77. Anderson, P., J. Davies and B. D. Davies: J. molec. Biol. **29**, 203 (1967).
78. Sparling, P. F., J. Modolell, Y. Takeda and B. D. Davis: J. molec. Biol. **37**, 407 (1967).

Discussion

Chandra (Frankfurt): Dr. Traub, it is supposed that ribosomal proteins are coded by r-RNA. Your studies clearly indicate that streptomycin-resistance is restricted to CP 30 protein. Have any fingerprint studies been done with 16 s RNA?

Traub (La Jolla, Cal.): Nothing has been done in this direction.

Chandra: How far are the 16 s, CP 30, and SP 30 fractions specific with respect to various bacterial species?

Traub: We did not try this with the core proteins and the split proteins, but we tried it with 16 s RNA and total protein from 30 s ribosomes. We could show that 16 s RNA from E. coli, B. stearothermophilus, and Azotobacter vinelandii are equally active in the reconstitution of 30 S ribosomes in combination with E. coli protein. By contrast, 16 s RNA from Micrococcus lysodeikticus was only poorly active in combination with 30 s ribosomal protein from E. coli.

Hülsen (Karlsruhe): Have you tried to find a binding of ^{14}C-streptomycin by incubating 30 s ribosomes with labelled streptomycin and separating afterwards into 23 s core particles and split proteins?

Traub: If I understood your question right you want to know whether after dissociation any one of the ribosomal components can bind streptomycin. No, we did not perform experiments of this type. However, Kaji could show that none of the dissociated ribosomal components can bind streptomycin. Only the complete particle with its native configuration is active in this binding reaction.

Chandra: I would like to ask Dr. Vazquez about chloramphenicol binding experiments. You have shown that the binding of chloramphenicol is inhibited by a number of antibiotics. One would, therefore, think that strains resistant to chloramphenicol should also be resistant to those antibiotics which inhibit its binding.

Vazquez (Madrid): It is very difficult to obtain chloramphenicol resistant mutants in which the resistance is localized in the ribosomes (as opposed to altered permeability or to factors which modify chloramphenicol). However, Cerná and Rychlik (1968) have isolated a mutant of *E. coli* with altered 50 s subunits, which has increased resistance to both erythromycin and chloramphenicol. Apirion (1967) has obtained lincomycin-sensitive mutants and shown that they are also sensitive to erythromycin.

Strominger (Cambridge, Mass.): Perhaps Dr. Vazquez would like to comment on the curious phenomenon which was observed by Weisblum; that is, cells which are normally sensitive to lincomycin become resistant to lincomycin in the presence of erythromycin, even though those cells are resistant to erythromycin. He termed that phenomenon conditional resistance.

Vazquez: We do not at present understand the relationships between antibiotic-binding sites on the 50 s subunit and modes of action of the antibiotics. For example, erythromycin competes with chloramphenicol and lincomycin for binding to the 50 s subunit, but does not inhibit the fragment reaction, even though chloramphenicol and lincomycin are very good inhibitors. We would expect erythromycin to reverse the inhibition by chloramphenicol of the fragment reaction, but we have not yet tested for this. It is probable that all of the antibiotics which compete for chloramphenicol-binding interact with the 50 s subunit at overlapping sites close to the peptidyl transferase catalytic centre, but that they have different effects due to their diverse sizes and structures. Alternatively, it is possible that the antibiotics act at different sites, and that effects on binding of other antibiotics and on peptidyl transfer take place by allosteric mechanisms.

Strominger: This is one of few examples of real antagonism between antibiotics that appeared in clinical medicine. If you try to treat, for example, a pneumococcal pneumonia which is sensitive to lincomycin and resistant to erythromycin, with both lincomycin and erythromycin, then you obtain no killing of pneumococcus due to antagonism.

Traub: Dr. Vazquez, you said that one of the split proteins SP 50 is identical with peptidyl transferase. Do you have any evidence for this? I understand that you lose the active center of the enzyme, but you cannot say that you split off the protein representing peptidyl transferase from the ribosome. It is possible that after dissociation of several ribosomal proteins by CsCl density gradient centrifugation the tertiary structure of the enzyme, which is still present in the ribosome, is altered in such a way that the active center is destroyed.

Vazquez: Yes, that is quite possible.

Traub: The dependence of the binding of the antibiotics discussed in your paper on potassium and magnesium ions indicates also that the binding depends on a specific configuration of the ribosome.

Vazquez: Both binding of antibiotics and the peptidyl transfer reaction are dependent on the presence of Mg^{++} and suitable monovalent cation, although there are some quantitative differences in response. We agree that cations most probably act by affecting the configuration of the ribosome (Refs. [18B, 54, 55] in Vazquez et al. p. 100).

W. Kersten (Erlangen): Have you any information whether the interaction between the antibiotics and the ribosomes is reversible?

Traub: Streptomycin binds tightly to 30 s ribosomes, but only after heating. After heating of the ribosome-streptomycin mixture to 30 °C, only one molecule of streptomycin binds to the 30 s ribosome in an apparently irreversible way. This is indicated by the fact that the antibiotic cannot be washed off from the ribosome by sucrose gradient centrifugation.

Vazquez: Concerning antibiotics active on the 50 s subunit, the binding is reversible in all cases we have so far tested, even though the binding constants are very low for certain antibiotics, such as streptogramin A, spiramycin III and erythromycin.

Inhibitors as Tools in Elucidating Hormone Action

A. KORNER

School of Biological Sciences, University of Sussex, England

Inhibitors have an honourable place in the history of biochemistry: their use has elucidated much of fundamental importance. These vital tools have been used by many workers in attempts to elucidate the mode of action of protein anabolic hormones, sometimes with success, sometimes with failure. Many criticisms are raised against the use of inhibitors and some of these criticisms are well taken. It is well to remember, however, that no technique must be applied uncritically and that, with care and self-criticism in the analysis of results, inhibitors can be useful tools in research. In this paper I discuss some of the uses of three or four inhibitors in uncovering the mechanism of action of protein anabolic hormones.

1. Actinomycin

One favoured hypothesis (KARLSON, 1963; KARLSON and SEKERIS, 1966) of the mechanism of hormone action on protein biosynthesis is that they act by a classical de-repression mechanism of the type outlined for bacterial genetic control by JACOB and MONOD (1961). In this view, hormones stimulate the synthesis of new molecules of messenger-RNA which act as templates for increased protein biosynthesis. The evidence for this view is essentially that hormonal treatment is followed by a rise in RNA biosynthesis as well as in protein biosynthesis (KENNEY and KULL, 1963, for example); that in a few cases it has been claimed that RNA extracted from tissues treated with a hormone can induce the production of specific proteins in cell-free systems (SEKERIS and LANG, 1964, for example); and that treatment with actinomycin can abolish the anabolic effect of some hormones (GREENGARD, SMITH and ACS, 1963, for example).

Because of the topic of this conference, I shall deal mainly with the third line of evidence but it should be mentioned with regard to the first line of evidence that hydrocortisone, for example, which stimulates bulk RNA synthesis and enzyme induction in rat liver, does the latter but not the former in cells grown in tissue culture (THOMSON, TOMKINS and CURRAN, 1966). It seems that RNA synthesis of a specific kind might be still needed for hormone action, because actinomycin inhibits it, but the great bulk of the RNA synthesis seen in the whole animal in fact resulted from some secondary action of the hormone such as altered blood flow through the organ and not from a primary action of the hormone on liver. It might also be mentioned that criticisms have been raised against the second line of evidence (WYATT, 1965; KORNER, 1967).

The evidence based on the use of actinomycin has also been questioned. The drug might have some action other than the inhibition of DNA-directed RNA synthesis. Certainly the material is very toxic so that inhibition of a hormone effect might not be caused only by the inhibition of RNA synthesis. It is also possible to argue that actinomycin might inhibit one reaction in a sequence which leads to increased protein synthesis but that the hormone stimulates a different reaction in the sequence. Because of these objections experiments in which abolition of a hormone effect by actinomycin is used to claim that the hormone acts through RNA synthesis are open to objection.

On the other hand, the reverse argument is on stronger grounds. Insulin (EBOUÉ-BONIS, CHAMBAUT, VOLFIN and CLAUSER, 1963) and growth hormone (KORNER, 1964; MARTIN and YOUNG, 1965) continue to exert protein anabolic effects in liver and isolated diaphragm of the rat even when RNA synthesis is inhibited by actinomycin. These hormones seem, then, not to act through prior synthesis of RNA because, although actinomycin might inhibit reactions other than RNA synthesis, the evidence that it does inhibit RNA synthesis is unquestioned. Since these hormones continue to exert their effect in the virtual absence of RNA synthesis, they cannot do so through RNA synthesis.

Actinomycin has been reported to have some apparently paradoxical effects. GARREN, HOWELL, TOMKINS and CROCCO (1964) have reported, for example, that actinomycin administered at the same time as hydrocortisone abolishes the hormone induction of tyrosine transaminase and tryptophan pyrrolase of rat liver. When, however, actinomycin was administered 6 h or so after the hormone, when hormonally induced enzyme activity is maximal, it results in a further boost in enzyme activity. This result which has been both confirmed (Grossman and Mavrides, 1967) and denied (Mishkin and Shore, 1967; Csanyi, Greengard and Knox, 1967) can also be obtained in cells grown in tissue culture (Gelehrter and Tomkins, 1967).

The explanation of Tomkins and his group for this effect of actinomycin is that when enzyme activity rises after hormone treatment a repressor is synthesized on a repressor m-RNA which inhibits production of the induced enzymes probably by degrading their m-RNA molecules. Addition of actinomycin, after enzyme levels have risen, results in inhibition of the synthesis of the m-RNA for the repressor rather than of m-RNA for the enzymes because the latter turns-over at a slower rate than the former. Hence superinduction of the enzyme by actinomycin results.

Grossman and Mavrides (1967) have argued that the synthesis of the putative repressor requires a pituitary factor, possibly growth hormone, because the hormonally stimulated enzyme activity does not fall as rapidly in hypophysectomized rats as in normal ones. Growth hormone can, under some circumstances, inhibit tyrosine transaminase in hypophysectomized or adrenalectomized rats (Kenney, 1967) but the response was reported to be erratic. In perfused liver growth hormone is reported to have both no effect (Hager and Kenney, 1968) and to stimulate enzyme activity (Ottolenghi and Cavagna, 1968). Labrie and Korner [1968 (1)] found that growth hormone treatment for 4 days did diminish activity of tyrosine transaminase and tryptophan pyrrolase in liver of adrenalectomized or hypophysectomized rats but that short-term treatment had no effect. Perhaps the varied time and conditions of treatment with growth hormone might help explain the differences in the results on this point obtained by the various authors. Growth hormone did, however, inhibit the stimulation of the activity of tyrosine transaminase and tryptophan pyrrolase by hydrocortisone [Labrie and Korner, 1968 (1)]. At first sight this result might be interpreted as support for the hypothesis that growth hormone stimulates the synthesis of a repressor of enzyme induction. The situation is, however, more complex. The supply of amino acids can influence the activity of these enzymes (Rosen, 1965) and, indeed, Labrie and Korner [1968 (1)] could overcome the growth hormone inhibition of the hydrocortisone effect by feeding an amino acid mixture to the rats. Later it was shown [Labrie and Korner, 1968 (2)] that amino acids could, alone, induce both enzymes by a mechanism which was inhibited completely, in the case of tyrosine transaminase, and partially, in the case of tryptophan pyrrolase, by actinomycin.

Because of this, it is possible to argue that growth hormone might effect the activity of cortisol-induced tyrosine transaminase and tryptophan pyrrolase indirectly by sequestering some amino acid(s) for the synthesis of proteins other than these enzymes. Similarly one could argue that the superinduction of enzyme activity by actinomycin could have been occasioned by some alteration in amino acid supply: the hypothesis of a repressor (Garren et al., 1964) is not the only possible one.

A more cogent objection to the Tomkins hypothesis of the mechanism of actinomycin superinduction comes from the recent experiments of Reel and Kenney (1968). They induced tyrosine transaminase with hydrocortisone in two cell lines grown in culture, and examined, simultaneously, the amount of tyrosine transaminase enzyme present by an immunological technique and the labelling of the enzyme by radioactive precursors. They found that, although actinomycin increased the actual amount of enzyme present in cells, the radioactivity of it simultaneously decreased. They argue that actinomycin is able to do two things: it can inhibit enzyme synthesis rather slowly, by inhibiting the synthesis of its m-RNA, but also it can inhibit enzyme degradation rapidly. The net effect is a rise in enzyme activity, not because of superinduction but because of inhibited degradation of the enzyme by actinomycin.

This result shows that actinomycin does have actions other than the inhibition of RNA synthesis. It emphasizes not only the dangers in using an inhibitor like actinomycin, but also the dangers in relying on incorporation of radioactivity or even of enzyme activity as measures of synthesis. Schimke, Sweeney and Berlin (1965) have pointed out the dangers of ignoring the rate of degradation of enzymes in studies on their rate of synthesis. Suppose two enzymes, A and B, are synthesized at the same rate but A is degraded twice as quickly as B. The pool size of A will be much smaller than that of B. Doubling the synthetic rates of both enzymes will be more rapidly apparent in A because of its small pool size. Similarly, a rapid change in activity could be obtained by alteration in degradation rate: under some circumstances this could be more rapid than changes in synthetic rate.

The finding that amino acids could induce the synthesis of tyrosine transaminase and tryptophan pyrrolase by an actinomycin sensitive mechanism [LABRIE and KORNER, 1968 (2)] raised the suggestion that amino acids might be acting through RNA synthesis. If it is argued that hydrocortisone acts in this way because actinomycin inhibits it, it must be equally valid (or invalid) to argue that amino acids act through the same mechanism. Because of the weakness of this argument we have looked (LABRIE and KORNER, 1969) directly at the question. We found that amino acids fed to rats could indeed stimulate labelling of RNA of rat liver by precursors.

2. Puromycin

It has been mentioned that the protein anabolic effects of neither insulin nor growth hormone are inhibited by actinomycin so that their primary effects must be on some aspect of the protein synthetic process other than RNA synthesis. There is evidence that both hormones can enhance the ability of liver and muscle ribosomes to synthesize protein *in vitro*. Per unit weight, the ribosomes from normal rats are better than those from hypophysectomized rats at amino acid incorporation in the absence or in the presence of excess polyuridylic acid (poly U). Some deficiency in the ribosome must have occurred as a result of hypophysectomy. Treatment of rats with growth hormone reverses this effect. Similar changes in activity occur with muscle ribosomes when rats are made diabetic or are treated with insulin.

One can now ask: is each ribosome less active after hypophysectomy or after diabetes, or is a smaller proportion of the ribosome population active? WOOL and KURIHARA (1967) devised an ingenious method of answering this question. Ribosomes are incubated with radioactive puromycin so that each of the nascent peptide chains attached to them is released, each with a radioactive puromycin attached. The number of ribosomes carrying a nascent chain can then be calculated from the radioactivity attached to the nascent peptides and the percentage of the total ribosomes which have reacted with puromycin can be calculated. It was reported that about 25% of ribosomes from normal tissue and only about 9% of those from diabetic muscle are active in this sense. The puzzle is that over 70% of the ribosomes in normal muscle are present as polysomes, yet only 25% appeared to carry a nascent peptide chain. WOOL suggests that some ribosomes might be sedimented along with the polysomes giving the appearance of more polysomes being present in the preparation. It seems possible to me that many ribosomes carrying nascent peptide chains could be unreactive to puromycin, and therefore be considered inactive by WOOL, for another reason. It is generally accepted that two sites exist on each ribosome where t-RNA molecules may be held: one is the amino acyl t-RNA binding site and the other is the nascent peptide t-RNA site. After peptide bond synthesis has occurred onto the amino acid on t-RNA in the amino acid site, the t-RNA carrying the nascent peptide now leaves the ribosome. At this point, the sole t-RNA left on the ribosome must change its site so as to allow the next t-RNA with its amino acid to enter. This step requires an enzyme usually called translocase.

Now suppose this reaction is slow compared with the peptide synthesis reaction: puromycin would be able to react only with those peptides on t-RNA molecules which are in the peptidyl site and not with those still in the amino acid site. A further point of interest emerges from this speculation. If it is true, some of the difference in ribosome reactivity towards puromycin might arise not from a difference in the number of ribosomes carrying a protein chain but from a difference in the rate of translocation between ribosomes from differently treated rats.

We have used this ingenious technique and have shown that liver ribosomes of hypophysectomized rats are less reactive to labelled puromycin than those of normal rats and that growth hormone treatment of the animals restores this diminished activity towards normal. We have obtained the same result by use of a different method. We noticed, however, that ribosomes prepared from liver without the use of detergent were more reactive towards puromycin than those prepared with it. This point might also help explain the low percentage of active ribosomes found in normal tissues when detergent is used. However they were prepared and however active the controls were towards puromycin, the ribosomes derived from rats which had circulating growth hormone were always considerably more active than those from rats without growth hormone.

3. Dextran Sulphate and Aurintricarboxylic Acid

If a higher percentage of ribosomes from rats with circulating growth hormone are active in protein synthesis one can ask, at what point in the process does the difference manifest itself? Is it at the initiation stage, or at the processes of t-RNA binding, peptide synthesis, translocation or of termination? In an attempt to analyse the point of action of growth hormone we have tried to inhibit the chain initiation reaction without inhibiting the rest of the process of protein biosynthesis. Dextran sulphate appears to be able to do this. When dextran sulphate is added to a ribosome cell-free system before poly U, it completely abolishes the usual stimulation of phenylalanine incorporation seen with poly U but it does not inhibit the incorporation of amino acids not coded for by poly U. Added after poly U, dextran sulphate inhibits phenylalanine incorporation to a decreasing extent as the interval between adding poly U and dextran sulphate increases. It would appear that dextran sulphate inhibits peptide chain initiation but not the rest of the protein synthetic process.

I found that addition of dextran sulphate to a liver cell-free system in the absence of poly U inhibited amino acid incorporation to a variable but significant extent, provided it was added to ribosomes before addition of the other components of the cell-free system. Added 2 min after incubation had commenced, it had little effect on incorporation; it seemed that initiation occurs in the cell-free system but that most of it takes place in the first 2 min of incubation.

Now when ribosomes preparations from normal, hypophysectomized and growth hormone-treated rats were compared in the presence of dextran sulphate to inhibit initiation, the differences in activity between them were still present. Even if initiation has been effected by growth hormone, and the results do not rule it out, some other change has occurred which renders the ribosomes more able to perform some of the other reactions in the translation process.

GROLLMAN and STEWART (1968) reported that the triphenylmethane dye, aurintricarboxylate (ATA) [probably the methyl quinone 3,3′,3″ — tricarboxy — 4,4′,4″-trihydroxytriphenylmethane] inhibited the attachment of $Q\beta$ or f_2 RNA to *E. coli* ribosomes. We have found that this compound stops peptide chain initiation in the liver cell-free system but does not inhibit the other protein synthesis reactions. The results with ATA confirm those obtained with dextran sulphate: the hormonally wrought differences persist after initiation has been inhibited. Initiation in the liver cell-free system is low, so that it is not easy to use the decrease in activity in the presence of ATA or dextran sulphate as an accurate measure of the difference in extent of initiation of normal and treated systems. However, it is clear that changed activity persists after the initiation reaction is eliminated from consideration.

Acknowledgements

The work reported is part of programme of a Group supported by the Medical Research Council to whom I express my thanks.

References

CSANYI, V., O. GREENGARD, and W. E. KNOX: J. biol. Chem. **242**, 2688 (1967).
EBOUE-BONIS, D., A. M. CHAMBAUT, P. VOLFIN, and H. CLAUSER: Nature (Lond.) **199**, 1183 (1963).
GARREN, L. D., R. R. HOWELL, G. M. TOMKINS, and R. M. CROCCO: Proc. nat. Acad. Sci. (Wash.) **52**, 1121 (1964).
GELEHRTER, T. D., and G. M. TOMKINS: J. molec. Biol. **29**, 59 (1967).
GREENGARD, O., M. A. SMITH, and G. ACS: J. biol. Chem. **238**, 1548 (1963).
GROLLMAN, A. P., and M. L. STEWART: Proc. nat. Acad. Sci. (Wash.) **61**, 719 (1968).
GROSSMAN, A., and C. MAVRIDES: J. biol. Chem. **242**, 1398 (1967).
HAGER, C. B., and F. T. KENNEY: J. biol. Chem. **243**, 3296 (1968).
JACOB, F., and J. MONOD: J. molec. Biol. **3**, 318 (1961).
KARLSON, P.: Perspect. Biol. Med. **6**, 203 (1963).
—, and C. E. SEKERIS: Acta endocr. (Kbh.) **53**, 505 (1966).
KENNEY, F. T.: J. biol. Chem. **242**, 4367 (1967).
—, and F. J. KULL: Proc. nat. Acad. Sci. (Wash.) **50**, 493 (1963).
KORNER, A.: Biochem. J. **92**, 449 (1964).
— Progr. Biophys. molec. Biol. **17**, 61 (1967).
LABRIE, F., and A. KORNER: (1) J. biol. Chem. **243**, 1120 (1968).
— — (2) J. biol. Chem. **243**, 1116 (1968).
— — (in preparation) (1969).
MARTIN, T. E., and F. G. YOUNG: Nature (Lond.) **208**, 684 (1965).
MISHKIN, E. P., and M. L. SHORE: Biochim. biophys. Acta (Amst.) **138**, 169 (1967).

Ottolenghi, C., and R. Cavagna: Endocrinology **83**, 924 (1968).
Reel, J. R., and F. T. Kenney: Proc. nat. Acad. Sci. (Wash.) **61**, 200 (1968).
Rosen, F.: J. cell. comp. Physiol. **66**, Supplement **1**, 146 (1965).
Schimke, R. T.: J. biol. Chem. **239**, 3808 (1964).
—, E. W. Sweeney, and C. M. Berlin: J. biol. Chem. **240**, 322 (1965).
Thompson, E. B., G. M. Tomkins, and J. F. Curran: Proc. nat. Acad. Sci. (Wash.) **56**, 296 (1966).
Wool, I. G., and K. Kurihara: Proc. nat. Acad. Sci. (Wash.) **58**, 2401 (1967).
Wyatt, G.: J. cell. comp. Physiol. **66**, Supplement **1**, 74 (1963).

Effects of Cortisol and Actinomycin D on RNA Polymerase Activity of Rat Liver Nuclei: Importance of Sequence of Administration

C. E. SEKERIS, J. HOMOKI, and M. BEATO

Physiologisch-Chemisches Institut der Universität Marburg/Lahn

An important aspect of the use of inhibitors for the elucidation of mechanisms of hormone action is the sequence of administration of the inhibitor and of the hormone. To illustrate this point, we will

Table 1. "*In vivo*" *effects of cortisol and actinomycin D on the RNA polymerase activity of rat liver nuclei*

	μμmol ^{14}C-UTP incorporated into RNA/mg protein Incubation time	
	4 min	8 min
Control	12.6	14.2
Cortisol	15.1	16.8
Actinomycin	5.6	8.6
Actinomycin, then cortisol	3.2	3.6

Four groups of rats were treated as follows: one group received i.p. 1.5 mg/100 g actinomycin D dissolved in tris-buffer containing 0.25 M sucrose, 0.025 M KCl and 0.01 M $MgCl_2$, pH 7.55 (TSS). Thirty min later 2.5 mg/100 g cortisol suspended in TSS was administered i.p. A second group of animals were treated as above, but instead of cortisol the same of TSS was injected. A third group received cortisol alone and a fourth group, acting as control, received only the corresponding amount of buffer. Forty-five min after the last injection, the animals were sacrificed by cervical dislocation and liver nuclei isolated as described in Ref. [2]. "Aggregate enzyme" was then prepared according to WEISS [3] and RNA polymerase activity measured in a system consisting of 0.25 μMol each of ATP, CTP and GTP; 0.1 μC ^{14}C-UTP, 2.5 μMol creatine phosphate, 5 μg creatine phosphokinase, 1.5 μMol mercaptoethanol, 1 μMol $MnSO_4$ and 12 μMol tris, pH 7.9, in a final volume of 0.150 ml. For each assay amounts of "aggregate enzyme" corresponding to 130 μg DNA were added. Aliquots were collected on filter paper discs and the radioactivity incorporated into RNA measured as described in Ref. [2]. (From HOMOKI, BEATO, and SEKERIS, 1968, slightly modified.)

Table 2. "*In vitro*" *effects of cortisol and actinomycin D on the RNA polymerase activity of rat liver nuclei*

	μμmol ^{14}C-UTP incorporated into RNA/mg protein Incubation time	
	4 min	8 min
Control	3.9	5.6
Cortisol	5.9	7.2
Actinomycin	2.0	2.1
Cortisol, then Actinomycin	2.0	1.9
Actinomycin, then Cortisol	1.3	1.6

Rat liver nuclei were incubated at 37° either with actinomycin D (20 μg/ml) dissolved in TSS or with TSS alone for 5 to 10 min and then in the presence or the absence of 5 μg/ml cortisol for another 10 min. In one experiment cortisol and actinomycin were added 15 min and 10 min respectively before completion of the incubation. The nuclei were then lysed in 0.05 M tris/HCl buffer pH 7.4. The nuclear sediment obtained after centrifugation at 8000 g for 10 min was suspended in 0.065 M tris-buffer pH 7.9 to a final concentration of 10 mg protein per ml and used for the assay of the RNA polymerase as described in the legend to Table 1. (From HOMOKI, BEATO and SEKERIS, 1968, slightly modified.)

briefly present experiments concerning the action of cortisol and actinomycin D on RNA synthesis in the rat liver. Administration of cortisol to rats results in a significant stimulation of RNA polymerase activity in liver nuclei [1], while injection of actinomycin D depresses RNA synthesis. Administration of both cortisol and actinomycin variously affects RNA polymerase activity depending on the sequence of injection of the two substances. If actinomycin is injected after cortisol administration, RNA synthesis is depressed to values approaching those caused by actinomycin alone whereas administration of actinomycin before treatment with cortisol inhibits RNA polymerase activity to a greater extent than that seen by actinomycin alone (Table 1).

The fact that isolated rat liver nuclei respond to cortisol with an increased RNA polymerase activity [2] led us to repeat the above mentioned experiments in vitro: under such conditions a more exact timing of the addition of the different agents is possible. The results are shown in Table 2.

Treatment of the nuclei with cortisol and subsequent addition of actinomycin D inhibits RNA polymerase activity to similar values as actinomycin alone, whereas addition of actinomycin first, followed by cortisol, results in inhibiton of the polymerase reaction to still lower values.

These results, independent of their interpretation (see [4] for discussion) stress the significance of the exact timing of hormone and inhibitor administration for studies concerning elucidation of mechanisms of hormone action. This work was supported by the Deutsche Forschungsgemeinschaft.

References

1. LANG, N., and C. E. SEKERIS: Life Sci. **3**, 391 (1964).
2. LUKÁCS, I., and C. E. SEKERIS: Biochim. biophys. Acta (Amst.) **134**, 85 (1967).
3. WEISS, S. B.: Proc. nat. Acad. Sci. (Wash.) **46**, 1020 (1960).
4. HOMOKI, J., M. BEATO, and C. E. SEKERIS: FEBS Letters **1**, 275 (1968).

Discussion

CHANDRA (Frankfurt): We have done some work on the action by polyanions in cell-free protein synthesis in bacterial systems, and dextran sulfate was one of them. We have found that dextran sulfate inhibition can partly be reversed by Mg^{++}. Have you studied such effects in liver?

KORNER: We examined the optimum magnesium level, both in the absence and in the presence of dextran sulfate. The amount of dextran sulfate we used is quite small, and we found that there is no difference in the optimum magnesium concentration in the liver system. Dextran sulfate does something else in the bacterial system; that is, to alter the subunit structure of ribosomes [MAYAZAWA, F., O. R. OLIJYNK, and C. J. TILLEY: Biochim. Biophys. Acta **145**, 96 (1967)]. We have shown that very low doses of dextran sulfate act as a ribonuclease inhibitor in the liver system, and this may complicate the issue.

STAEHELIN (Basle): Dr. KORNER has given evidence for the existence of broken polysomes in rat liver. This may make any interpretation of the biosynthetic activity of mammalian ribosomes very difficult. Since Dr. KORNER has indicated methods which would release the ribosomes from these broken polysomes and then measure their amount, I wonder whether he could give an estimate on the relative amount of broken polysomes in a preparation from rat liver.

KORNER: We find that about 60% of the liver ribosomes will react with puromycin. If one makes ribosomes with detergents, they are less sensitive to puromycin than they are when made without detergent.

For muscle, the corresponding figure of active ribosomes is 25%.

H. Kersten (Münster): Dr. Korner, if you use ribosomes from hypophysectomized rats and the enzymes from normal rat liver, do you get a stimulation in the biological activity of the partially inactive ribosomes?

Korner: There is no major effect of cell sap factors. However, there is a minor effect which might be due to difference in ribonuclease activity.

Kroon (Groningen): I would like to comment on Dr. Vazquez' talk. I think that some of the antibiotics he showed and which are active on 80 s ribosomal systems, are well-known to be not very toxic in clinical use. I think that this is due to the higher concentration at which these antibiotics inhibit in the in vitro system. Dr. Chandra, would you like to comment on your studies with tetracycline?

Chandra: I am glad that Dr. Kroon has brought up this point for discussion. We have observed some dose-dependent differences in the sensitivity of bacterial and mammalian systems towards chloramphenicol and tetracycline. These antibiotics at a concentration 1 to 10 μg/ml cause a complete inhibition of protein synthesis in systems obtained from sensitive bacteria. The mammalian systems isolated from liver, spleen, thymus and bone marrow (human) were sensitive only above 150 μg/ml concentration. To obtain a 50% inhibition in bacteria, about 8 μg/ml of both the antibiotics were needed, whereas concentrations up to 600 μg/ml were not as effective in liver. However, using a concentration range of 100 to 600 μg/ml we observed differences in the sensitivities of various systems isolated from mammals. Under our experimental conditions, spleen system was comparatively more sensitive to tetracycline than liver and thymus, whereas bone marrow system was very sensitive (300 to 600 μg/ml) to chloramphenicol. Intraperitoneal injections of tetracycline (6 mg/250 g b.w.) to rats were found to inhibit the antibody formation against sheep red blood cells (SRBC). This treatment was started on the first day on which SRBC were injected and continued till 4th day. The antibody titer was estimated on the 5th day. Under these conditions we observed that the antibody titer and the protein synthesis in liver were inhibited.

These experiments do not conclude solely the causes of clinical damages like aplastic anemia etc., but may influence such effects. The dose differences as observed between bacteria and mammalian systems are of a magnitude 1:100, and may be of importance from phylogenetic standpoint.

Kroon: In the eukaryotic cell, there are clearly two different types of targets for antibiotic action. Since the mitochondrial system is inhibited in most organisms, not only by chloramphenicol but also by tetracyclines, it seems necessary to point out that the inhibitions in the mitochondrial system are present at concentrations at which there is also antibacterial action. The eukaryotic system needs much higher concentrations which most likely are not reached in vivo during antibacterial treatment.

W. Kersten (Erlangen): Tetracyclines accumulate in the bone at special places. Does anyone know the reason for this accumulation of tetracycline?

O. Wieland (Munich): One reason is that tetracyclines form very strong complexes with calcium ions and therefore are incorporated in bone and teeth especially during growth. This constitutes a bad complication in so far as teeth become yellowish or even brownish, and this lasts for the whole life of the individual. Many people are now looking to avoid this complication which definitely invalidates the therapeutic use of this class of antibiotics, especially in children.

W. Kersten: Dr. Kroon, at the FEBS-Meeting in Madrid you showed that chloramphenicol administered to rats finally affects the cytochrome in mitochondria. Could you perhaps present these results here again and comment on how these explain the toxic effects in humans?

Kroon: In fact, it is possible to block the formation of cytochrome oxidase completely at very low serum levels of chloramphenicol in the intact animal (about 5 to 10 μg/ml serum). These are the serum levels at which the toxic effects in patients are also found. Thus, the levels in serum which are measured in patients with blood dyscrasia are the same as those used in the experimental animals by us. Further details on this point are published elsewhere [Kroon, A. M.: This volume, p. 159., and ref. [7] therein; —, F. Fase-Fowler, and H. DeVries: FEBS-Meeting, Madrid, 1969, Abstract 681.]

Chandra: The experimental evidence available today allows one to believe that the regulation of protein biosynthesis by hormones is not only at the level of transcription, but also that the translational activity and structural disposition of ribosomes play an important role. On the other hand, Wicks and Kenny have [Fed. Proc. **20**, 600 (1965)] reported a 2- to 3-fold increase in the synthesis of transfer RNA (t RNA) by steroids. In the light of recent experiments on enzyme induction in bacterial systems we know that tRNA-patterns are subject to alteration under various physiological conditions. May I ask you, Dr. Korner, whether any studies on these lines related to hormone action are known?

Korner: I don't know of any evidence for changes in tRNA patterns by hormones. Amino acid pools have been looked at after hormone treatment, but one should look at the tRNA's. There are some, as yet unpublished, studies with diabetic rat diaphragm, but as far as I know, there is no dramatic absence of a particular aminoacyl tRNA.

III. Supramolecular Structures

Incorporation of Amino Acids into Mitochondrial Membrane Proteins

W. Sebald, A. Schwab, and Th. Bücher

Institut für Physiologische Chemie und Physikalische Biochemie der Universität München

With 8 Figures

1. Intrinsic and Extrinsic Contribution to the Formation of Mitochondria

In recent years, it has been clarified in its essential features how genetic information is reduplicated and used in the synthesis of single protein macromolecules. Furthermore, our understanding of multienzyme complexes has progressed. However, our insight into morphogenetical laws of supramolecular units, such as cellular organelles, is still very limited.

Most important is the point of view that cytoplasmic supramolecular units may contribute to their morphogenetic processes with an input of intrinsic information (recent review in [1]). This was first supposed when Correns described the phenomenon of cytoplasmic inheritance [2], that is the inheritance of a certain phenotype from the maternal cell only. The discovery of DNA together with the components of a protein synthesizing system in various cellular organelles, for instance in mitochondria and chloroplasts, have substantiated this idea.

When we study the biogenesis of supramolecular units we are consequently confronted with the following question: What contributes the intrinsic system of an organelle, and what contributes the extrinsic system governed by the nucleus to the formation of a supramolecular unit? We will treat this question in our presentation, dealing with the incorporation of amino acids into membrane proteins of mitochondria.

Some possibilities of the experimental approach to this problem are compiled in Table 1.

Many workers have studied the incorporation of amino acids into isolated mitochondria from fast growing as well as from stationary cells, for instance from rat liver. As a matter of fact, these mitochondria isolated from their cellular environment still incorporate amino acids into protein. ROODYN, SUTTIE and WORK [3] have shown in 1962 that these amino acids are incorporated exclusively into the insoluble protein fractions of mitochondrial

Table 1. *Experimental approaches to the differentiation of extrinsic and intrinsic contributions to the incorporation of amino acids into mitochondrial proteins*

1. Isolated mitochondria (*in vitro* experiments).
2. Intact cells (*in vivo* experiments).
   a. Kinetics of incorporation.
   b. Cytoplasmic mutants.
   c. Specific inhibitors of extrinsic system.
   d. Specific inhibitors of intrinsic system.

membranes suggesting that most of the matrix and intercristae proteins are formed by the extrinsic system. These findings have been extended by NEUPERT et al. [4] and by BEATTIE et al. [5]. They demonstrated the nonincorporation of amino acids into the mitochondrial outer membrane *in vitro*. So by experiments with isolated mitochondria only certain proteins of the mitochondrial inner membrane are left over for the intrinsic system, and we will show later on that these are only a few ones.

One may ask to what extent these *in vitro* results are artifacts due to the isolation of the mitochondria from their natural environment. Hence it is desirable to find experimental approaches avoiding the disrupture of the cellular integrity. Such possibilities are listed in the lower part of Table 1.

2. Cycloheximide

Specific inhibitors are available which differentiate between the systems of ribosomal protein synthesis in eukaryotic cells of higher organisms and in prokaryotic cells, as bacteria. Cycloheximide has been found to be a potent inhibitor of protein synthesis in fungi and mammalian cells and to be nonactive on bacterial systems. It has been postulated that mitochondrial ribosomes are similar to the ribosomes of bacteria. In consequence, cycloheximide might be a useful tool for the differentiation between the intrinsic

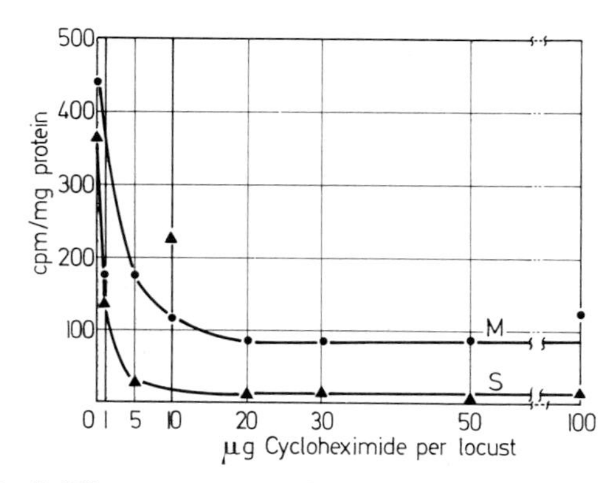

Fig. 1. Effect of different amounts of cycloheximide on the incorporation *in vivo* of C-14 phenylalanine (0.2 μC per locust) into the proteins of whole mitochondria (M, ● —— ●) and of the 20,000 × g supernatant (S, ▲ —— ▲) of the flight muscle of *Locusta migratoria*. The precursor was injected immediately after the cycloheximide. The locusts were killed after a 30 min labelling period (for experimental conditions see Ref. [6])

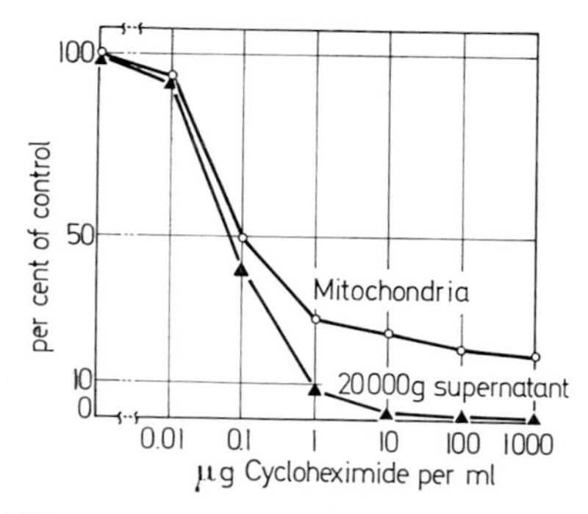

Fig. 2. Effect of different amounts of cycloheximide on the incorporation *in vivo* of C-14 leucine (0.5 μC per 50 ml culture) into the proteins of whole mitochondria (o——o) and of the 20,000 × g supernatant (▲ —— ▲) of *Neurospora crassa*. Hyphae were preincubated for 5 min with cycloheximide before the 10 min labelling period

and the extrinsic contribution to mitochondrial biosynthesis in whole cells.

Fig. 1 demonstrates the action of varying doses of cycloheximide on the incorporation of C-14-phenylalanine into the protein fractions of the fast growing wing depressor of a locust. While the incorporation into the cytosolic proteins, marked S, is almost entirely inhibited, this is not the case with the mitochondrial proteins. Here about 15% of the incorporation are found to be resistant. The same is found with *Neurospora crassa* wild type as shown in Fig. 2. We will go into some details with this organism.

3. Cellular Subfractions

A constant concentration of 100 μg of cycloheximide per ml has been applied in the experiment of Table 2. Here the influence of cycloheximide on the incorporation of C-14 amino acids into cellular subfractions is shown. The hyphae were divided into two parts and incubated under identical conditions, with the exception that to one part cycloheximide was added 5 min prior to the addi-

Table 2. *Effect of cycloheximide on the in vivo incorporation of amino acids into mitochondrial subfractions of Neurospora crassa*

Protein fraction		Control		Cycloheximide	
		cpm per mg protein			
Cytosolic (20,000 g supernatant)		130,000	(93%)	3,000	(5%)
Mitochondrial	whole	120,000	(86%)	28,000	(47%)
	extractable	105,000	(75%)	3,100	(5%)
	residual[a]	140,000	(100%)	60,000	(100%)

[a] The further separation of these fractions is demonstrated in Figs. 4A, B and 5.

Percentages are in reference to the insoluble mitochondrial proteins (residual) in each experiment.

Hyphae grown for 18 h in five 50 ml cultures were incubated for 30 min with 0.1 μC per ml of each C-14 leucine, C-14 isoleucine and C-14 phenylalanine, followed by a 30 min chase (2 μMol per ml of each C-12 leucine, C-12 isoleucine and C-12 phenylalanine). In the cycloheximide experiment the hyphae were incubated for 5 min with 100 μg cycloheximide per ml prior to the addition of the labelled amino acids.

For fractionation conditions see Ref. [7].

tion of labelled amino acids. For further experimental details we may refer to the text in the table. It should be mentioned, however, that the labelled amino acids have been diluted by a factor 10^4 or more by the corresponding inactive amino acids in a 30 min chase period prior to the disruption of the hyphae. Therefore, labelled proteins and peptides may be assumed to be essentially complete ones. Under these conditions the cycloheximide insensitive labelling of mitochondrial proteins, which emerged already from the experiment in Fig. 2, can now be clearly attributed to the insoluble proteins of mitochondrial membranes. Their specific activity still amounts up to 40% of the control, while the incorporation into the proteins of the cytosol and into the mitochondrial matrix proteins is reduced to two percent as compared to the control. This is similar to results found with the locust flight muscle [6]. In both experimental objects the action of cycloheximide supports earlier findings with isolated mitochondria by an independent method. This is further extended below.

4. Amino Acid Pool

From the results shown in Table 2 we might conclude that about 40% of membrane proteins, that is 20% of whole mitochondrial protein, are formed by the cycloheximide insensitive intrinsic system of the mitochondria. This conclusion is premature as far as the given percentage is concerned. Dilution of the labelled amino acid by the cellular pool has to be considered. By the inhibitory action of cycloheximide on the cellular protein synthesis the amino acid pool may change dramatically. Hence, dilution by the cellular pool under cycloheximide may be different from the control. This is shown in Fig. 3 where the relative size of the leucine pool as compared to the control was determined after different times of cycloheximide incubation. In fact, the pool size increases up to eight fold at 20 min action of cycloheximide. From these measurements we have calculated the actual rate of mitochondrial protein synthesis after different times of cycloheximide preincubation. Extrapolation of this curve to zero time leads to a production rate of 8% as compared to that without cycloheximide. We therefore believe that about 8% of the whole mitochondrial protein is synthesized by the intrinsic system.

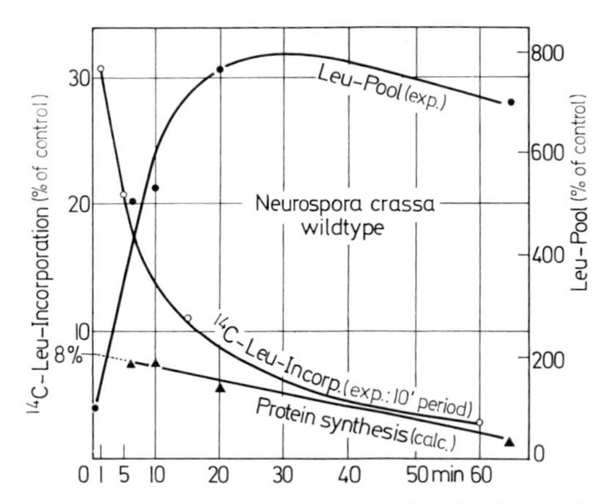

Fig. 3. o——o C-14 leucine incorporation *in vivo* in a 10 min labelling period (0.5 μC per 50 ml culture). The hyphae were preincubated with 100 μg cycloheximide per ml for the times plotted in the abscissa. The radioactivity incorporated without cycloheximide was taken as 100%. ●——● Leucine pool per 50 ml culture after different times of cycloheximide (100 μg/ml) incubation. The leucine pool without cycloheximide was taken as 100%. For the incorporation and the pool experiment parallelly grown hyphae were used (one 50 ml culture per point). The hyphae were grown from an inoculum of 2×10^6 conidia per ml in 50 ml of Vogel's minimal medium plus 2% sucrose at 25 °C for exactly 18 h before the addition of cycloheximide. ▲——▲ Actual mitochondrial protein synthesis after different times of cycloheximide preincubation as calculated from the pool size and the leucine incorporation. For this calculation the following assumptions were made: The mitochondrial proteins contain 7% (w/w) leucine. Without cycloheximide all components of the exponentially growing hyphae enhance proportionally with a doubling time of 4 h. This rate of synthesis was set as 100%. The protein synthesis of the control cannot be calculated from leucine incorporation because the added label is diluted very rapidly. (The turnover of the cellular leucine pool is less than 2 min)

5. Electrophoretic Bands

8% of total mitochondrial protein correspond to about 16% of mitochondrial membrane proteins. In Fig. 4A the gelelectrophoretic separation of these (insoluble) membrane proteins into some 20 bands is shown. The proteins have been stained with amido black. The bands are numbered beginning with the slowest moving ones. The smooth line in Fig. 5 represents the densitogram of the strip shown in Fig. 4A. For the evaluation of the labelling pattern autoradiographs, as presented in Figs. 4B, C and 6, have

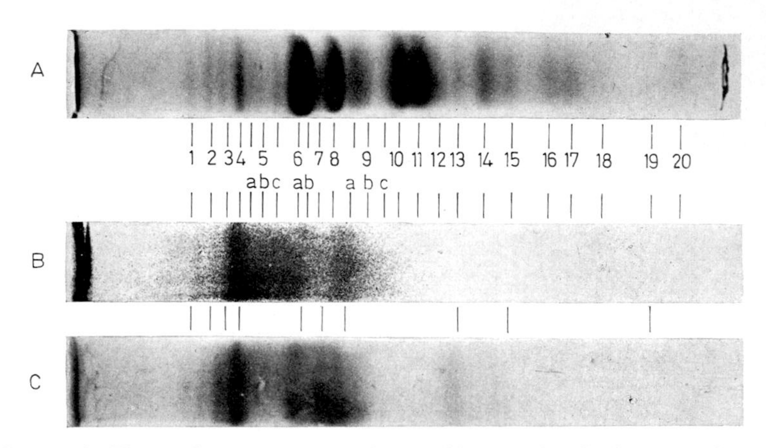

Fig. 4. A. Electrophoretic pattern of insoluble mitochondrial protein from *Neurospora crassa*. Bands were stained with amido black. B. Autoradiograph corresponding to the pherogram after labelling *in vivo* plus cycloheximide (for conditions see Table 2). C. Autoradiograph after labelling *in vitro*. (For conditions see Ref. [7])

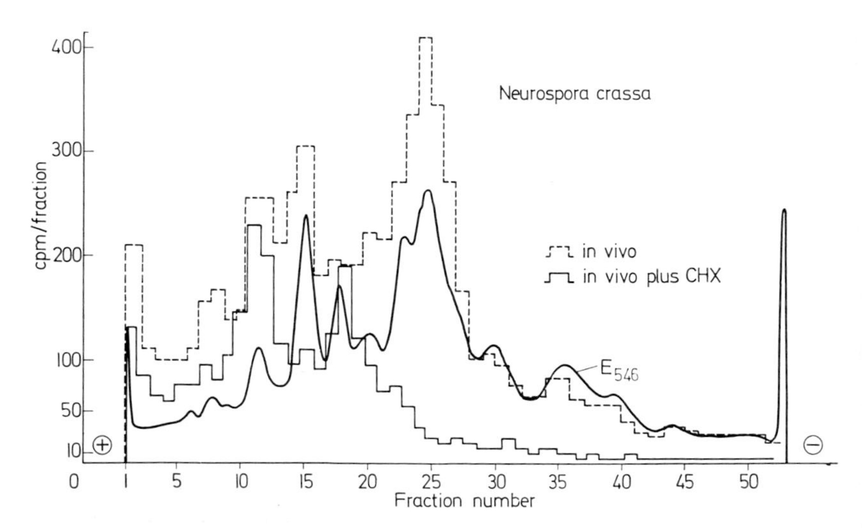

Fig. 5. Densitogram of amido black stained insoluble mitochondrial protein from *Neurospora crassa* after gel electrophoresis (smooth curve) and distribution of radioactivity over the pherograms (edged lines) after incorporation *in vivo* (- - - - -) and *in vivo* plus cycloheximide (———). (For labelling conditions see Table 2)

been exposed. In addition the pherograms have been sliced. The counts per 1 mm-slice are plotted in the stepped lines in Figs. 5 and 6. The continuous step line in Fig. 5 shows the radioactivity which had been incorporated in presence of cycloheximide. The residual insoluble fraction of the experiment shown in Table 2 (right hand column) had been subjected to the electrophoresis.

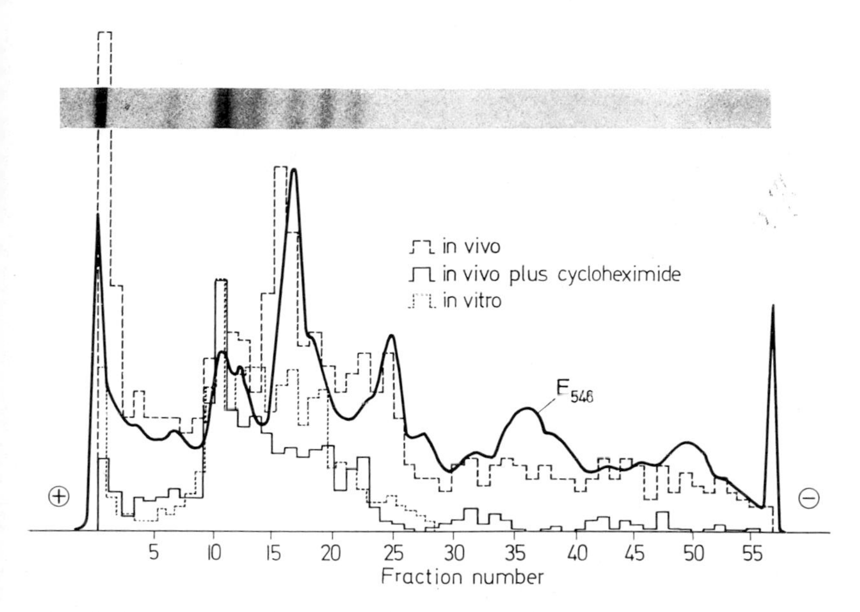

Fig. 6. Densitogram of amido black stained insoluble mitochondrial protein from the flight muscle of *Locusta migratoria* after gel electrophoresis (smooth curve), and distribution of radioactivity over the pherograms (edged lines) after incorporation *in vivo* (- - - - -), *in vivo* plus cycloheximide (———) and *in vitro* (......). (For labelling conditions see Ref. [6]). The upper part of the figure presents the autoradiograph after incorporation of amino acids *in vivo* plus cycloheximide in the same expansion as the densitogram

The radioactivity is incorporated mostly into fraction 11, corresponding to band 4, one of the slowly moving components. Other maxima appear in fractions 15 and 19, corresponding to bands 6 and 8. This suggests that only a small number of mitochondrial proteins or peptides localized in the bands mentioned above are synthesized by the intrinsic mitochondrial system. As a control the broken step curve shows the radioactivity of the corresponding (left hand column) fraction of Table 2. Here the amino acids are incorporated nearly proportional to the amido black staining, suggesting that all proteins are synthesized with about the same rate in the control. Interestingly enough, with the electrophoretic separation of the proteins the incorporation under the action of cycloheximide is found to be as efficient as in the control for some "cycloheximide insensitive" fractions (11, 19). The radioactivity pattern resulting from amino acid incorporation by the cycloheximide resistant system *in vivo* may now be compared with the pattern obtained after incorporation *in vitro*, in isolated mitochondria. This is illustrated by the autoradiographs in Figs. 4B and 4C. In both cases the same protein bands (4, 6, and 8) are labelled, with a predominance of band 4.

In experiments with *Locusta migratoria* similar results are obtained, as shown in Fig. 6. Here the smooth curve represents a densitogram of the pherogram which was subjected to autoradiography, shown in the upper part of the figure. Again by the cycloheximide resistant protein synthesis (autoradiograph and smooth step line) amino acids are incorporated *in vivo* into the same few fractions as *in vitro* (dotted step line), while in the control (broken step line) all bands are labelled.

In summary, the biological validity of earlier experiments with isolated mitochondria is supported by these studies on the action of cycloheximide. With two independent methods the same answer is found in that the mitochondrial intrinsic system produces a few protein fractions of the inner membrane. According to two independent estimations (see also [7]) these proteins make up about 8% of whole mitochondrial protein or 16% of the membrane proteins.

So far only negative answers are available with concern to the function of the material in the labelled electrophoretic bands. They do not represent the so-called structural protein [7]. Also some membrane bound components of the respiratory chain may be excluded. Here the specific radioactivity decreased in the course of the isolation procedure in preliminary experiments. Even the question whether the observed amino acid incorporation represents true protein synthesis is open to some extent. From the

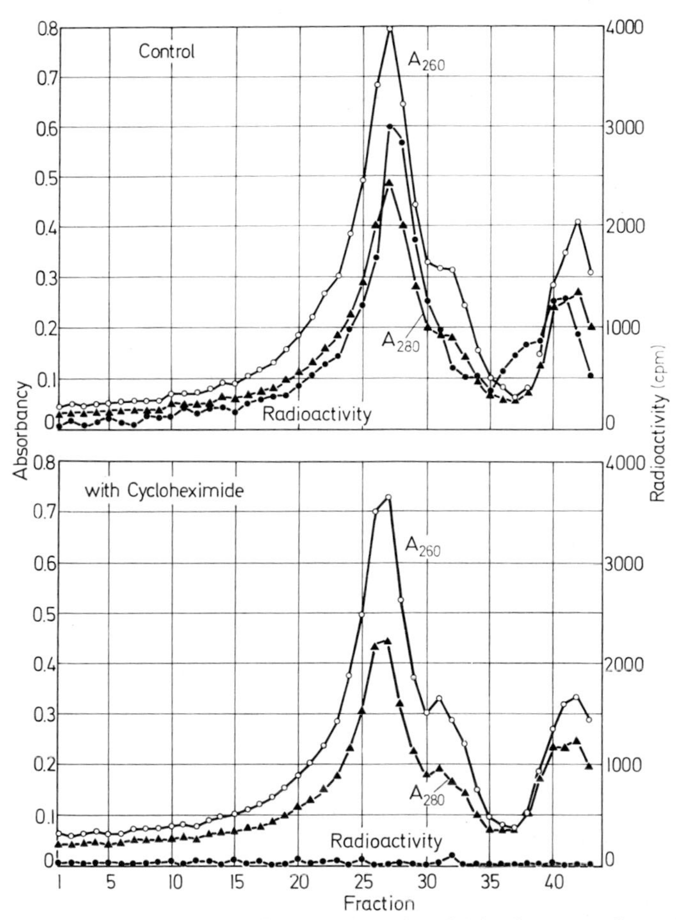

Fig. 7. Density gradient profiles of mitochondrial ribosomes from *Neurospora crassa* as measured by the absorbancy at 260 and 280 nm, and distribution of radioactivity incorporated *in vivo* (Fig. 7a) and *in vivo* plus cycloheximide (Fig. 7b). Ribosomes isolated from mitochondria were purified by sucrose gradient centrifugation. Mitochondria were lysed with 1% Triton X-100 in standard buffer (100 mM NH_4Cl, 10 mM TRIS, 10 mM $MgCl_2$, pH 7.6), and the supernatant from a centrifugation at 30,000 xg for 30 min was centrifugated again at 150,000 xg for 3 h. The resulting yellowish pellet was resuspended in standard buffer and 0.2 ml (5-10 OD_{260}) were used for centrifugation (2 h) at 41,000 rpm in the Spinco SW 41 rotor through an isokinetic convex sucrose gradient as described by NOLL [8]. Radioactivity was incorporated by adding C-14 leucine, C-14 isoleucine and C-14 phenylalanine (each 6,7 nC per ml) to the cultures for 20 min. Then the C-12 amino acids were added each to a final concentration of 2 mM for 20 min. In the cycloheximide experiment, 100 μg cycloheximide per ml was added 10 min before the addition of the radioactivity

experiments which W. NEUPERT will communicate in his prepared discussion, it may be assumed, however, that puromycin releasable peptides are formed on the mitochondrial ribosomes. In contrast, the proteins of the mitochondrial ribosomes are formed by the extrinsic system. This will be discussed in the next section.

6. Amino Acid Incorporation into the Proteins of Mitochondrial Ribosomes

In cooperation with W. NEUPERT, mitochondrial ribosomes have been isolated from *Neurospora crassa* with the methods developed by KÜNTZEL and NOLL [8] and by RIFKIN, WOOD, and LUCK [9]. These ribosomes can be prepared in a pure state. Their sedimentation behaviour as well as the composition of their RNA and protein moieties are distinct from that of the cytosolic ribosomes. In the experiment shown in Fig. 7 a preparation of mitochondrial ribosomes was centrifuged through a sucrose gradient. The absorbancy at 260 and 280 mμ was determined as well as the radioactivity incorporated *in vivo*. Again the 20 min labelling period was followed by a 20 min chase period with unlabelled amino acids prior to the disruption of the hyphae. Therefore the peptide chains just formed on the ribosomes at the time of disruption will incorporate predominantly unlabelled amino acids during the chase period. Consequently, the radioactivity incorporated in the control experiment (Fig. 7a) into polysomes (fraction 10 to 15) and monosomes (fractions 20 to 30) may be attributed to ribosomal proteins. No radioactivity was incorporated when the hyphae were preincubated for 10 min with cycloheximide (Fig. 7b), whereas the mitochondrial membrane fractions were labelled to the same extent as previously shown. This result indicates that the mitochondrial ribosomal proteins are synthesized by the extramitochondrial protein synthesis. This has also been recently communicated by KÜNTZEL [10].

So we are confronted with the phenomenon that part of the intrinsic system of mitochondrial protein synthesis is synthesized by the extrinsic system. Interestingly enough, this would mean that the mitochondrial ribosomes, behaving like ribosomes from prokaryotic cells with respect to the noninhibition by cycloheximide and the inhibition by chloramphenicol (see below), are synthesized on ribosomes of the eukaryotic cell type.

7. Modified Intrinsic System

In the experiments described until now we have concentrated on the inhibition of the extrinsic system. At the end we would like to present some results on the modification of the intrinsic system. Chloramphenicol is an inhibitor of protein synthesis in prokaryotic cells and also in isolated mitochondria. It has been used in investigations on the problems discussed here by several groups with

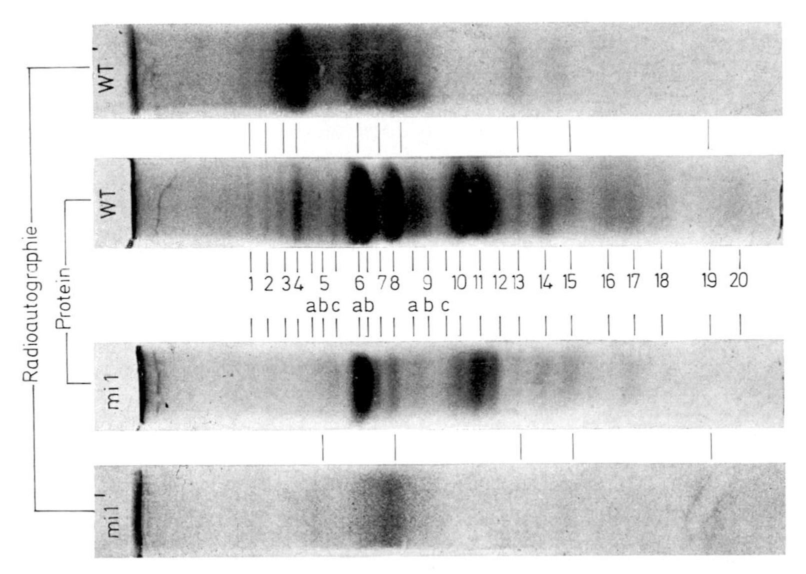

Fig. 8. Electrophoretic pattern of insoluble mitochondrial protein from *Neurospora crassa* wild type (WT) and cytoplasmic *mi-1* mutant (*mi-1*). Inward, amido black staining; outward, autoradiographs corresponding to the pherograms after amino acid incorporation *in vitro*. (For experimental conditions see Ref. [7])

yeast cells (for example [11]). The effect of chloramphenicol on amino acid incorporation by the intrinsic mitochondrial system *in vivo* can be studied using cycloheximide and chloramphenicol simultaneously. When hyphae from *Neurospora crassa* are preincubated with both inhibitors, the labelling of the mitochondrial proteins is reduced to about 20% as compared to the labelling under the influence of cycloheximide alone. On the other hand, hyphae grown in the presence of high concentrations of chloramphenicol develop altered mitochondria. The content of cytochrome c is increased and that of the cytochromes b and a/a_3 is strongly decreased. A cytochrome pattern [12] similar to the one observed in the cytoplasmic *mi-1* mutant of *Neurospora* results. In addition, after electrophoretic separation of the membranes less protein is found in band 4, which is the one mostly labelled by the intrinsic system as we have shown.

Equally the mitochondrial membranes of the cytoplasmic *mi-1* mutant contain less band 4 protein as shown by the protein pattern in Fig. 8. In addition, no amino acids are incorporated into this fraction by isolated *mi-1* mitochondria, as demonstrated by the autoradiograph of the pherogram.

8. Discussion

The mitochondrial inner membrane has a defined composition similar to a multienzyme complex. Consequently, the mitochondrial and extramitochondrial systems of protein synthesis must be coordinated in the biogenesis of this supramolecular unit. This interdependency is demonstrated in the cytoplasmic mutants and in hyphae grown in the presence of chloramphenicol. In the case of the mutants we have to assume that the mitochondrial DNA has mutated. In the case of chloramphenicol the function of the mitochondrial ribosomes is inhibited. In both instances the alterations observed in the mitochondria are similar. The content of cytochrome a is strongly decreased [11, 13, 14] and the content of cytochrom c is increased [14]. These proteins are synthesized by the extrinsic system [15—17]. This means that we have to discriminate between the primary defects caused by the modification of the intrinsic system and the secondary alterations. This complicates the evaluation of the observed phenotype.

The incorporation of amino acids by the intrinsic system into electrophoretically defined protein bands provides a first insight into the immediate products. But until now the label could not be enriched in any functionally characterized protein fraction. In addition to the technical difficulties of preparing undenatured membrane proteins we have to consider the possibility that the peptide chains synthesized by the intrinsic system may not be integrated into functionally active proteins when the extrinsic system is eliminated simultaneously. This would concern experiments *in vitro* as well as *in vivo* under cycloheximide action. Nevertheless, it is remarkable that the mitochondrial protein synthesis continues to operate at least for 1 h when the extrinsic system is eliminated by cycloheximide. This indicates that the two systems are not strongly coupled or that the coupling of the two systems is weakened by the action of the antibiotic.

In speculating about the function of the material produced by the intrinsic mitochondrial protein synthesis we may consider different possibilities. We have to differentiate between stoichiometric and catalytic contributions to the biogenesis of the mitochondria. A stoichiometric contribution would indicate that building stones are produced which fit in a molar proportion into the mitochondrial architecture. Such stones might be enzymes or coordinating structural elements of the multienzyme complex. A catalytic function would relate to the process of membrane formation. In this case the products of the intrinsic system would contribute in a nonmolar proportion to the protein pattern of the membrane. With respect to a catalytic contribution of the intrinsic system we can consider the following possibilities:

1. The protein produced might be active in the synthesis of coenzymes belonging to apoenzymes synthesized outside the mitochondria. For instance, ferrochelatase is known to be part of the inner membrane [18], while the apocytochromes *a* and *c* are assumed to be synthesized by the extrinsic system [15—17].

2. The product of the intrinsic system might function in the translocation or the modification of peptide chains synthesized by the extrinsic system. In this way the specific localization of enzymes in the mitochondria could be explained.

3. The protein produced might be active in the mitochondrial system of DNA replication and in the mitochondrial systems of RNA and protein synthesis.

In the literature, arguments may be found which favour one or the other of the speculative possibilities listed above. A promising approach to the solution of the open questions may be the further characterization of the electrophoretic protein fractions which are specifically labelled by the intrinsic mitochondrial system.

The authors wish to express their most sincere appreciations to F. KAUDEWITZ of the Institut für Genetik der Universität München for his help and support, and for the possibility to perform part of the experiments in the laboratories of that institute. This work was supported by the Deutsche Forschungsgemeinschaft, Schwerpunktsprogramm "Biochemie der Morphogenese".

References

1. ROODYN, D. B., and D. WILKIE: The biogenesis of mitochondria. London: Methuen Co. Ltd. 1968.
2. CORRENS, C.: Handbuch Vererbungswiss., 22. Berlin: Bornträger 1937.
3. ROODYN, D. B., J. W. SUTTIE, and T. S. WORK: Biochem. J. **83**, 29 (1962).
4. NEUPERT, W., D. BRDICZKA, and TH. BÜCHER: Biochem. biophys. Res. Commun. **27**, 488 (1967).
5. BEATTIE, D. S., R. F. BASFORD, and S. B. KORITZ: Biochemistry **10**, 3099 (1967).
6. SEBALD, W., TH. HOFSTÖTTER, D. HACKER, and TH. BÜCHER: FEBS Letters **2**, 177 (1969).
7. —, TH. BÜCHER, B. OLBRICH, and F. KAUDEWITZ: FEBS Letters **1**, 235 (1968).
8. KÜNTZEL, H., and H. NOLL: Nature (Lond.) **215**, 1340 (1967).
9. RIFKIN, M. R., D. D. WOOD, and D. J. L. LUCK: Proc. nat. Acad. Sci. (Wash.) **58**, 1025 (1967).
10. KÜNTZEL, H.: Nature (Lond.) **222**, 142 (1969).
11. CLARK-WALKER, G. D., and A. W. LINNANE: J. Cell Biol. **34**, 1 (1967).
12. TISSIERES, A., and H. K. MITCHELL: J. biol. Chem. **208**, 241 (1954).
13. SHERMAN, F., and P. P. SLONIMSKI: Biochim. biophys. Acta (Amst.) **91**, 1 (1964).
14. HASKINS, F. A., A. TISSIERES, H. K. MITCHELL, and M. B. MITCHELL: J. biol. Chem. **200**, 819 (1953).
15. TUPPY, H., and G. D. BIRKMAYER: Europ. J. Biochem. **8**, 237 (1969).
16. GONZALEZ-CADAVID, N. F., and P. N. CAMPELL: Biochem. J. **105**, 443 (1967).
17. KADENBACH, B.: In: SLATER, E. C., J. M. TAGER, S. PAPA, and E. QUAGLIARIELLO: Biochemical aspects of the biogenesis of mitochondria, p. 415. Bari: Adriatica Editrice 1968.
18. JONES, M. S., and O. T. G. JONES: Biochem. biophys. Res. Commun. **31**, 977 (1968).

Puromycin Sensitivity of Ribosomal Label after Incorporation of 14-C-Amino-Acids into Isolated Mitochondria from *Neurospora crassa*

W. NEUPERT

Institut für Physiologische Chemie and Physikalische Biochemie der Universität München

With 1 Figure

Mitochondrial ribosomes from *Neurospora crassa* have been isolated and characterized by KÜNTZEL and NOLL [1] and by RIFKIN et al. [2]. Radioactivity has been found in these ribosomes after labelling of isolated mitochondria by incorporation of 14-C leucine [1]. However, no distinction was made between labelling of the structural proteins of the ribosomes and the peptide chains being actually synthesized.

This distinction is relevant in two respects. A labelling of growing peptide chains would suggest that mitochondrial ribosomes are active in synthesizing proteins. Therefore, similar physical and chemical properties of cytoplasmic and mitochondrial ribosomes would correspond to a similar function. On the other hand, a labelling of the ribosomal proteins would indicate that these proteins are of mitochondrial origin.

Puromycin, which is known to release the growing peptide chain from the ribosome, was used to examine this question.

The experiment was carried out in the following way: Mitochondria isolated from *Neurospora* cells [3] were incubated with radioactive amino acids [4]. After 20 min of incubation the mitochondria were divided into two equal portions. One portion served as a control. Puromycin (0.4 mM) was added to the other portion. The incubation was continued for additional 7 min. Then the ribosomes were isolated from both control and puromycin treated mitochondria by lysis with Triton X 100 and differential and density gradient centrifugation. The specific radioactivities of all fractions of this procedure were determined. This is shown in Table 1 and Fig. 1.

In the control preparation (Table 1, left hand columns), the total radioactivity incorporated into the crude ribosomal fraction is less than 10% of the radioactivity of the mitochondrial lysate.

Table 1

Fraction	Control		Puromycin incubated	
	cpm/mg prot.	cpm (total)	cpm/mg prot.	cpm (total)
Mitochondria after incubation	7000	525000	4900	343000
Mitochondrial lysate	7210	392000	4960	238000
Sediment of mitochondrial lysate 30 min, 24000 x g	7920	13050	3650	6930
Crude ribosomes	17660	33500	4160	5830
Supernatant after sedimentation of ribosomes	6185	180700	7110	242000

Radioactivity incorporated into different fractions of mitochondria labelled *in vitro* for 20 min with 14-C-leucine, 14-C-isoleucine and 14-C-phenylalanine (each 0.1 μC/ml incubation medium) [4]. Control mitochondria were withdrawn before further incubation with 0.4 mM puromycin for 7 min. After incubation the mitochondria were washed twice with sucrose medium [5] and centrifuged for 1 h at 25000 rpm in the Spinco SW 25/2 rotor through a linear gradient of 25 to 68% sucrose in a buffer containing 0.1 M NH_4Cl, 10 mM Tris, and 10 mM $MgCl_2$, pH 7.6. This buffer was also used for the following procedures. The mitochondria were lysed by homogenization for 5 min in 1% Triton X 100. Crude ribosomes were prepared by centrifuging 30 min at 24000 x g and the resulting supernatant 3 h at 150000 x g.

The specific radioactivity of the ribosomes, however, is higher by a factor of 2.5 than that of the mitochondrial lysate. This low incorporation into the ribosomal fraction concerns optimal conditions for incorporation into whole mitochondria. Under non-optimal incorporation conditions these relationships are different. In an experiment in which incorporation into whole mitochondria was lower by a factor of 12.5 as compared to the experiment of Table 1, the specific radioactivity of the crude ribosomes was higher by a factor of 7.5 than that of whole mitochondria. As much as 25% of the total radioactivity incorporated was found in crude ribosomes in this case.

Puromycin incubation (Table 1, right hand columns) for 7 min results in a decrease of specific radioactivity of the crude ribosomal fraction by a factor of about 4 as compared to the control fraction. An even greater decrease of the total radioactivity is observed. Also the total and specific radioactivities of whole mitochondria

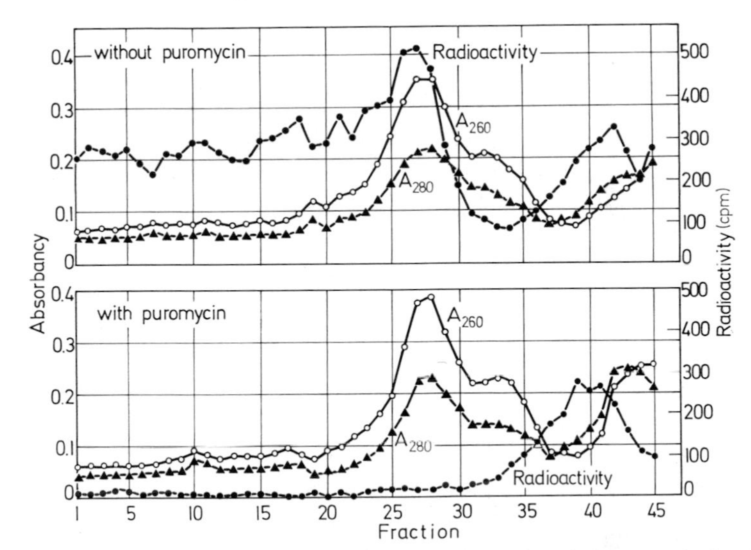

Fig. 1. Gradient profiles and incorporated radioactivity of ribosomes isolated from mitochondria labelled *in vitro* with and without successive incubation with puromycin. The crude ribosomal fractions mentioned in Table 1 were submitted to isokinetic sucrose gradient centrifugation as described by NOLL [6]

decreases. This may be at least partially explained by a loss of the smaller peptide chains released by the action of puromycin. These chains may possibly not be precipitated by trichloracetic acid during the protein preparation procedure.

The results are more clearcut when the crude ribosomal fraction is further purified by density gradient centrifugation as shown in Fig. 1. In the control preparation (without puromycin) the largest part of the radioactivity is found in the polysome (fractions 1 to 23) and monosome (fractions 24 to 30) regions, the polysomes having a much higher specific radioactivity than the monosomes. By a preceeding incubation with RNase this label is shifted from the polysome region into the monosome peak. A smaller part of the radioactivity is found at the top of the gradient (fractions 40 to 45) in a region where the absorption at 280 nm is higher than at 260 nm. After incubation with puromycin no radioactivity is associated with the monosomes and polysomes, and only the contaminating protein at the top of the gradient retains its radioactivity.

We would like to draw the following conclusions:

1. Mitochondrial ribosomes incorporate amino acids into polypeptide chains. At least part of the ribosomes are active as polysomes. This confirms and extends recent experiments of KÜNTZEL [5], who demonstrated a poly-U dependent activity of amino acid incorporation with mitochondrial ribosomes isolated from *Neurospora crassa*.

2. Isolated mitochondria do not synthesize significant amounts of the proteins of their ribosomes. It might be still assumed that ribosomal precursor proteins or peptides are synthesized by the mitochondrial system which are not integrated into the ribosomal proteins under these *in vitro* conditions.

3. Under appropiate conditions the largest part of the amino acids incorporated are not found in peptide chains on the ribosomes, but bound to the insoluble mitochondrial membrane. On electrophoresis at least part of these non-ribosome-bound peptide chains can be detected as definite bands [4]. Therefore, it appears likely that ribosomes in isolated mitochondria synthesize definite proteins.

References

1. KÜNTZEL, H., and H. NOLL: Nature (Lond.) **215**, 1340 (1967).
2. RIFKIN, M. R., D. D. WOOD, and D. J. L. LUCK: Proc. nat. Acad. Sci. (Wash.) **58**, 1025 (1967).
3. LUCK, D. J. L.: J. Cell Biol. **16**, 483 (1963).
4. SEBALD, W., TH. BÜCHER, B. OLBRICH, and F. KAUDEWITZ: FEBS Letters **1**, 483 (1968); see also this volume, p. 140.
5. KÜNTZEL, H.: Nature (Lond.) **222**, 142 (1969).
6. NOLL, H.: Nature (Lond.) **215**, 360 (1967).

On the Effects of Antibiotics and Intercalating Dyes on Mitochondrial Biosynthesis

A. M. Kroon

Department of Medical Enzymology, Laboratory of Biochemistry, University of Amsterdam, and Laboratory of Physiological Chemistry, State University, Groningen, The Netherlands

It has been known for a long time that mitochondrial protein synthesis is inhibited by chloramphenicol, and during the last few years it has been shown that a large number of antibacterial agents that inhibit bacterial multiplication at the level of replication, transcription or translation, are interfering also with the biosynthesis of mitochondria (for reviews and references to the original literature, see refs. 1—3). The purpose of this paper is to summarize our experiments on the effects of different inhibitors of mitochondriogenesis in animal tissues. We have been working along three lines. Firstly, we have studied the effects of these inhibitors on the incorporation of radioactive amino acids into protein by isolated mitochondria that were either intact or swollen by hypotonic treatment in water. We have further looked into the inhibitory effects on the growth and mitochondrial composition of rat-heart cells in tissue culture. Finally, we have examined the effects of chloramphenicol on mitochondriogenesis in regenerating rat liver.

The results of our studies so far, which are summarized in Table 1, lead to a number of conclusions and considerations.

1. Mitochondrial protein synthesis can be specifically inhibited by antibiotics interfering with bacterial protein synthesis. This is completely in line with the accumulating evidence — especially for lower organisms — that mitochondria contain bacterial type ribosomes, bacterial type aminoacyl-t-RNA synthetases, and bacterial type transfer RNA.

2. In contrast to yeast mitochondria [1], protein synthesis in mitochondria from rat tissues is insensitive to lincomycin and the

macrolides (e.g. erythromycin, oleandomycin). This insensitivity is apparently not due to differences in the properties of mitochondrial ribosomes from yeast and rat, since after swelling also

Table 1. *Effects of various inhibitors on the biosynthetic activities of mitochondria of rat tissues in vivo and in vitro. The detailed experimental conditions for the different types of experiments are published elsewhere: for amino acid incorporation in intact mitochondria, see* Kroon [4], *for amino acid incorporation in swollen mitochondria, see* Kroon et al., [5], *for experiments on beating heart cells, see* Kroon *and* Jansen [6], *for experiments regarding liver regeneration see* Kroon *and* de Vries [7]

Inhibitor	Mitochondrial protein synthesis *in vitro*		Specific inhibition of cytochrome *c* oxidase formation	
	Intact mitochondria	Swollen mitochondria	Cultured heart cells	Regenerating liver
Antibiotics				
Actinomycin D	–	+	0	0
D(–)*threo*-Chloramphenicol	++	++	++	++
L(+)*threo*-Chloramphenicol	–	–	–	0
Oxytetracycline	++	++	++	0
Streptomycin	+	+	+	0
Lincomycin	–	+/++[a]	–	0
Erythromycin	–	++	–	0
Oleandomycin	–	+/++[a]	0	0
Sparsomycin	++	++	0	0
Puromycin	++	++	0	0
Cycloheximide	–	–	+	0
Intercalating dyes				
Acriflavin	++	++	++	0
Ethidium bromide	++	++	++	0

++ = 50 to 100% inhibition; + = 20 to 50% inhibition; – = no inhibition; 0 = not yet tested.

[a] Based on two different experiments only.

rat-liver mitochondrial protein synthesis is inhibited by these antibiotics. The lack of inhibition in intact mitochondria is, therefore, to be ascribed to a permeability barrier at the level of the mitochondrial membrane as is also the case for some of the erythromycin-resistant mutants of yeast described by THOMAS and WILKIE [8]. In yeast this permeability appears to be controlled by the nucleus.

The permeability barrier may well turn out to be an important tool in the search for antibiotics inhibiting bacterial protein synthesis without impairing mitochondrial functions. In view of the relatively long half-life of mitochondrial components, this is specially important if longterm antibiotic treatments are desired.

3. The synthesis of functionally active cytochrome *c* oxidase in cultured rat-heart cells is inhibited by those antibiotics that interfere with protein synthesis in intact mitochondria. We are to conclude, therefore, that a product of mitochondrial protein synthesis plays a key role in the formation of this enzyme. However, also cycloheximide, *not* inhibiting protein synthesis in either intact or swollen mitochondria, prevents the formation of active cytochrome *c* oxidase. We, therefore, favour the idea that cytochrome *c* oxidase is synthesized *outside* the mitochondria, but that its synthesis or assembly is strongly controlled by a product of mitochondrial protein synthesis. The fact that TUPPY and BIRKMAYER [9] have found that the apoprotein of cytochrome *c* oxidase is also present under conditions where mitochondrial protein synthesis is not operating, supports this hypothesis.

4. All the effects of chloramphenicol are specific for the D(−) *threo*-isomer and are obtained at concentrations at which there is no effect on oxidation or phosphorylation whatsoever. *In vivo* inhibition in regenerating liver is obtained only if a minimal serum level of about 10 μg/ml is maintained during the total time of the experiments (2 to 4 days in our case). The inhibitory effect of chloramphenicol is reversible. Once the antibiotic is withdrawn, mitochondrial protein synthesis and cytochrome *c* oxidase formation resume.

5. The inhibitions by the intercalating agents acriflavin and ethidium bromide are irreversible and occur at very low concentrations. The mechanism of their action is not yet completely established. We favour the hypothesis that the inhibitions are due to a preferential binding to the mitochondrial DNA. This is in agreement with the fact that both dyes induce preferentially cytoplasmic mutations in yeast at similar concentrations [1—3]. If our explanation is correct, this implies that mitochondrial protein syn-

thesis is continuously dependent on DNA-directed RNA synthesis as we have proposed earlier [10] on the basis of the inhibition of mitochondrial protein synthesis by actinomycin D.

In summary we may say that the inhibitors described have been and will certainly continue to be useful for elucidating the mechanism of mitochondrial biosynthesis.

I am indebted to Dr. P. Borst for his valuable criticism. This work was aided in part by the Netherlands Foundation for Chemical Research (S.O.N.) with financial aid from the Netherlands Organization for the Advancement of Pure Research (Z.W.O.).

References

1. Slater, E. C., J. M. Tager, S. Papa, and E. Quagliariello, Eds.: Biochemical aspects of the biogenesis of mitochondria. Bari, Italy: Adriatica Editrice 1968.
2. Borst, P., and A. M. Kroon: Int. Rev. Cytol 1969 (in press).
3. Kroon, A. M. In: Lima de Faria, A., Ed.: Handbook of molecular cytology, p. 943. Amsterdam: North Holland Publishing Co. 1969.
4. — Biochim. biophys. Acta **91**, 145 (1964).
5. —, I. J. Vries, and J. L. J. Smit: (In press).
6. —, and R. J. Jansen: Biochim. biophys. Acta **155**, 629 (1968).
7. —, and H. de Vries: FEBS Letters **3**, 208 (1969).
8. Thomas, D. Y., and D. Wilkie: Genet. Res. **11**, 33 (1968).
9. Tuppy, H., and G. D. Birkmayer: Europ. J. Biochem. 8, 237 (1969).
10. Kroon, A. M.: Biochim. biophys. Acta **76**, 165 (1963).

Discussion

Westphal (Freiburg): I think these three presentations are a very good example of the whole subject of our colloquium, showing how valuable antibiotic inhibitors may be for general research in the field of the synthesis of cellular subunits.

Staehelin (Basle): I have a question on the time course relationship between mitochondrial function and inhibition of mitochondrial protein synthesis. In the adrenal cortex, cycloheximide blocks the action of ACTH. Whereas the cytoplasmic reactions still proceed — such as activation of adenyl cyclase, splitting of cholesterol etc. — the step that is specifically blocked is the first reaction occurring in the mitochondrium, namely, cholesterol side chain cleavage. The inhibition of ACTH action by cycloheximide occurs very fast, within a few minutes. My question is: How soon after the addition of an inhibitor of mitochondrial protein synthesis can any change in the mitochondrial function be observed?

Kroon (Groningen): We are not experienced with the system you referred to. We know that with intact cells it lasts some time before the function of the mitochondria is impaired in the sense of a deficiency of their capacity for oxidative phosphorylation. After partial hepatectomy of rats, regeneration proceeds although no functional mitochondria are synthesized any more.

With respect to your statement on cycloheximide, I do not think that your results can be explained on the basis of inhibition of mitochondrial protein synthesis because cycloheximide does not inhibit mitochondrial protein synthesis.

Bücher (Munich): I think nobody can give a direct answer to these very interesting observations. However, generally we could say that we have to distinguish between the mitochondria of growing tissues as the flight muscle of the Locust and Neurospora crassa, and the mitochondria of stationary tissues as liver and perhaps the adrenal gland. In the liver of adult rats we know the turnover (half live values) of different parts of the mitochondria labelled by ^{35}S-methionine [1]. It is about 4 days for the outer membrane, about 13 days for the inner membrane and about 12 days for the soluble proteins of the mitochondrial matrix. With the exception of cytochrome c no single protein has been followed up hitherto in such studies. Hence they do not exclude that certain mitochondrial enzymes have much higher turnover rates. From measurements of the induction of the enzyme activity of δ-aminolevulinate synthetase, inhibited by cycloheximide but not by chloramphenicol, an apparent half life time of 68 min has been concluded for this mitochondrial enzyme [2]; cf. also [3].

1. Brunner, G., and W. Neupert: FEBS Letters **1**, 153 (1968).
2. Hayashi, N., B. Yoda, and G. Kikuchi: Arch. Biochem. **131**, 83 (1969).
3. Zuyderhoudt, F. M., P. Borst, and F. Huising: Biochim. biophys. Acta **178**, 408 (1969).

Lardy (Madison, Wisc.): Dr. Kroon, what treatment was done to get the three antibiotics lincomycin, erythromycin, and oleandomycin into the mitochondria? How extensive must the mitochondria be swollen in order to get the antibiotics in?

Secondly, can you use this technique to determine the degree to which mitochondria swell under various physiological conditions? There are conjectures that the swelling phenomena may be connected with some physiological functions. Can you use the antibiotics to prove this question?

Kroon: Concerning your first question: The mitochondria were treated under mild hypotonic conditions with water 5 to 10 min at 0 °C. Then the mitochondria were added to the incubation medium for amino acid incorporation. There are two possibilities: We add the antibiotic to the water during the hypotonic treatment, or we treat the mitochondria, as described above, by adding the antibiotic to the incubation medium.

Concerning your second question, I have no idea.

W. Kersten (Erlangen): Dr. Traub, you said that cycloheximide inhibits only 80 S ribosomes. Can this inhibitor be used as a tool to really differentiate between different kinds of ribosomes and their protein synthesizing machinery?

Traub (La Jolla, Cal.): I think so. I believe Dr. Vazquez did some experiments with 80 S and 70 S ribosomes with bacterial and mammalian systems, and he could show that the bacterial system was not inhibited by this antibiotic.

W. Kersten: Dr. Kroon, the alkylating agents do not only bind to DNA but also to ribosomes. You might explain your observation simply by the binding to the ribosomes which might then inhibit protein synthesis as well.

Kroon: I am aware of these interactions with ribosomes and with tRNA. But in the experiments published on this subject, the concentrations of the alkylating agents were much higher than that needed for the maximal effect on mitochondriogenesis. When growing heart cells are treated for 1 day with ethidium bromide, the development of fully active mitochondria is inhibited, even 8 to 10 days after having changed to medium without ethidium bromide for many times. As far as I know, the binding of proflavin to tRNA is reversible.

W. Kersten: So is the binding to DNA.

Kroon: Indeed, but just as in the case of the cytoplasmic mutants, it appears that the damage to the DNA is irreversible. I thought that in the case of tRNA the binding is reversible and the activity is restored.

Horstmann (Erlangen): Dr. Neupert, do you have any information concerning the site of synthesis of ribosomal proteins of the mitochondrial ribosomes? Have you compared the disc electrophoretic patterns of ribosomal proteins from cytoplasmic and mitochondrial ribosomes?

Neupert (Munich): What I can say, and this is in agreement with the experiments of Luck, is that the protein pattern of these two types of ribosomes is clearly distinct. The mitochondrial ribosomes appear to have at least 30 to 40 different proteins.

Horstmann: If the proteins of mitochondrial ribosomes are synthesized outside of the mitochondria, as your experiments suggest, and if these proteins are distinct from those of the cytoplasmic ribosomes, then there is the question on the origin of the genetic message for these ribosomal proteins: nuclear or mitochondrial DNA?

Neupert: I think it is not justified to conclude from the in vitro experiments you are referring to — and I have not made that conclusion — that mitochondria don't synthesize their own ribosomal proteins, because the system could be rather damaged. RNA synthesis may be lacking, and therefore the synthesis of ribosomal proteins may be blocked.

With special regard to the experiments shown by SEBALD, concerning the cycloheximide effect, we would conclude that these mitochondrial ribosomal proteins are made outside the mitochondria because the synthesis is cycloheximide-sensitive, a criterion for extramitochondrial synthesis.

KROON: Dr. SEBALD, it has been shown by THOMAS and WILKIE (Ref. [8] in KROON, this volume, p. 159) that in yeast a cytoplasmic mutant can be obtained which is erythromycin-resistant. One of the explanations they gave is that this mutation would give rise to an alteration of one of the ribosomal proteins. Do your experiments exclude that cytoplasmic mutations can be expressed in the ribosomal protein of mitochondria?

SEBALD (Munich): I think that THOMAS and WILKIE have interpreted their experiments more carefully. They didn't say the mitochondrial ribosomal proteins, but rather more generally, the ribosomes are changed.

KROON: My question is whether your experiments are enough sensitive to exclude this, so that we are left with the one possibility that there is an alteration in the ribosomal RNA cistron.

SEBALD: Under our experimental conditions in the presence of cycloheximide the labelling of the mitochondrial ribosomal proteins is less than 1% of the control. So we cannot exclude that a minor component, comprising less than 1% of the ribosomal proteins, is synthesized by the intrinsic system.

There may be another, sophisticated, possibility; namely, that a trigger protein with very fast turnover synthesized outside the mitochondria is necessary to induce inside the mitochondria the synthesis of the ribosomal proteins.

But we favor another explanation of the cytoplasmic inheritance of resistance to antibiotics. There are some indications that the mitochondrial ribosomal RNA is coded by the mitochondrial DNA.

WESTPHAL: Have any investigations of this kind been made with reticulo-endothelial cells such as lymphocytes or macrophages or plasma cells?

KROON: We looked into the in-vitro system, recently, by isolating mitochondria from bone marrow cells. These mitochondria are equally sensitive to chloramphenicol and tetracyclin. We started this experiment because we liked the hypothesis (KROON, A. M., F. FASE-FOWLER, and H. DEVRIES: 6. FEBS-Meeting, Madrid 1969, Abstract Nr. 681) that the pancytopenia and agranulocytosis are just caused by a deficiency of energy generating capacity in the bone marrow cells. We are still left with the problem that tetracyclin is not a potent inhibitor of bone marrow function whereas chloramphenicol is.

WESTPHAL: I was thinking of lymphocytes. They have a very long half life time. They may be taken as a very stable system of cells with half life times of over years. Under these conditions, one could exclude the formation of new cellular units.

Kroon: That is correct. There is some information in the literature about the immunosuppressive action of chloramphenicol, and there, of course, you have no stable system. If you inhibit mitochondrial protein synthesis in that system, you get a very fast diluting out of the preexisting fully active mitochondria, and these cells can therefore become deficient in their capacity of oxidative phosphorylation.

Morphogenetic Processes in Acetabularia

GÜNTHER WERZ

Max-Planck-Institut für Zellbiologie, Wilhelmshaven

With 14 Figures

The classification of all living organisms into distinct species is based mainly on their morphology. The mechanisms involved in morphological expression during onto- and phylogenesis, therefore, have been and still are prime targets of cell biological research. Two, of the many, questions to be asked are of predominant importance: 1. In what cellular substances are the morphogenetic informations stored, and how are they passed on from generation to generation? 2. By what mechanisms are the morphogenetic informations expressed during ontogenesis? The first question was answered by geneticists: In general, the program of morphogenesis is being stored in deoxyribonucleic acids of the cell nucleus. The answer to the second question is also well established by now, although certain details are still awaiting further clarification.

Since the discovery of DNA and its function, little doubt was left that the transmission of morphogenetic programs from the cell nucleus to the cytoplasm, where morphogenesis takes place, ought to employ vehicles of a different chemical composition than DNA itself. The first proof for the existence of such vehicles was presented by JOACHIM HÄMMERLING in the nineteenthirties [1]. He demonstrated that the cell nucleus synthesizes species-specific substances and subsequently transfers them to the cytoplasm where they are first stored for periods of up to several months, until they finally express morphogenesis. HÄMMERLING's experimental objects were *Acetabularia*. These marine green algae grow in the shallow shore waters of the Mediterranean Sea and of the warmer regions of the Atlantic and the Pacific ocean. *Acetabularia* can be kept in laboratory cultures. They grow and multiply under carefully maintained conditions without any sign of dedifferentiation. The only difference between cultured *Acetabularia* and the ones in nature is even of experimental advantage. Cultured plants lack the cell wall calcification which invariably occurs in the sea. Most species of *Acetabularia* grow up to 10 cm long. One species, *Acetabularia gigas*, even approaches lengths of 20 cm. All species of *Acetabularia* have a unique feature in common: They consist of only one cell which carries, until shortly before multiplication, a

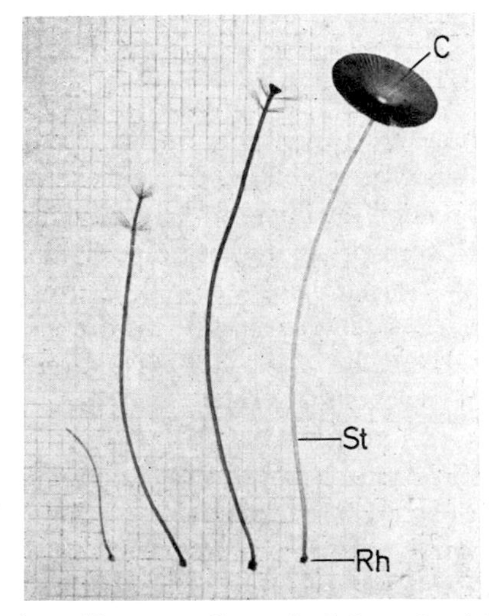

Fig. 1. *Acetabularia mediterranea.* From the left to the right: different stages of development. At the right: adult cell with a fully developed cap

single nucleus. The most frequently used species is *Acetabularia mediterranea* (Fig. 1). Its morphological features are a bulky rhizoid which houses the single nucleus, a long stalk, and on top of it an umbrella-like structure, commonly called "cap". In the course of ontogenesis, the stalk grows gradually out of the rhizoid. During stalk growth, the so-called whorls can be observed. They are nonpermanent brush-like structures which branch off the growing stalk in unpatterned intervals. Finally, cap-formation completes the growth period of the plant. Each species of *Acetabularia* develops a cap of a characteristic shape by which they can be easily distinguished from each other (see Fig. 10). The caps are sectioned into a multitude of compartments, resembling pieces of a cut cake. The cytoplasm of the cap compartments remains connected to the stalk cytoplasm by narrow bridges. The function of these bridges is to assure the transport of the secondary nuclei into the cap compartments, where the formation of gametangia takes

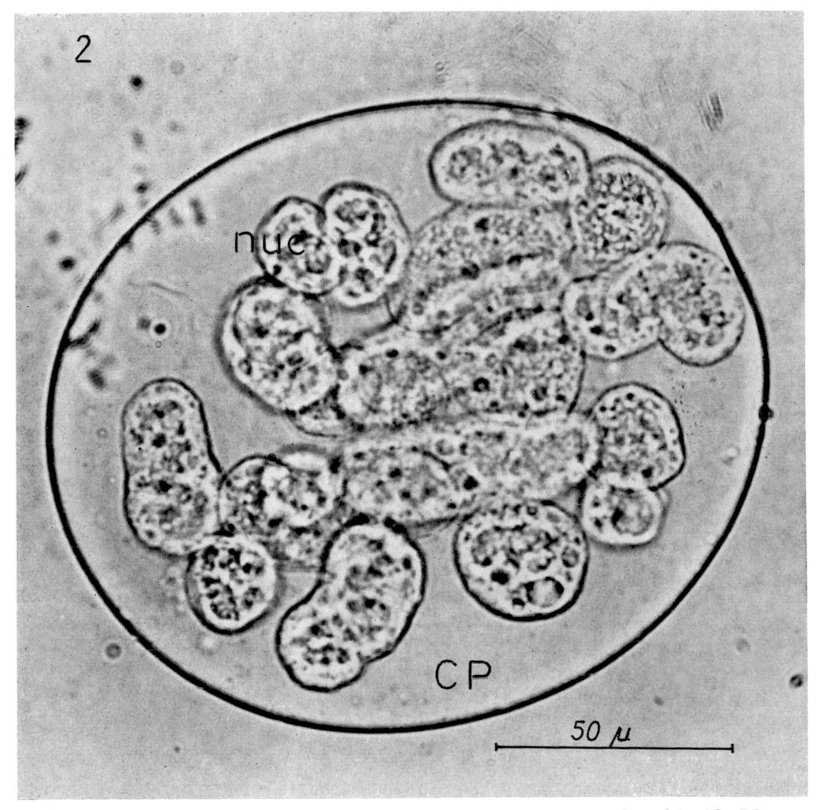

Fig. 2. Nucleus of *A. mediterranea*, isolated alife from the rhizoid. Many nucleoli (*nuc*) are present within the homogeneous caryoplasm (*cp*)

place. Secondary nuclei arise from the primary nucleus in the rhizoid after the completion of the cap. They travel to the cap compartments by route of the stalk cytoplasm. The primary nucleus of an *Acetabularia* cell (Fig. 2) is, in contrast to the minute secondary nuclei, very large. It grows from a zygote nucleus of only

5 μ in diameter to an easily visible ball with a diameter of 0.3 mm. The otherwise homogeneous caryoplasm contains sausage-like structures which are not chromosomes but nucleoli, stuffed with small particles, resembling ribosomes [2].

It is obvious that the giant size of the *Acetabularia* cell and of its nucleus allow experimental operations which create almost unsurmountable difficulties if attempted with commonly sized cells. An intact *Acetabularia* can be "transformed" into an enu-

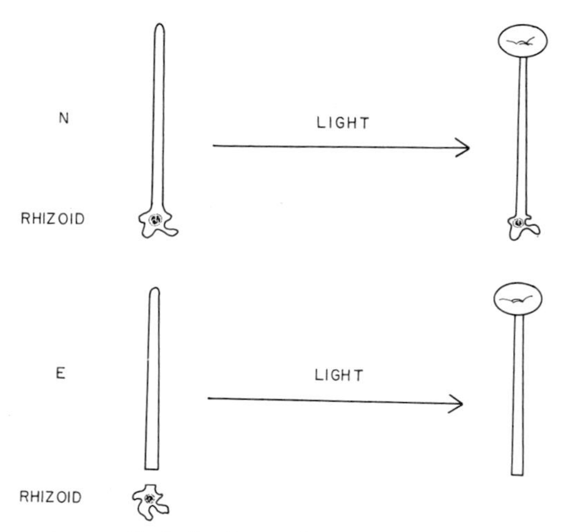

Fig. 3. The morphogenetic behaviour of enucleated *Acetabularia* cells (E). They form caps like the nucleated cells (N)

cleated cell by simple amputation of the nucleus-containing rhizoid [1—3]. The amputated cell survives the operation as long as 4 months. In this special case, survival does not just mean maintenance of the structure present at the time of amputation, but actual continuation of morphological development. The stalk grows in the absence of a nucleus, and a species-specific cap is formed like in an intact cell (Fig. 3). HÄMMERLING concluded from this phenomenon that "morphogenetic substances", which later exert the formation of the cap, must be already present in the stalk cytoplasm at the time of amputation. Subsequent experiments showed clearly the nuclear origin of the morphogenetic substances [4]. The potency to grow is not evenly distributed along the stalk of an enucleated cell (Fig. 4). An otherwise intact stalk completes the full pattern of morphogenesis. The same is true for the apical stalk region, but not for basal stalk section from which the rhizoid and the stalk apex were cut off. These basal stalk sections do survive, but are no longer able to grow. They regain the capacity to grow and to develop a cap by implantation of a "cytoplasm-free" nucleus (Fig. 4). Experiments of this type do not only prove the nuclear origin of the morphogenetic substances, which could also arise from DNA-containing cytoplasmic structures

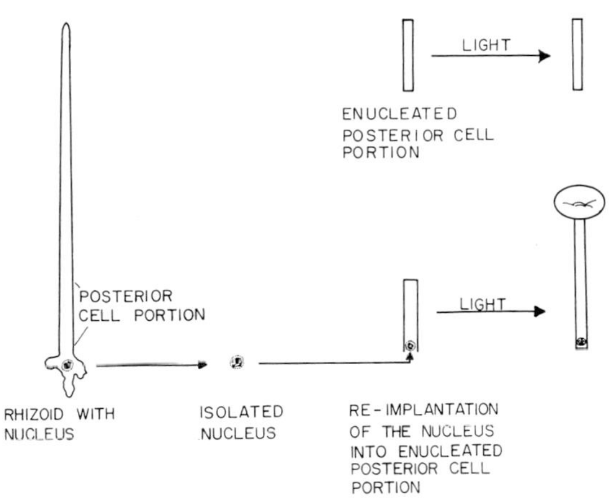

Fig. 4. Implantation of an isolated, living nucleus into a non-growing stalk portion of *Acetabularia*. Growth and cap-formation are induced by the implanted nucleus

like mitochondria and chloroplasts [lit. in 15], but also indicate their species-specificity. When the transplanted nucleus is taken from a species different from that of the basal stalk segment, the shape of the resulting cap corresponds to that of the donor.

Although these early key-experiments left little doubt in the existence of morphogenetic substances, their chemical nature remained obscure. Today we know that DNA transcribes its inherent genetic code to base-complementary messenger-RNA's from which it is translated into specific proteins. The application of the molecular-genetic scheme on the morphogenesis of *Acetabularia* appears to be inevitable, except for one disturbing fact. Even though the thesis of a rapid turnover of m-RNA has been extended in the meantime, *Acetabularia* demands an exception from the rule which is truly unusual. If the morphogenetic substances of *Acetabularia* are represented by m-RNA's, ribonucleic acids must remain stable in the cytoplasm for as long as 4 months. This poses the question of a different identity of the morphogenetic substances, for which proteins are the next suspects in line.

Up to now, the problem has resisted direct experimental attack. Attempts to induce morphogenesis in one species of *Acetabularia* by the injection of RNA- and protein fractions from another species were so far unsuccessful. One major handicap in experiments of this kind are probably the concentrations of the morphogenetic substances in the algae, which are possibly not related to the unusual size of *Acetabularia*. The processing of thousands of plants may be necessary to obtain sufficient quantities of the substances in question in pure state, a tedious enterprise if one considers that it takes 3 months for an *Acetabularia* to reach its full size. With these difficulties at hand, it became necessary to take a different approach to elucidate the chemical nature of the morphogenetic substances. We therefore investigated the influence of inhibitors on the morphogenesis of *Acetabularia*. The substances used were selected according to their mode of action: actinomycin-D as an inhibitor of transcription, puromycin as an inhibitor of translation, and colchicine as an inhibitor of products of translation.

Since the mechanisms of action of actinomycin and puromycin have been thoroughly discussed in preceding lectures of this symposion, I shall restrict myself to a description of their influence on morphogenetic events in *Acetabularia*. Some effects of actinomycin-D are shown schematically in Fig. 5. Cells which are about to develop a cap, do so even in the presence of the antibiotic. The same is true for the apical portion of an enucleated cell of similar age. Cap formation is inhibited if actinomycin is added to the culture-medium of basal stalk sections and of basal cell segments with intact rhizoid [5]. These results are in agreement with the assumption that the morphogenetic substances of *Acetabularia* are represented by messenger-RNA. They can be interpreted as follows:

1. Actinomycin inhibits morphogenesis in the nucleus-containing basal cell segment, because no m-RNA or only insufficient

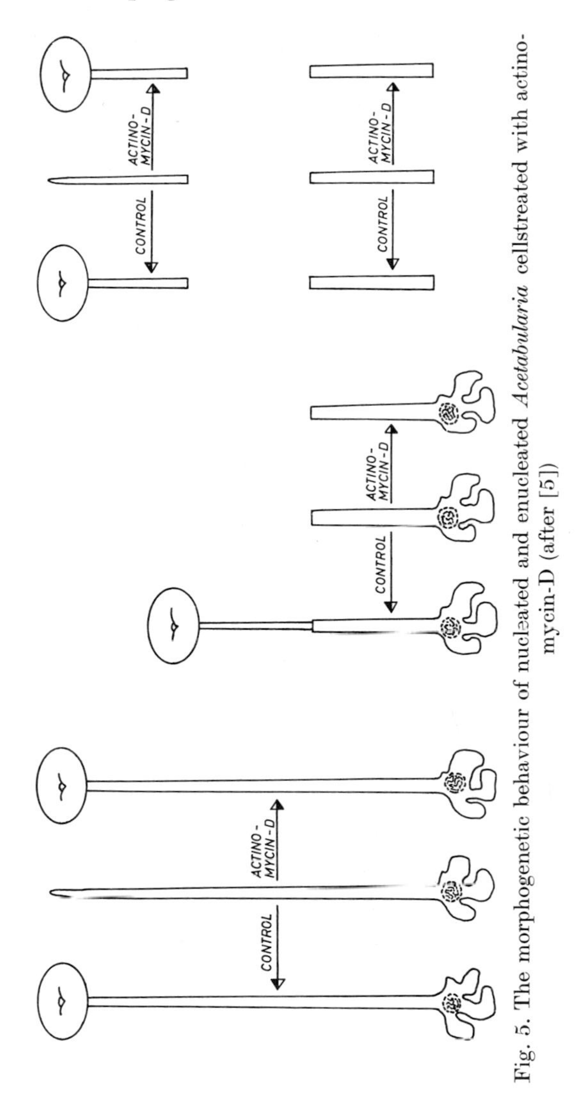

Fig. 5. The morphogenetic behaviour of nucleated and enucleated *Acetabularia* cellstreated with actinomycin-D (after [5])

quantities of it are present in the cytoplasm and the synthesis of m-RNA is (irreversibly) suppressed.

2. Enucleated basal stalk sections contain likewise none or too little m-RNA.

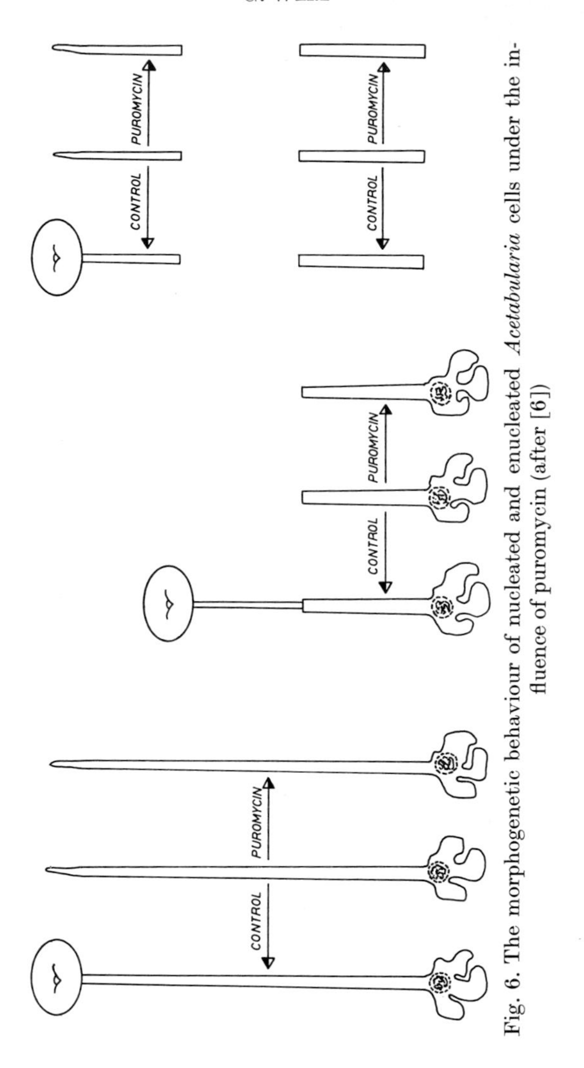

Fig. 6. The morphogenetic behaviour of nucleated and enucleated *Acetabularia* cells under the influence of puromycin (after [6])

3. In contrast, sufficient quantities of m-RNA are accumulated in the apical regions of the stalks of intact and enucleated cells. Actinomycin, therefore, can not interfere with cap formation.

This interpretation is confirmed by the results of similar experiments with puromycin (Fig. 6). If translation from m-RNA follows transcription in the course of *Acetabularia* morphogenesis, the inhibitory effect of actinomycin on cap formation should be complemented by puromycin, which is the case. Under puromycin treatment, cap formation is inhibited in apical stalk sections too. The action of puromycin is reversible. Intact cells and basal stalk sections with adherent rhizoid regain the capacity to grow and to form caps after being transferred to normal medium [6].

In the preceding experiments, the effect of inhibitors on morphogenesis was read only from their interference with the development of gross morphological features. These, of course, come about by a framework of reactions which are scheduled to

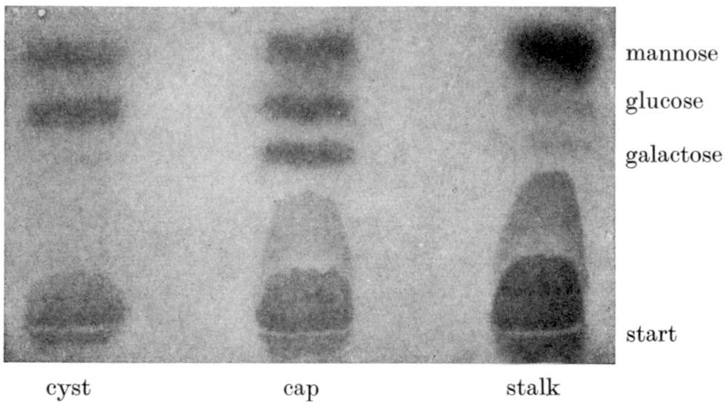

Fig. 7. Comparison of sugars constituting cell walls of the stalk, and of the cap of *A.* (*Polyphysa*) *cliftonii*. Note the increased galactose-content in the cap-wall hydrolysate. TLC on Eastman-Kodak polycarbonate sheet

occur at predetermined times and locations. Two of the many reactions participating in *Acetabularia*-morphogenesis were selected to provide additional evidence for the conclusions drawn above.

The cell walls of *Acetabularia* consist mainly of polysaccharides which are almost exclusively composed of mannose and galactose [7]. The proportions of these hexoses do not only vary in the cell wall polysaccharides of different species but also in a characteristic manner within a single plant (Fig. 7). Mannose predominates in the polysaccharides of stalk cell wall, while galactose is present in a higher proportion in cap cell wall polysaccharides [7]. The change in sugar composition during cap development could be brought about by an increased galactose synthesis at this stage of morphogenesis. This, in turn, would then either be caused by a mere

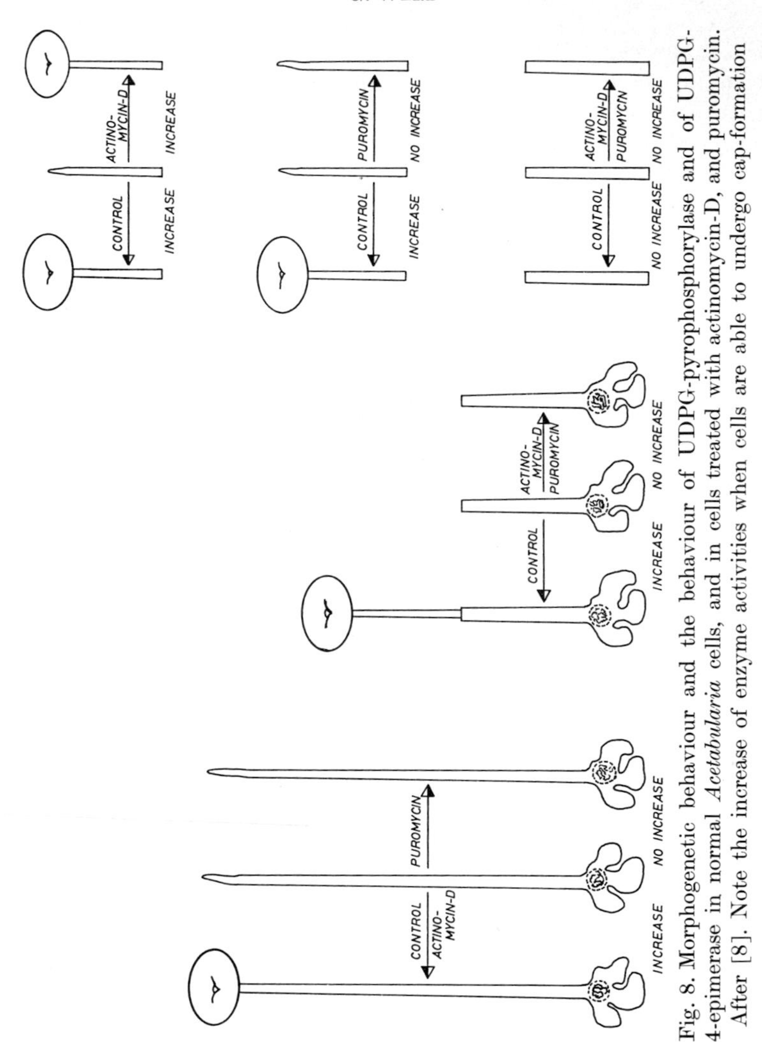

Fig. 8. Morphogenetic behaviour and the behaviour of UDPG-pyrophosphorylase and of UDPG-4-epimerase in normal *Acetabularia* cells, and in cells treated with actinomycin-D, and puromycin. After [8]. Note the increase of enzyme activities when cells are able to undergo cap-formation

enzyme activation or by *de-novo* synthesis of enzymes. Two important enzymes for the synthesis of galactose from glucose-1-phosphate are uridinediphosphateglucose-pyrophosphorylase and uridinediphosphateglucose-4-epimerase [8].

Puromycin inhibits the synthesis of the two enzymes and the increase of galactose-production (Fig. 8). This indicates that the change in sugar composition of cell wall polysaccharides at the moment of cap formation is indeed caused by an enhanced synthesis of galactose producing enzymes. The effect of puromycin on enzyme synthesis is reversible in the same way as is its inhibition of cap formation. A similar analogy is observed for actinomycin with respect to its action on cap formation and on enzyme synthesis (Fig. 8). It can be concluded, therefore, that the m-RNA's for UDPG-pyrophosphorylase and UDPG-4-epimerase must be present in the stalk apex well in advance of the sudden increase of enzyme synthesis.

The results of all actinomycin- and puromycin experiments described here, and of others of similar nature, fit nicely into the molecular-genetic scheme of information transmission and expression. The "morphogenetic substances" of *Acetabularia* appear in essence to be identical with m-RNA's, the extreme longevity of which must be accepted as a further extension of the original scheme.

When, in spite of this plausible explanation, we went on to investigate a possible influence of a modification of translation products on the morphogenesis of *Acetabularia*, so not in order to eliminate last doubts in the nature of the "morphogenetic substances", but rather to gain a better insight into posttranslational processes of morphogenesis. Easy as it was to select appropiate inhibitors of transcription and translation, it was difficult to choose an inhibitor of translation products. Impressed by the fine work of TAYLOR's group [9], we finally resorted to colchicine, an alkaloid of *Colchicum autumnale*. Its best known action is the inhibition of nucleus and cell division, but it also causes other structural and functional deviations, which result, e.g., in the development of atypically formed, so-called apolar cells [see 10]. Working with tritiated colchicine, TAYLOR and coworkers [9] found that the alkaloid is preferentially bound by a protein fraction of microtubules. These microtubules are structural elements of the spindle-apparatus, of cilia and flagella. In plant cells, microtubules are believed to have an orientating function in the deposition of cellulose microfibrils during the formation of the secondary cell wall. A first characterization of the colchicine-binding protein fraction extracted from microtubules by TAYLOR et al. revealed a sedimentation coefficient of 6 S and an approximate molecular weight of 100,000.

In all of our experiments, colchicine was added to the culture medium to a final concentration of 10^{-3} molal. The alkaloid does not interfere with the continuance of stalk growth, neither in normal nor in enucleated cells. Curves similar to the ones in Fig. 9 for *Acetabularia cliftonii* are obtained with all species of *Acetabularia* so far under investigation (see [11]). In contrast, cap formation is most impressively inhibited by the alkaloid, in the

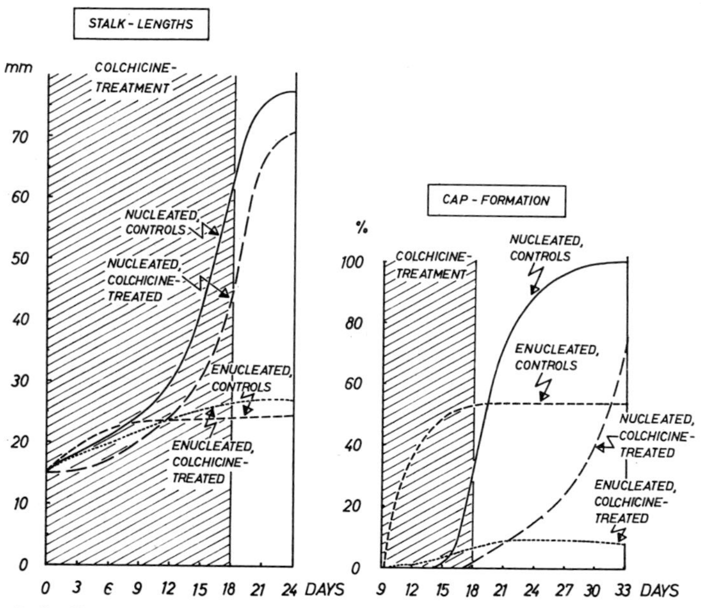

Fig. 9. Stalk growth and cap-formation in untreated and in colchicine-treated, nucleated and enucleated cells of *A.* (*Polyphysa*) *cliftonii* (after [11])

presence as well as in the absence of a nucleus. Intact cells regain their cap-forming ability if they are subsequently transferred to colchicine-free medium. This is not true for enucleated cells, unless they receive a nucleus transplant after colchicine treatment. The suggestion of a nuclear site of action of colchicine by these results is obscured by the following experiment: If a colchicine-treated intact cell is transferred to colchicine-free medium and is denucleated at the same time, cap formation takes place. This excludes an interaction with the nucleus itself, but rather points to a nuclear product or a successive cytoplasmic component as the target of the alkaloid. The mechanism of colchicine poisoning is further pinpointed by another observation. Intact and enucleated cells continue to develop a complete cap in the presence of colchicine if the first signs of cap growth were already visible at the time the alkaloid was added to the medium. Colchicine apparently can elicit its effect only during a very limited period of time by interacting with cellular components which are either only present at that time, or whose sensitivity toward colchicine is transient, or both. It is obvious that the colchicine-sensitive factors must have a

Fig. 10. Typical caps of species *A. mediterranea* (left), and *A. crenulata* (right), and intermediate cap (center), resulting from transplantation experiments (see text)

trigger-like function for the onset of morphogenesis. Additional evidence is provided by experiments in which the nucleus is replaced after colchicine treatment by a nucleus of a different species. The caps formed after transplantation are of an "intermediate" type, containing morphological characteristics of both species (see Fig. 10).

In addition to cap formation, at least one more morphogenetic process of *Acetabularia* is inhibited by colchicine. In the final stage of *Acetabularia* morphogenesis the species-specific cell wall is formed. Structure and chemical composition of the cell wall are, as already mentioned, determined by nucleus-dependent processes of the cytoplasm [see 12, 13]. The possible implication of the cell wall in the shaping of the cell has been subject of a lengthy discussion until it became evident that the cytoplasm aquires the final shape of the cell already before the cell wall deposition begins. The main reason why it took a long time to settle the question is the usually

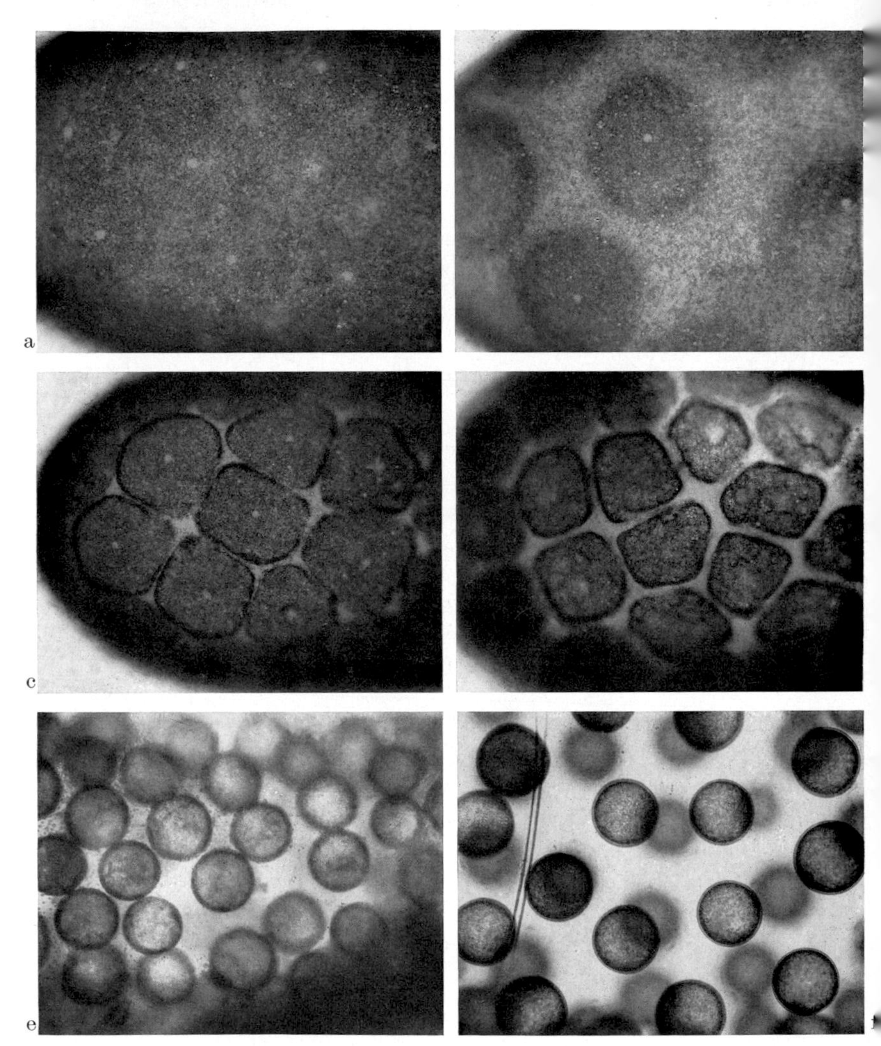

Fig. 11 a—f. Normal cyst development within the cap chambers of *A. crenulata*. Note the formation of the plasmatic cyst (e) on which later cyst wall is deposited (f)

very quick succession of these two processes. Again, *Acetabularia* offers an exception from this rule during the course of its morphogenesis, which proved helpful in the further elucidation of colchicine-action (Fig. 11). In the first stage of multiplication, the rhizoid nucleus "divides" into a host of small secondary nuclei. These secondary nuclei migrate through the cytoplasm of the stalk into the cap-chambers where the formation of gametangia, so-called cysts, takes place. To that goal, the flat plasma layer of the cap chamber folds around a secondary nucleus, and gradually aquires the characteristic ball-shape appearance of a cyst. Finally, the "plasmatic" cyst is covered with the specific cell wall, which can be easily recognized by a color reaction with chlorine-iodine-zinc reagent. The whole sequence of events proceeds also *in vitro* with isolated nuclei-containing cap chamber cytoplasm, so-called protoplasts (Fig. 12).

Colchicine arrests cyst-formation *in vivo* and *in vitro* [11]. In the presence of colchicine, the protoplast does not assume the shape of the plasmatic cyst (Fig. 13). If the latter stage of cyst development has been already reached, colchicine is without effect on the further differentiation, i.e. cell wall deposition (Fig. 13). This narrow timing is in remarkable agreement with the influence on cap formation, exerted by the alkaloid.

The interpretation of the effects of colchicine on the morphogenesis of *Acetabularia* opens a wide field of speculations. Of the many hypotheses possible, I would like to restrict myself to only one which has the advantage to cover all of our observations. It is the modification of one or several specific proteins by colchicine, which was deduced by TAYLOR and coworkers from their experiments on other objects. One discrepancy ought to be mentioned first. So far, no microtubules, which according to TAYLOR harbor the colchicine-sensitive proteins, have been found in growth regions of *Acetabularia* [14]. But this, naturally, does not exclude the existence of such proteins in *Acetabularia*, which may be present in other cellular structures as well. Our results are summarized in Fig. 14 to facilitate the discussion.

What can be said about the function and the synthesis of the hypothetical, colchicine-sensitive protein of *Acetabularia*? It obviously is a trigger of morphogenetic processes which initiates a sequence of events at an exactly determined stage of differentiation. The nucleus restores the capacity of previously colchicine-poisoned cytoplasm to synthesize the trigger (line 1). This restoration can only be achieved by the rhizoid nucleus, but not by the young secondary nucleus (line 8). An enucleated cell loses the capacity for trigger synthesis permanently (line 2) unless it receives

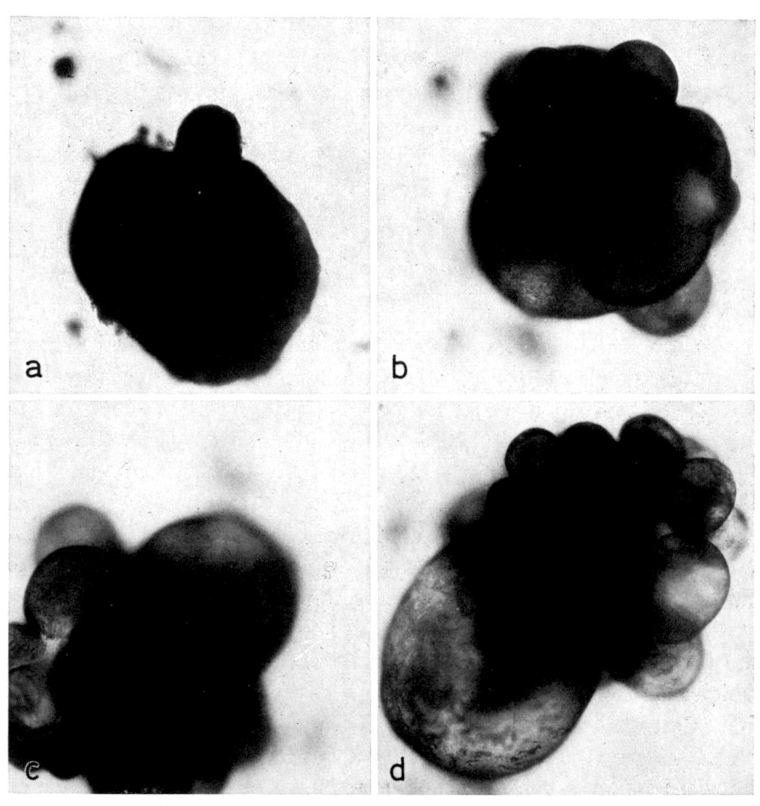

Fig. 12 a—d. Differentiating protoplasts of *A.* (*Polyphysa*) *cliftonii in vitro*. "Cysts" (d) are formed from the isolated plasma droplets (a)

a nucleus transplant after colchicine treatment (line 3). The tremendous speed in which the nucleus restores the trigger-synthesizing-capacity of the cytoplasm becomes evident from line 5. Of special interest is the experiment in line 4. It proves that the trigger is not species-specific, and that its function is limited to the initiation of species-specific reactions, the information-carriers of which are already present in the cytoplasm.

Our working hypothesis can be summarized in two points:

1. Colchicine reacts with a non-species-specific protein of the cytoplasm which is a trigger for species-specific morphogenetic processes.

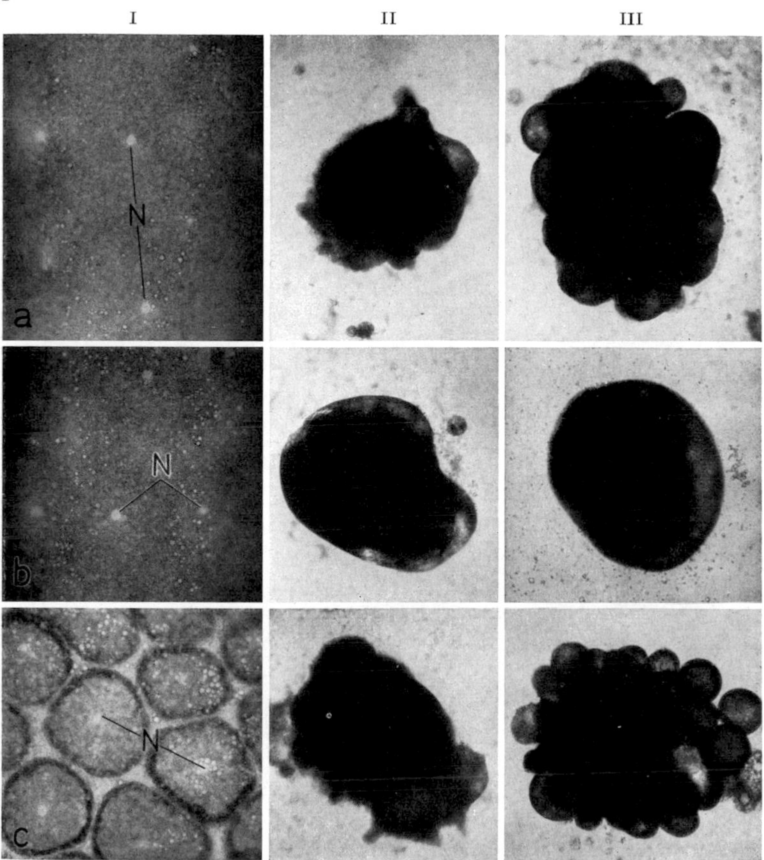

Fig. 13 a—c. *A.* (*Polyphysa*) *cliftonii*. The influence of colchicine on protoplast differentiation *in vitro*. (a) Control; (b) inhibition of "cyst" formation by colchicine-treatment of protoplasts, isolated in early stages of development. (c) Colchicine-treatment of protoplasts isolated in later stages of development does not interfere with "cyst" formation. I = stage of differentiation of the cap plasm *in situ*; II = protoplast shortly after its isolation; III = protoplast differentiation *in vitro*. N = secondary nuclei

2. This trigger protein is coded by the nucleus. Its m-RNA has a short half-life time, in contrast to the very stable m-RNA's of species-specific morphological features of *Acetabularia*.

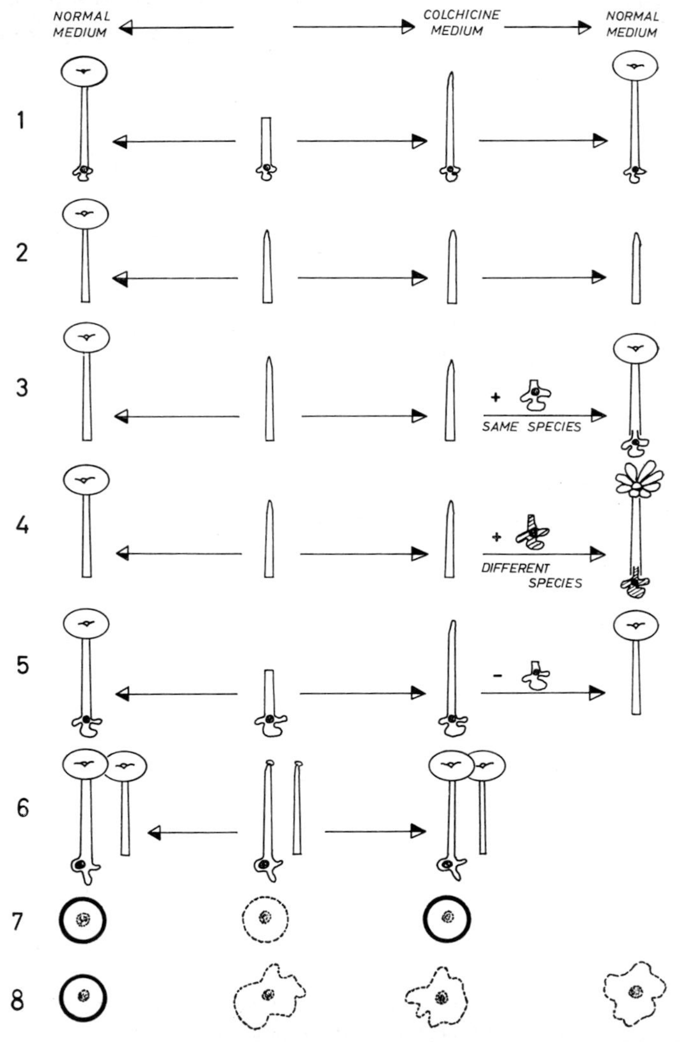

Fig. 14. Summary of the results of colchicine-experiments performed with nucleated and enucleated *Acetabularia* cells (1 to 6), and with cap plasm *in situ* and *in vitro* (7 to 8). For details see text

The trigger-like function of the hypothetical protein for the initiation of cap- and cyst-formation resembles that long sought for as "inductors" of animal cells. We are now working on the isolation of the "inductor" of *Acetabularia* morphogenesis and are engaged in a detailed analysis of the chemistry of its interaction with colchicine to prove the hypothesis.

It was the goal of this lecture to demonstrate with some pertinent examples how selectively-acting inhibitors can be used to elucidate complex phenomena like the morphogenesis of *Acetabularia*. The experiments with actinomycin-D and puromycin helped to identify the "morphogenetic substances" of *Acetabularia* as stable m-RNA's. A first attempt to investigate processes beyond the transcription and translation of morphogenetic informations has been made with the aid of colchicine which led to the discovery of a non-species-specific initiation of morphogenetic events. The final stages of morphogenesis are still not understood. It must be hoped, therefore, that new specific inhibitors become available to proffer further support.

References

1. Hämmerling, J.: Wilhelm Roux' Arch. Entwickl.-Mech. Org. **131**, 1 (1934).
   — Zool. Jb. **56**, 441 (1936).
2. Werz, G.: Brookhaven Symp. Biol. **18**, 185 (1965).
3. Hämmerling, J.: Ann. Rev. Plant. Physiol. **14**, 69 (1963).
4. — Biol. Zbl. **74**, 420 (1955).
5. Schweiger, H. G., u. E. Schweiger: Naturwissenschaften **50**, 620 (1963).
   Zetsche, K.: Z. Naturforsch. **19b**, 751 (1964).
6. Zetsche, K.: Planta (Berl.) **64**, 119 (1965).
7. Werz, G.: Planta (Berl.) **60**, 322 (1963).
   — Planta (Berl.) **60**, 540 (1964).
   Zetsche, K.: Planta (Berl.) **76**, 326 (1967).
8. Zetsche, K.: Biochim. biophys. Acta (Amst.) **124**, 332 (1966).
   — Z. Naturforsch. **23b**, 369 (1968).
9. Borisy, G. G., and E. W. Taylor: J. Cell Biol. **34**, 525, 535 (1967).
   Shelansky, M. L., and E. W. Taylor: J. Cell Biol. **34**, 549 (1967).
10. v. Wettstein, D.: Handb. Pflanzenphysiologie 15/1, 275. Berlin-Heidelberg-New York: Springer 1965.
11. Werz, G.: Protoplasma (Wien) **67**, 117 (1969).
12. — Protoplasma (Wien) **65**, 81 (1968).
13. — Protoplasma (Wien) **65**, 349 (1968).

14. Werz, G.: Unpubl.
Boloukhére, M.: Personal communication.
15. Werz, G.: Planta (Berl.) **68**, 256 (1966).
—, and G. Kellner: J. Ultrastruct. Res. **24**, 109 (1968).

Discussion

Gibian (Berlin): May the puromycin-inhibited cap formation be restituted by substitution of UDP-galactose?

Werz: No, this is not the case.

Westphal (Freiburg): Is this due to the fact that UDP-galactose does not get to the site of action?

Werz: It is very difficult to get the substance to the right position in the cell because we know that the cell wall formation is dependent on some structural elements, and the substance alone does not make morphogenesis.

Westphal: You did not speak of the transferase which catalyzes the incorporation of the sugar into the polymer. Then you would not expect to get anything by the addition of UDP-galactose.

Werz: Concerning the transferase system, we have no experience.

Szabo (Orsay): When you restitute the cap formation by washing out the inhibitor, is the chemical composition of the cap the same as in normal Acetabularia?

Werz: It is absolutely normal.

Penicillin-Sensitive Enzymatic Reactions in Bacterial Cell Wall Synthesis *

Jack L. Strominger

Biological Laboratories, Harvard University, Cambridge, Massachusetts 02138

With 14 Figures

We have been searching for the mechanism of action of penicillin for 15 years. In this lecture I would like to share with you the things that had to be done in the effort to find the mechanism by which penicillin kills bacterial cells.

Structure of Bacterial Cell Walls

Bacterial cell walls are made by disintegrating bacterial cells, usually with glass beads. The internal content of the cells spills out through a nick in the wall made by the glass beads. The cell wall fraction is then separated by differential centrifugation and purified. It is seen as a rigid bag-shaped molecule.

The cell wall is by all odds the largest macromolecule in the cell. It is a three-dimensional structure which completely envelops the bacterial cell. A great deal of effort has been spent in elucidating the structure of this macromolecule (Fig. 1). Bacteriolytic enzymes provided the tools for these investigations [1]. The fundamental units in the cell wall of bacteria are the glycan strands composed of two alternating sugars, represented in the figure by X (acetylglucosamine) and Y (acetylmuramic acid). Four glycan strands are represented in Fig. 1, but to account for the dimensions of the wall, many more strands would be needed.

* The work described in this lecture has been generously supported by the U.S. Public Health Service (AI-09152 and AM-13230) and the National Science Foundation (GB-7853). I am very appreciative of the invitation from the German Society for Biological Chemistry to participate in the annual Mosbach Colloquium.

Acetylmuramic acid is the 3-O-D-lactic acid ether of N-acetylglucosamine. The carboxyl group of this sugar is substituted by a tetrapeptide, which, in the genus *Staphylococcus aureus*, has the sequence, L-alanyl-D-isoglutaminyl-L-lysyl-D-alanine. Virtually all of the acetylmuramic acid residues are substituted in this way in the cell wall of *S. aureus*, thus forming peptidoglycan strands.

The peptidoglycan strands are in turn cross-linked to each other by means of an interpeptide bridge. In the case of *S. aureus*,

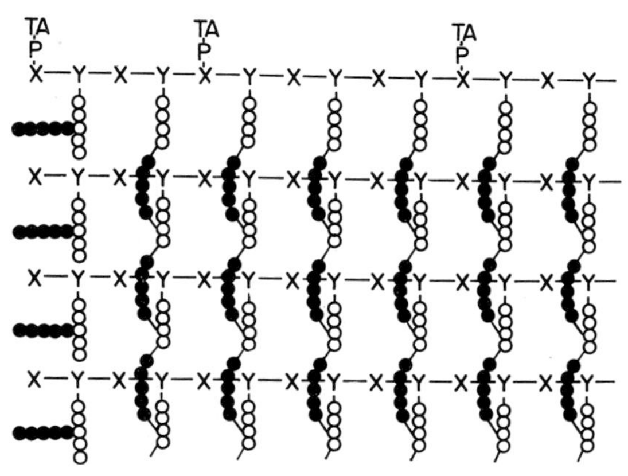

Fig. 1. Structure of the peptidoglycan of the cell wall of *S. aureus*. In this representation X (acetylglucosamine) and Y (acetylmuramic acid) are the two sugars in the peptidoglycan. Open circles represent the four amino acids of the tetrapeptide, L-alanyl-D-isoglutaminyl-L-lysyl-D-alanine. Closed circles are pentaglycine bridges which interconnect peptidoglycan strands. The nascent peptidoglycan units bearing open pentaglycine chains are shown at the left of each strand. TA-P is the teichoic acid antigen of the organism which is attached to the polysaccharide through a phosphodiester linkage

the interpeptide bridge consists of a pentaglycine chain which extends from the carboxyl group of the terminal D-alanine residue of the tetrapeptide to the ε-amino group of lysine, the third amino acid in the tetrapeptide. To some extent, the nature of the interpeptide bridge is a genus-specific characteristic, and only in the genus *S. aureus* is it pentaglycine. In this way a two-dimensional network is built up. However, the wall is a three-dimensional structure. Present physical methods are not adequate to investigate the three-dimensional structure of non-crystalline ordered networks of this kind, and we can therefore only speculate that the third dimension of the structure might be built up by pentaglycine chains extending not in the plane of the figure, but extending to another peptidoglycan strand in a plane in front of or to a plane in back of that represented by the figure.

The cell wall of *S. aureus* was the first whose structure was investigated in great detail, and it still represents the most thoroughly studied cell wall structure [1—3]. The cell walls of other genera of bacteria have the same general pattern. The most prominent difference among bacterial cell walls is the nature of the additional (often antigenic) substances attached to the peptidoglycan. In the case of *S. aureus*, this component is a teichoic acid which is attached in some manner as a phosphodiester (represented in the figure as TA). The interpeptide bridge varies greatly among genera of bacteria. The bridge may contain different amino acids and can vary in size from one amino acid to a pentapeptide bridge such as that found in *S. aureus*, or the bridge may be a direct link between tetrapeptide chains without the intervention of another amino acid. Variations also occur in the tetrapeptide sequence, the most common of these being the substitution of meso-diaminopimelic acid or of another dibasic amino acid for L-lysine. Other substitutions also occur, however, e.g. the substitution of glycine for L-alanine as the first amino acid in the sequence or the substitution of L-homoserine for L-lysine. In the latter case, a most unusual bridge occurs in that the tetrapeptide contains no extra amino group for its attachment, and therefore, the bridge is a dibasic amino acid (D-ornithine or D-lysine) which connects the α-carboxyl group of D-glutamic acid in one tetrapeptide with the carboxyl group of D-alanine at the end of another tetrapeptide. An excellent review of cell wall structure has recently been published which describes all of the variations which are known to occur [3].

Biosynthesis of Uridine Nucleotide Precursors of the Cell Wall

This macromolecular structure is synthesized in three distinct stages which occur at three different sites in the bacterial cell. At each site there are specific antibiotic inhibitors of the biosynthetic sequence. The first site is the soluble cytoplasmic fraction. At this

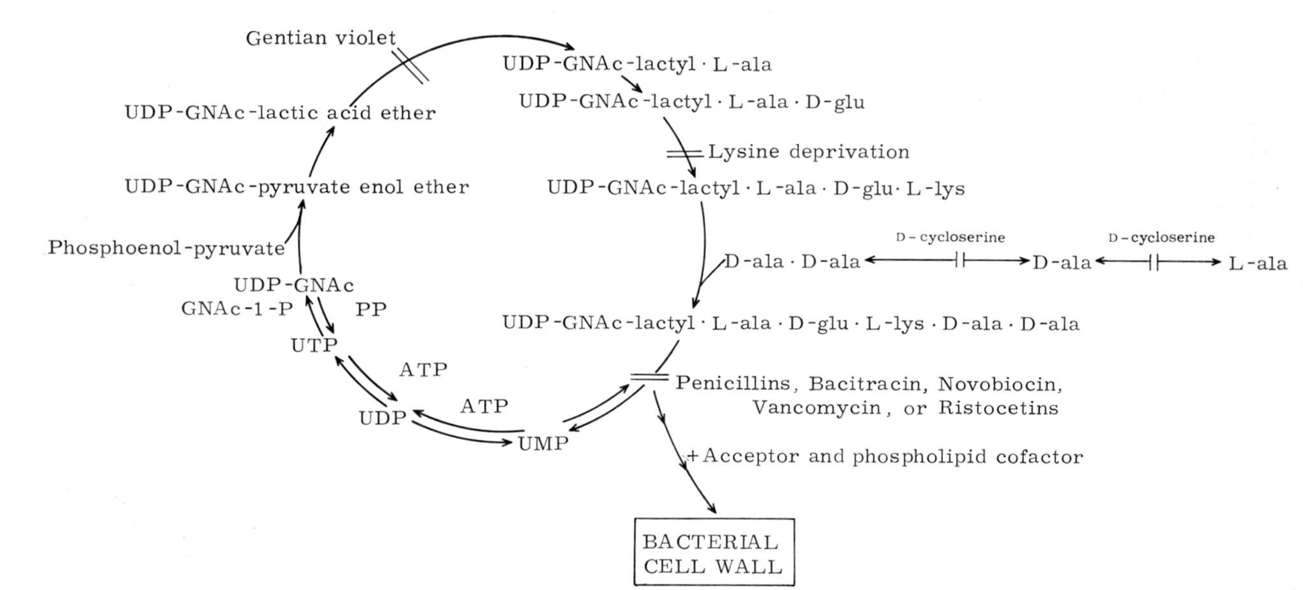

Fig. 2. Biosynthesis of the uridine nucleotide precursors of the peptidoglycan. The points of inhibition by various substances are indicated

site, the reactions which lead to the synthesis of UDP-acetyl-muramyl-pentapeptide occur (Fig. 2) [4]. This compound was first isolated by PARK and JOHNSON in 1949 [5]. Its accumulation in very large amounts in penicillin-inhibited *S. aureus* made possible its isolation.

The first series of reactions lead to synthesis of the nucleotide, UDP-acetylglucosamine. Then a 3-carbon fragment at the oxidation level of pyruvic acid is added to it and then reduced to the oxidation level of lactic acid. The step-wise addition of three amino acids to form UDP-acetylmuramyl-tripeptide then occurs. Finally, a dipeptide, D-alanyl-D-alanine, is added to the tripeptide to form UDP-acetylmuramyl-pentapeptide [4].

Two antibiotics, D-cycloserine and O-carbamyl-D-serine, are competitive inhibitors of the reactions which lead to the synthesis of the dipeptide [6, 7]. These two reactions are catalyzed by alanine racemase which leads to the formation of D-alanine from L-alanine and by D-alanyl-D-alanine synthetase which leads, in the presence of ATP, to the formation of the dipeptide from D-alanine. D-cycloserine is a true competitive inhibitor of both of these enzymatic reactions, while O-carbamyl-D-serine is a competitive inhibitor only of alanine racemase. The K_m for the substrate, D-alanine, is of the order 5×10^{-3} M for each of these enzymes, while the K_i for D-cycloserine is 100 times smaller, of the order 5×10^{-5} M in each case. These enzymes therefore bind a substance which is unnatural for them 100 times as effectively as they bind their natural substrate. No explanation of the relatively tight binding was immediately apparent.

Another observation also was puzzling. Alanine racemase catalyzes the reversible interconversion of L-alanine and D-alanine. D-cycloserine, the antibiotic, is a competitive inhibitor of this interconversion whether one measures the reaction in the direction D-ala $\rightarrow$ L-ala, or L-ala $\rightarrow$ D-ala. However, L-cycloserine, a synthetic substance, did not inhibit this reaction at very high concentrations when measured in either direction. Since D-cycloserine is a competitor for D-alanine, then L-cycloserine ought also to have been a competitor for L-alanine.

An explanation was found in an examination of the molecular models of the antibiotic and the substrates [8]. The insertion of an oxygen atom to close the ring in D-cycloserine and L-cycloserine has a very important consequence for these molecules. It results in a fixed conformation for these molecules by preventing rotation at the carbon-carbon bonds. The substrates, D-alanine and L-alanine, can have many possible conformations because of the possibility of rotation at these bonds. In one conformation, the substrate D-alanine is remarkably similar to the antibiotic D-cycloserine, and the other substrate, L-alanine, can be rotated into the same conformation. On the other hand, L-cycloserine, the synthetic substance, because of the closure of the 5-membered ring, cannot assume this conformation. These observations suggest that the conformation required by the substrate binding site on alanine racemase is the conformation in which D-cycloserine is fixed. The fact that L-cycloserine cannot assume this conformation provides a plausible explanation of its failure to inhibit this enzyme and of the fact that it is a poor antimicrobial agent. These observations also indicated that in some respects a D-amino acid and L-amino acid can resemble each other. This point was important later in considering the mechanism of penicillin action.

Biosynthesis of Linear Peptidoglycan Strands

The second stage of bacterial cell wall synthesis occurs in the membrane of the cell. At this site, the intracellular precursors, UDP-acetylmuramyl-pentapeptide and UDP-acetylglucosamine.

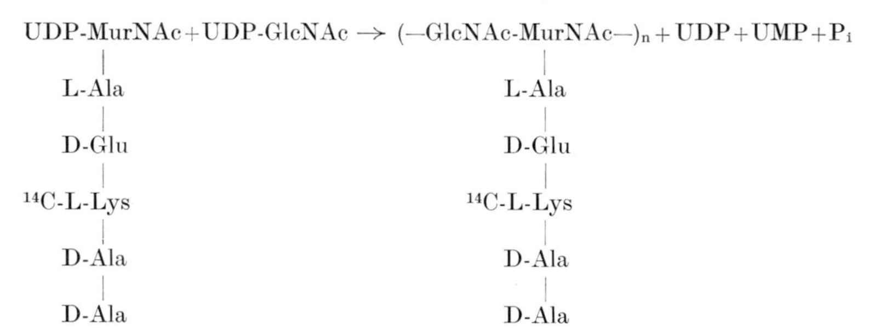

Fig. 3. Enzymatic synthesis of peptidoglycan from the two uridine nucleotide substrates

are utilized to form a linear peptidoglycan (Fig. 3) [9]. This linear peptidoglycan retains both of the D-alanine residues which are found in its pentapeptide precursor, although as was mentioned earlier, the final assembled cell wall product contains a tetrapeptide, rather than a pentapeptide, substituted on acetylmuramic acid. Later, in discussing the last stage of cell wall synthesis, the mechanism by which the last amino acid of the pentapeptide is lost to form the final cell wall product will be considered.

The biggest surprise in studying the formation of the linear peptidoglycan reaction was the finding that, although UDP is formed in this reaction in the transglycosylation involving UDP-acetylglucosamine (as had been found for many other reactions of this kind, beginning with the study of sucrose synthesis in Leloir's laboratory in 1950), no UDP was formed from UDP-acetylmuramyl-pentapeptide. Instead, UMP and inorganic phosphate were the primary products of the transglycosylation involving UDP-acetylmuramyl-pentapeptide. A clue to the complex reaction mechanism which accounted for these unusual products was provided by the observation of a smudge of radioactivity at the solvent front in the chromatographic system used for assay. This material, which had been ignored for a long time, turned out to be lipid intermediates in the reaction sequence. The reaction sequence which evolved beginning with those observations is shown in Fig. 4.

The initial reaction is the transfer of phosphoacetylmuramyl-pentapeptide from the nucleotide to a membrane-bound phospholipid with the generation of UMP. The product is acetylmuramyl (-pentapeptide)-P-P-lipid. This step is fully reversible. The second step in the reaction sequence is the addition of the second sugar from the second substrate, UDP-acetylglucosamine, to form disaccharide(-pentapeptide)-P-P-lipid with the generation of UDP. Then, the disaccharide-pentapeptide fragment of the lipid intermediate is transferred to an endogenous acceptor with the addition of a new disaccharide unit to a growing peptidoglycan strand and the generation of lipid pyrophosphate. Finally, lipid-P-P is dephosphorylated to yield inorganic phosphate and regenerate lipid-P, the lipid carrier which can then recycle to participate in the addition of a second unit to the growing peptidoglycan strand.

Three antibiotic inhibitors of this stage of the reaction sequence are known. Ristocetin and vancomycin at low concentrations are specific inhibitors of the transfer of the disaccharide-pentapeptide

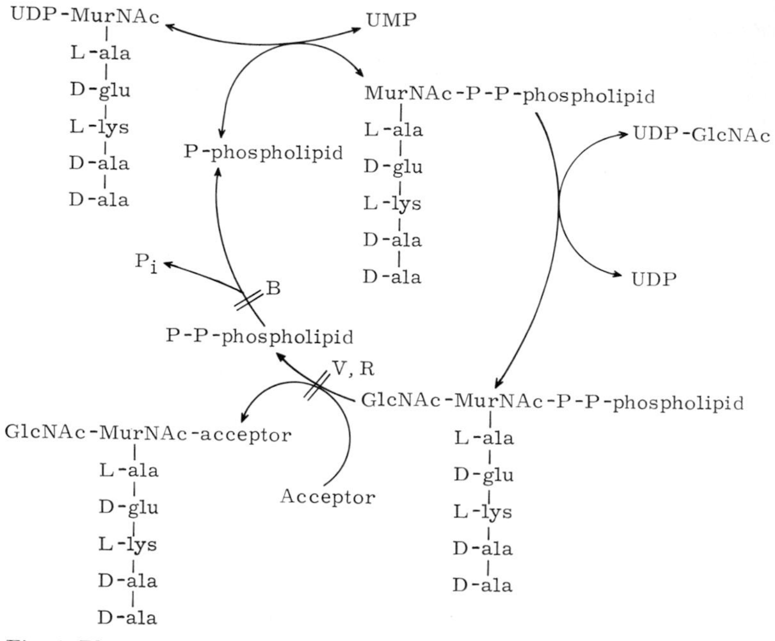

Fig. 4. Phospholipid cycle in peptidoglycan synthesis. The portion of the cycle common to both *S. aureus* and *M. lysodeikticus* is shown, as are the sites of inhibition by vancomycin (V), ristocetins (R) and bacitracin (B)

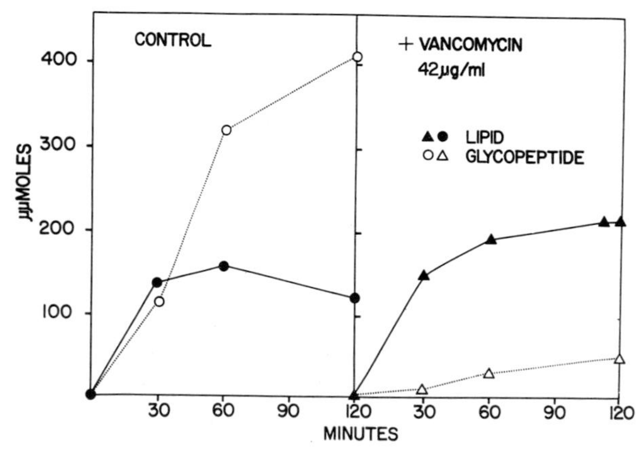

Fig. 5. Effect of vancomycin on the synthesis of the lipid intermediates and peptidoglycan

unit from the lipid intermediate to the cell wall acceptor. In the presence of either of these substances at low concentrations, the lipid intermediate can be formed normally, but it cannot be used to form the peptidoglycan (Fig. 5). Bacitracin is a specific inhibitor of the phosphatase which catalyzes the dephosphorylation of lipid-P-P. Dr. SIEWERT will describe the effects of bacitracin in more detail in a following paper (p. 210).

Identification of the Lipid Carrier: a C_{55}-Isoprenoid Alcohol

The particulate enzyme is derived from the membrane and contains both lipid and protein. The lipid and protein were separated by solvent extraction at low temperature. The extracted pro-

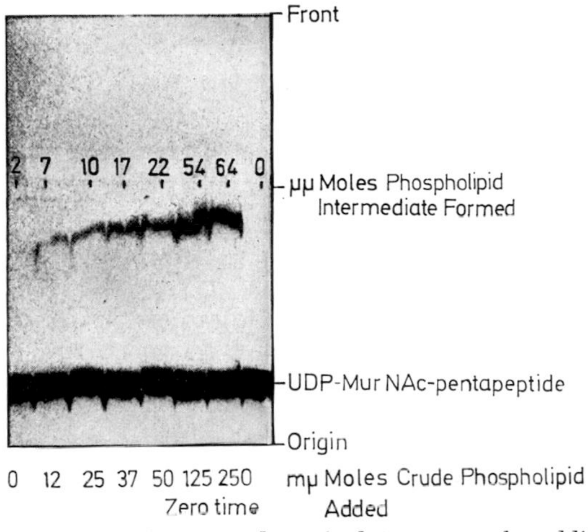

Fig. 6. Reconstitution of extracted particulate enzyme by addition of crude phospholipids. The particulate enzyme was resolved into protein and lipid components by extraction with chloroform-methanol (1:1) at −17 °C. The crude phospholipid added back was obtained by evaporation of the chloroform-methanol phase

tein had no enzymatic activity, but on the addition back to it of crude phospholipid, its enzymatic activity was restored (Fig. 6). The component of the crude phospholipid fraction which was active in restoring the activity of the protein fraction was purified. The first step in the purification was chromatography on a column of DEAE-cellulose, using the technique devised by ROUSER for the separation of the phospholipids of cells (Fig. 7). Rouser's solvents, however, did not elute the radioactive lipid intermediate from the column. A new solvent (numbered 8) was devised to elute it. It was eluted together with a very small amount of organic phosphate, an

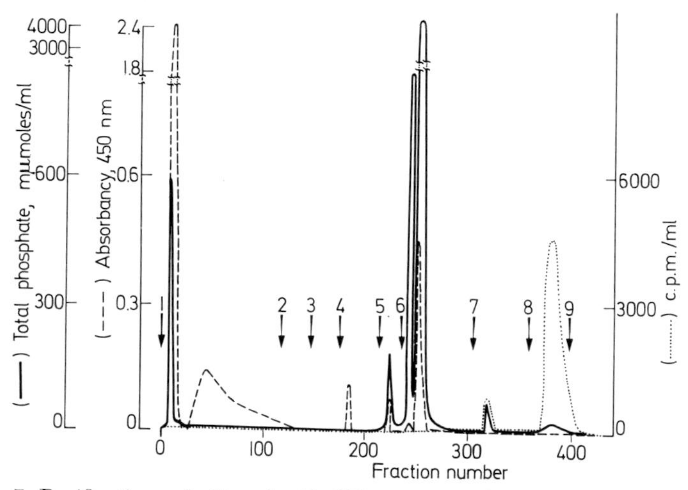

Fig. 7. Purification of disaccharide-^{14}C-pentapeptide-P-P-phospholipid on DEAE-cellulose. The phospholipid intermediate is the radioactive compound eluted by solvent 8. Note that a small amount of organic phosphate is also eluted at this position. There are no other radioactive compounds in the elution profile

amount which corresponded to approximately 0.2% of the total phospholipid of the bacterial cell. This fraction was not pure despite the enormous purification which had been obtained in this step, and additional purification steps were employed. Its structure

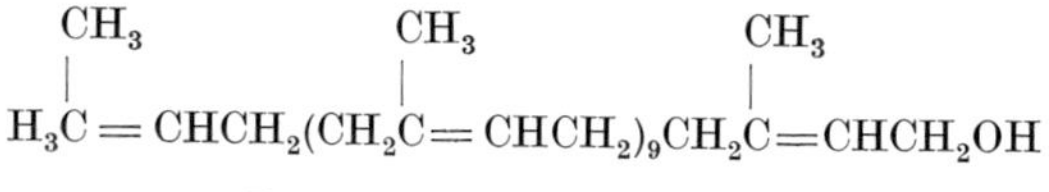

$$H_3\overset{\overset{\displaystyle CH_3}{|}}{C}=CHCH_2(CH_2\overset{\overset{\displaystyle CH_3}{|}}{C}=CHCH_2)_9CH_2\overset{\overset{\displaystyle CH_3}{|}}{C}=CHCH_2OH$$

Fig. 8. C_{55}-isoprenoid alcohol

was then readily ascertained by mass spectrometry [10]. The lipid is a C_{55}-isoprenoid alcohol (Fig. 8). It contains 11 isoprene units in a chain ending in an alcoholic function to which the disaccharide-pentapeptide fragment is attached by a pyrophosphate bridge. In the past 5 years, a large number of long-chain isoprenoid alcohols of this kind have been isolated from plants, animals and bacteria.

Isoprenoid Alcohol Phosphokinase

In the course of these studies, it had been observed that ATP greatly stimulated peptidoglycan synthesis with enzyme preparation from *S. aureus* but not with preparations from other bacteria. However, none of the reactions described thus far requires ATP. An explanation of the ATP stimulation of cell wall synthesis in *S. aureus* was therefore sought and is provided by the occurrence of an enzyme, isoprenoid alcohol phosphokinase, which catalyzes the phosphorylation of free C_{55}-alcohol to yield the C_{55}-alcohol phosphate [11]. In addition to the stimulation of the biosynthetic reaction which occurs on the addition of ATP, an additional stimulation was obtained by adding the C_{55}-alcohol, ficaprenol, isolated from *Ficus elasticus*, the household rubber plant. The enzyme which catalyzes this reaction has an extremely unusual property. It is soluble in butanol, methanol and other organic solvents in which it is also very stable, but it is insoluble in water or even in 80% methanol. This enzyme is derived from the membrane and is therefore an enzyme which normally occurs in the lipid phase, rather than in the aqueous phase, of the cell. It prefers organic solvents to water. It has recently been found that this enzyme is composed of two components: a protein fraction (which is insoluble both in water and in organic solvents), and a phospholipid, phosphatidyl glycerol (which restores both solubility in organic solvents and catalytic activity to the protein) [12]. Further investigation of the nature of the enzymes in the membrane which catalyze the reaction sequence which leads to cell wall synthesis may give us a great deal of information about the structure and function of membranes in general.

Utilization of tRNA in the Formation of Interpeptide Bridges

The reaction cycle discussed earlier is, in fact, a cycle which never operates in the bacterial cell. It can be made to operate in a test tube, but in the bacterial cell, a more complex cycle occurs (Fig. 9), i.e. modifications of the lipid intermediate occur before it is utilized for peptidoglycan synthesis. In the case of the genus

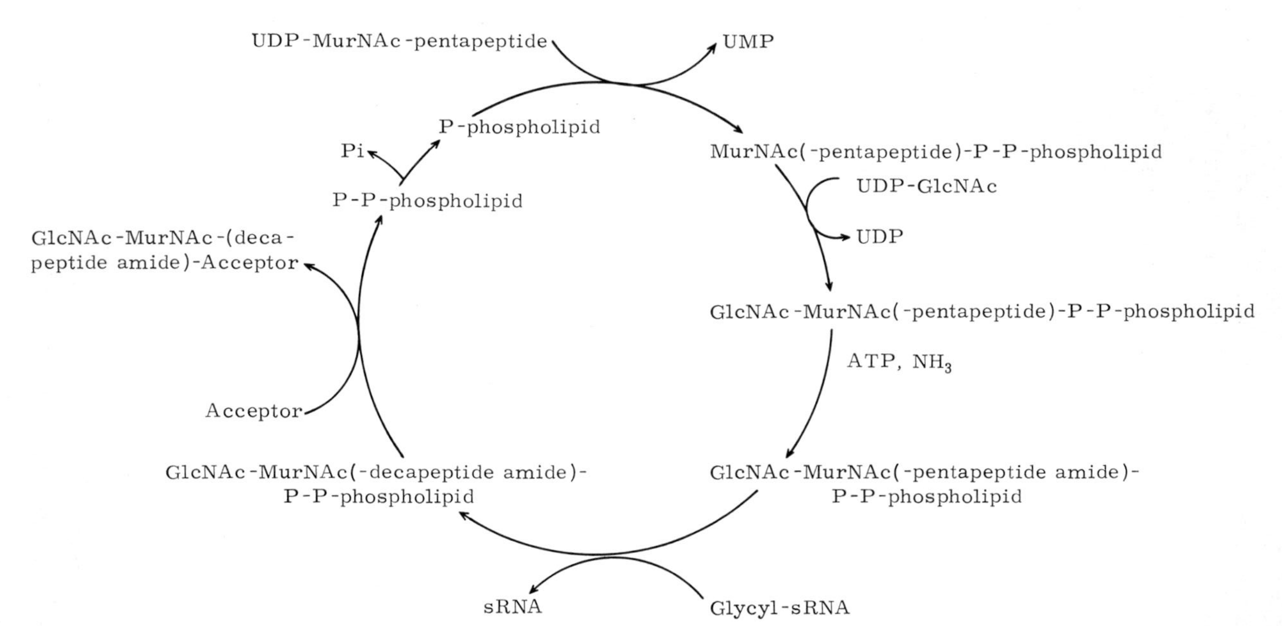

Fig. 9. Phospholipid cycle in peptidoglycan synthesis in *S. aureus*. The reactions in which the lipid intermediates are modified are included in this cycle

S. aureus, the modifications include the amidation of the α-carboxyl group of D-glutamic acid in the pentapeptide to yield D-isoglutamine, a reaction which requires ATP and ammonia, and the addition of the elements of the pentaglycine chain to form disaccharide (-decapeptide amide)-P-P-lipid [9]. This intermediate contains a preformed subunit of the wall of *S. aureus*, and this unit is then transferred to add a new subunit to a growing cell wall. Glycyl-tRNA is the intermediate in the addition of glycine to the lipid intermediate in *S. aureus*. A number of other microorganisms were investigated in an effort to answer the question of whether this requirement for an aminoacyl-tRNA was specific to the genus

Table 1. *Structure of interpeptide bridges and participation of aminoacyl-tRNA in bridge synthesis in various bacteria*

		Intermediate
S. aureus	$(gly)_5$	gly-sRNA
S. epidermidis	$(gly_3, L\text{-}ser_2)$	L-ser-sRNA gly-sRNA
M. roseus	$L\text{-}thr\text{-}(L\text{-}ala)_3$	L-thr-sRNA L-ala-sRNA ?
A. crystallopoietes	L-ala	L-ala-sRNA

S. aureus or whether it was a general phenomenon in bacteria. A similar phenomenon involving other amino acids was discovered in *S. epidermidis*, *M. roseus* and *A. crystallopoietes* (Table 1). There is one case in which a D-amino acid is found in the interpeptide bridge of the bacterial cell wall — D-aspartic acid which occurs in many lactobacilli. In that case, tRNA was not required for the synthesis of the interpeptide bridge. The intermediate is β-D-aspartyl phosphate. The question of whether there is some specific function of tRNA in cell wall synthesis similar to its adaptor function in protein synthesis is of great interest, but is beyond the scope of the present discussion.

Cross-Linking of Peptidoglycan Strands

The final step in cell wall synthesis is the cross-linking of the linear peptidoglycan strands. This reaction occurs at the outside of the cell membrane, at which site new units have been added to the growing wall. No ATP is available at this "extracellular" site to catalyze the final synthetic reaction which is required. Possibly for this reason, the final step is a transpeptidation which does not require any input of energy. The amino end of a pentaglycine chain in one linear peptidoglycan strand interacts with the terminal peptide bond in another peptidoglycan strand to form the cross-

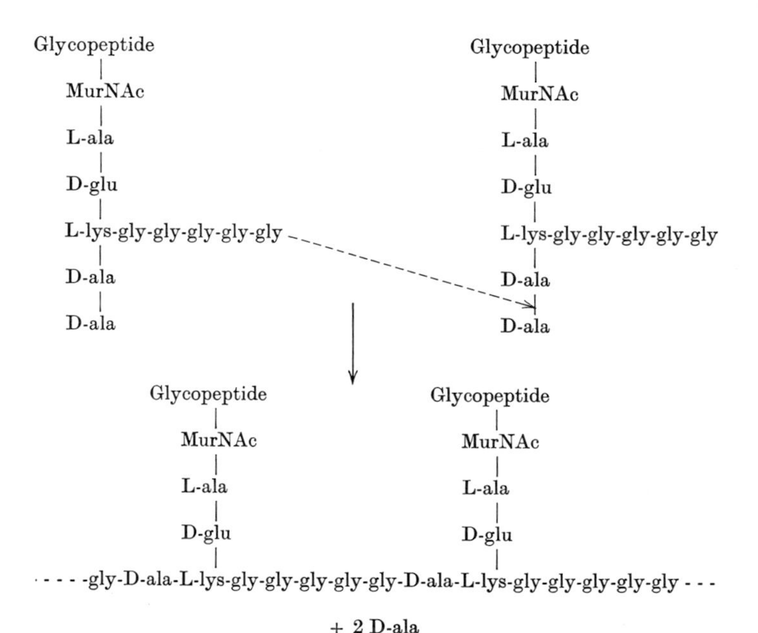

Fig. 10. Transpeptidation of two linear peptidoglycan strands with closure of the interpeptide bridges and elimination of D-alanine

linked peptidoglycan and liberate D-alanine (Fig. 10). It is this final step in cell wall synthesis which is inhibited by penicillins and cephalosporins. A free carboxyl group greatly enhances the biological activity of penicillins, although it is not absolutely essential for biological activity, i.e., penicillins with a blocked carboxyl group such as a methyl ester or amide have some biological activity, but it is exceedingly low. A carboxyl group in the peptidoglycan substrate which the carboxyl group in penicillin might resemble was therefore sought. Initially, there were two candidates, the α-carboxyl group of D-glutamic acid and the terminal carboxyl group of D-alanine. However, the α-carboxyl group of glutamic acid was found to be amidated, leaving only the latter possibility. Penicillin is a cyclic dipeptide of two amino acids, L-cysteine and D-valine. Was it possible that this cyclic L,D-dipeptide is an analogue of the D,D-dipeptide at the end of the peptido-

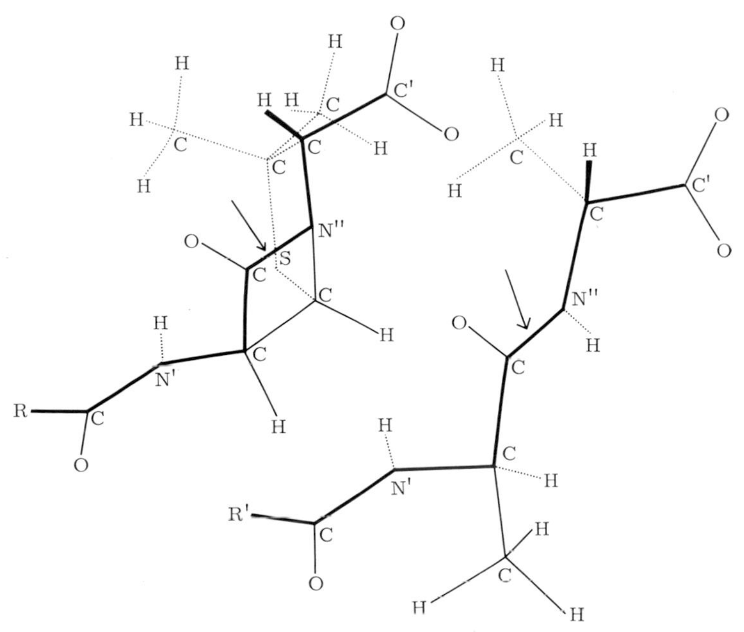

Fig. 11. Dreiding stereomodels of penicillin (left) and of the D-alanyl-D-alanine end of the peptidoglycan strand (right). Arrows indicate the position of the CO-N bond in the β-lactam ring of penicillin and of the CO-N bond in D-alanyl-D-alanine at the end of the peptidoglycan strand

glycan strand? Earlier, in the case of the cycloserines, there was an example where, from a conformational standpoint, an L-amino acid and a D-amino acid resembled each other. Dreiding stereomodels of the cyclic L,D-dipeptide penicillin and the D,D-dipeptide found at the end of the chain were therefore assembled (Fig. 11) [13]. The conformation of one edge of the penicillin molecule was nearly the same as the conformation of the backbone of the D-alanyl-D-alanine. A very important feature of these models is the fact that the highly reactive CO-N bond in the β-lactam ring of the penicillin molecule (the bond which is susceptible to acid hydrolysis or is attacked by the enzyme penicillinase, or is responsible for the nonenzymatic acylation of serum protein to give the penicilloyl allergen) lies in exactly the same position as the CO-N bond in D-alanyl-D-alanine which is involved in the transpeptidation. It

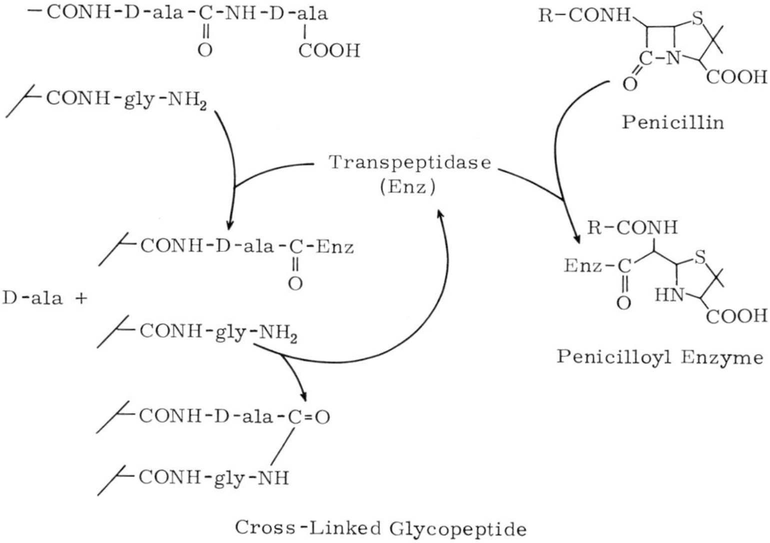

—CONH-D-ala-C(=O)-NH-D-ala(COOH)

R-CONH (β-lactam ring, C=O, -N-, S, COOH)

Penicillin

CONH-gly-NH_2

Transpeptidase (Enz)

CONH-D-ala-C(=O)-Enz

R-CONH

Enz-C(=O) (HN-, S, COOH)

D-ala +

CONH-gly-NH_2

Penicilloyl Enzyme

CONH-D-ala-C=O

CONH-gly-NH

Cross-Linked Glycopeptide

Fig. 12. Proposed mechanism of inhibition of transpeptidation by penicillins

was therefore hypothesized that penicillin might act as a substrate analogue of the end of that chain which it conformationally resembled.

In the normal reaction sequence, by analogy with other similar reactions, the transpeptidase might be expected to react with the end of the chain to give an acyl enzyme intermediate and eliminate D-alanine. This activated intermediate would then react with the amino end of another chain to close the cross-bridge (Fig. 12). Penicillin might then enter the substrate-binding site normally occupied by D-alanyl-D-alanine. The CO-N bond in the β-lactam ring would occupy the same position as the bond involving the transpeptidation, and penicillin might then acylate the transpeptidase and thereby irreversibly inactivate it.

It took some time to obtain a cell-free preparation which would catalyze the transpeptidation reaction. That was finally accomplished, not using *Staphylococcus aureus*, but using enzymes from *Escherichia coli* in which meso-diaminopimelic acid replaces L-lysine as the third amino acid in the peptide sequence. There are in fact two termination reactions in *Escherichia coli*, one of them

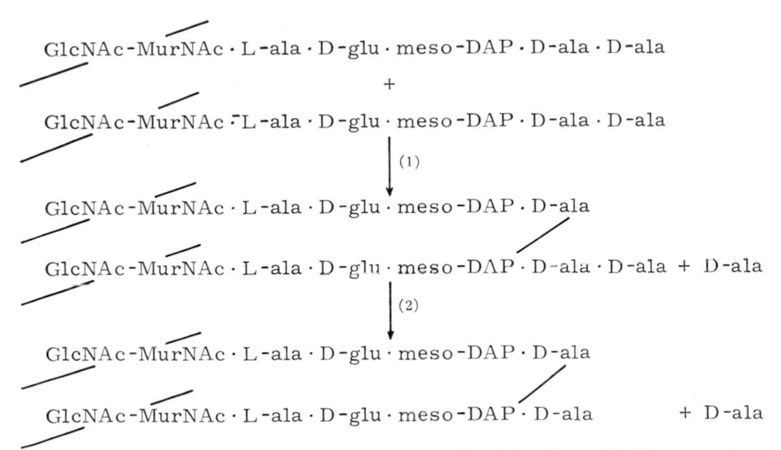

Fig. 13. Penicillin-sensitive enzymatic reactions in *E. coli*. The reactions shown are catalyzed by peptidoglycan transpeptidase [1] and D-alanine carboxypeptidase [2]

the transpeptidation in which a cross-link is introduced between two peptidoglycan strands, and the second a reaction catalyzed by a D-alanine carboxypeptidase in which the terminal D-alanine residue of the pentapeptide in the other strand is removed (Fig. 13) [9]. At some stage, the removal of the second D-alanine residue prevents further propagation of the cross-linking system. The cross-linked peptide units in *E. coli*, as was first found by WEIDEL and his collaborators [14], is limited to a dimer, while in *S. aureus*, very large cross-linked peptides, as large as decamers, occur.

Both of these reactions are sensitive to penicillins (Table 2). The carboxypeptidase is inhibited by concentrations of penicillins which are far below the growth inhibitory concentration for the organism. Therefore, the inhibition of the carboxypeptidase is either not a lethal inhibition (because at a concentration which inhibits the carboxypeptidase completely, growth of the cells is certainly not inhibited), or penicillins do not have access to the intracellular site of the carboxypeptidase in the intact microbial cells.

In the case of the transpeptidase, with one important exception, the concentration of the penicillin required to inhibit growth was virtually identical to the concentration required to inhibit the

Table 2. *Inhibition of growth and enzymes of E. coli by antibiotics*

Antibiotic	Growth	Concentrations required for 50% inhibition, μg/ml		
		Glycopeptide Synthetase	Glycopeptide Transpeptidase	D-alanine Carboxy-peptidase
Ampicillin	3	—	3	0.02
Penicillin G	30	—	3	0.02
Cephalothin	50	—	50	1
Methicillin	1000	—	1000	1
Ristocetin	1000	3	—	—
Vancomycin	100	10	—	—
Bacitracin	1000	40	—	—

— Not inhibited

enzyme (Table 2). The exception was penicillin G, which inhibited the enzyme at far lower concentrations than it inhibited the growth of these cells of *E. coli*. This presumably indicates that penicillin G, unlike ampicillin for example, does not have adequate access to the transpeptidase in the intact cell. This phenomenon is perhaps even better illustrated by the case of the three antibiotics, ristocetin, vancomycin and bacitracin, which inhibit growth of cells of *E. coli* only at very high concentrations. However, the enzymes from *E. coli* which are sensitive to these three substances are as sensitive as they are in *S. aureus*. The failure of these three substances to inhibit growth of intact cells of *E. coli* must be due to the fact that these antibiotics are unable to penetrate to the site of these enzymes in the microbial cell.

The carboxypeptidase has been obtained in a purified form and is inhibited in a true competitive fashion by penicillins [15]. Penicillin G and ampicillin are extremely effective competitors for the natural substrate of these enzymes, the K_i values being of the order of 10^{-3} M. 6-Amino-penicillanic acid is also a competitive inhibitor, but only at concentrations which are 100-fold higher than the concentrations required of penicillin G and ampicillin.

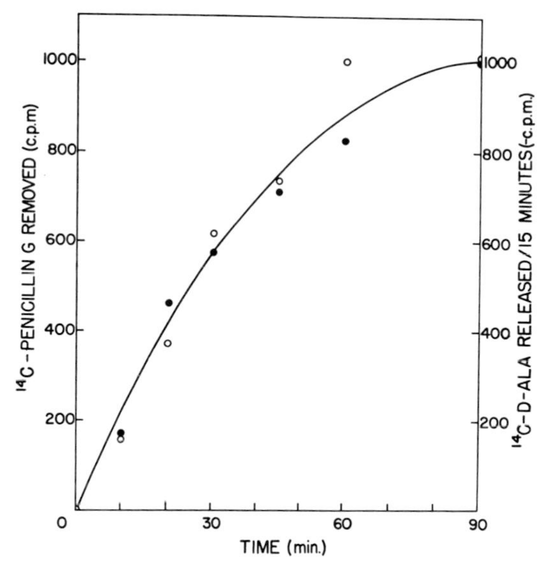

Fig. 14. Simultaneous removal of ^{14}C-penicillin G by hydroxylamine and restoration of activity of particulate D-alanine carboxypeptidase from *B. subtilis* [17]

By contrast, the transpeptidase is inactivated by penicillin [16]. Activity cannot be restored by washing out the penicillin or by treating the enzyme with penicillinase. Moreover, radioactive penicillin is firmly bound to the particulate enzyme which contains the inhibited transpeptidase.

Recently, a particulate D-alanine carboxypeptidase in *Bacillus subtilis*, which may be an uncoupled transpeptidase, has been studied [17]. It is also inactivated by penicillin G and also binds radioactive penicillin G. The binding of penicillin G to this enzyme has been reversed, and reversal restores activity to the inhibited enzyme. The reversal of binding of penicilln G was accomplished in two ways. Hydroxylamine was reacted with the enzyme containing bound ^{14}C-penicillin G. ^{14}C-penicilloyl hydroxamate was recovered. The inhibited enzyme containing ^{14}C-penicillin was also treated with ethylmercaptan. The resulting thioester of penicilloic acid was methylated and α-methyl-β-ethylthio-penicilloate was recovered and shown to be identical to an authentic sample of this compound synthesized by Dr. E. WAGNER of Eli Lilly and Co. in the course of studies of the penicillin allergen. The recovery of these two derivatives shows that in fact penicillin inactivates this enzyme by penicilloylation. The removal of penicillin G is exactly paralleled by the restoration of enzymatic activity (Fig. 14) [17].

Efforts to repeat these experiments with the transpeptidase of *Escherichia coli* are in progress. Those experiments are made more difficult by the problem of assaying the transpeptidase independently of the integrated sequence of reactions shown in Figs. 4 and 13. However, it is hoped that such an assay can be developed. It would make possible purification and characterization of this protein. It is hoped then to use penicillin as a labeling agent for the active site of this enzyme and, as other workers have done with other labeling agents for active sites of enzymes, to use the penicilloylation of the transpeptidase as a means of investigating the structure of its active site.

References[1]

1. STROMINGER, J. L., and J.-M. GHUYSEN: Science **156**, 213 (1967).
2. KATO, K., and J. L. STROMINGER: Biochemistry **7**, 2754 (1968).
3. GHUYSEN, J.-M.: Bact. Rev. **32**, 425 (1968).
4. STROMINGER, J. L.: In: The bacteria, Vol. III, p. 413. (GUNSALUS, I. C., and R. Y. STANIER, Eds.). New York: Academic Press 1962.
5. PARK, J. T., and M. JOHNSON: J. biol. Chem. **179**, 585 (1949).
6. STROMINGER, J. L., E. ITO, and R. H. THRENN: J. Amer. chem. Soc. **82**, 998 (1960).
7. NEUHAUS, F. C.: In: Antibiotics, Vol. I, p. 40. (GOTTLIEB, D., and P. SHAW, Eds.). Berlin-Heidelberg-New York: Springer 1967.
8. ROZE, U., and J. L. STROMINGER: Molec. Pharmacol. **2**, 92 (1966).
9. STROMINGER, J. L., K. IZAKI, M. MATSUHASHI, and D. J. TIPPER: Fed. Proc. **26**, 9 (1967).
10. HIGASHI, Y., J. L. STROMINGER, and C. C. SWEELEY: Proc. nat. Acad. Sci. (Wash.) **57**, 1878 (1967).

[1] Only a limited number of references have been provided. Full lists can be found in the references cited.

11. Higashi, Y., G. Siewert, and J. L. Strominger: Abstracts, Fed. Proc. **27**, 294 (1968).
12. — Fed. Proc. **28**, 657 (1969).
13. Tipper, D. J., and J. L. Strominger: Proc. nat. Acad. Sci. (Wash.) **54**, 1133 (1965).
14. Weidel, W., and H. Pelzer: Advanc. Enzymol. **26**, 193 (1964).
15. Izaki, K., and J. L. Strominger: J. biol. Chem. **243**, 3193 (1968).
16. —, M. Matsuhashi, and J. L. Strominger: J. biol. Chem. **243**, 3180 (1968).
17. Lawrence, P. J., and J. L. Strominger: Fed. Proc. **28**, 473 (1969).

In Vivo Action of Penicillin on Cell Walls of Proteus Mirabilis

H. H. MARTIN

Institut für Mikrobiologie, Technische Hochschule, Darmstadt

Professor STROMINGER and his colleagues have given us a beautiful and clear-cut picture of penicillin action in cell-free systems. For some time we have tried to study penicillin action on intact growing Gram-negative bacteria. Here the picture is still less clear. The gross effects of penicillin on growing Gram-negative bacteria are well known. They are: 1) loss of rigidity and shape of the cell wall; 2) formation of spheroplasts from rod-shaped bacteria, some of which, as in the case of Proteus mirabilis, will grow and multiply indefinitely as so called L-form, even in the presence of very high penicillin concentrations. Biosynthesis of peptidoglycan (= murein) is not inhibited in these spheroplasts. However, the spheroplast murein is morphologically and mechanically defect. Surprisingly, the overall chemical composition of normal murein and murein synthesized in the presence of penicillin is virtually identical. Both display the same molar ratio of amino acid components: D-glutamic acid = 1, m-diaminopimelic acid = 1, D + L-alanine = approximately 2; and this is not what one would expect from the in vitro model of penicillin action. Penicillin inhibition of peptide crosslinkage should result in the incorporation of uncrosslinked pentapeptide side chains (L-ala — D-glu — m-dap — D-ala — D-ala) which could be recognized by their "alanine excess" over normal murein. However, no such alanine excess is present in spheroplast murein.

As an explanation I have suggested an alternative function of the penicillin inhibited peptide crosslinking enzyme. The enzyme might interact with the terminal D-ala — D-ala-group of newly inserted peptide side chains under any condition, also in the presence of penicillin. The function of the enzyme as transpeptidase might then be blocked by penicillin, causing the enzyme to act as a carboxypeptidase, instead. — The separate "regulatory" D-alanine carboxypeptidase of the murein biosynthesis system appears to be excluded as the agent of "alanine ejection" in our case, since in E. coli, at least, this enzyme, according to STROMINGER, is even more sensitive to penicillin than the transpeptidase. It might be possible, of course, that the carboxypeptidase of Proteus mirabilis is not penicillin sensitive.

Inhibition of Bacterial Peptidoglycan Synthesis by Bacitracin

Gerhard Siewert

Abteilung Chemische Mikrobiologie, Schering AG, Berlin

With 2 Figures

As Dr. Strominger already pointed out in his lecture, bacitracin, a cyclic peptide antibiotic, interferes with bacterial peptidoglycan synthesis by inhibiting the hydrolysis of lipid pyrophosphate to lipid phosphate. It thus prevents the lipid carrier from further participating in the reaction cycle of peptidoglycan synthesis. Instead, lipid pyrophosphate accumulates [1].

These findings are illustrated by the following two figures. Fig. 1 shows a radioautogram of a paperchromatographic separation of reaction mixtures, which were obtained by incubating the substrates of peptidoglycan synthesis, UDP-acetylmuramyl-pentapeptide and UDP-acetylglucosamine, with particulate enzyme from *Micrococcus lysodeikticus* in the absence and presence of bacitracin. The UDP-acetylmuramyl-pentapeptide was doubly labeled with ^{14}C in the lysine residue and with ^{32}P in both phosphates.

As has already been explained by Dr. Strominger and is again shown on the left side of the radioautogram, in the absence of bacitracin acetylmuramyl-pentapeptide-1-phosphate is first attached to the lipid phosphate, followed by acetylglucosamine, to form ^{14}C, ^{32}P-lipid intermediate, in which only one of the two phosphates of the pyrophosphate bridge is labeled. The second ^{32}P of the substrate is liberated as ^{32}P-UMP. The ^{14}C-disaccharide unit of the lipid intermediate is then transferred to the growing peptidoglycan acceptor and the remaining ^{32}P-lipid pyrophosphate is immediately hydrolyzed to inorganic ^{32}P-phosphate and unlabeled lipid phosphate.

If, on the other hand, bacitracin is present in the reaction mixture, no ^{32}P-inorganic phosphate is liberated and instead ^{32}P-lipid pyrophosphate accumulates, as is shown on the right side of the radioautogram.

The amount of ^{14}C-peptidoglycan synthesized in the presence of bacitracin depends upon the reaction conditions. If the substrate concentrations and with them the reaction velocity are kept sufficiently low, so that every lipid phosphate molecule present in the crude enzyme preparation participates, on the average, only once or less than once in the reaction cycle, the amount of ^{14}C-peptidoglycan synthesized is not affected by the addition of bacitracin, and the amount of lipid pyrophosphate accumulated is equivalent to the inorganic phosphate released in the absence of the antibiotic.

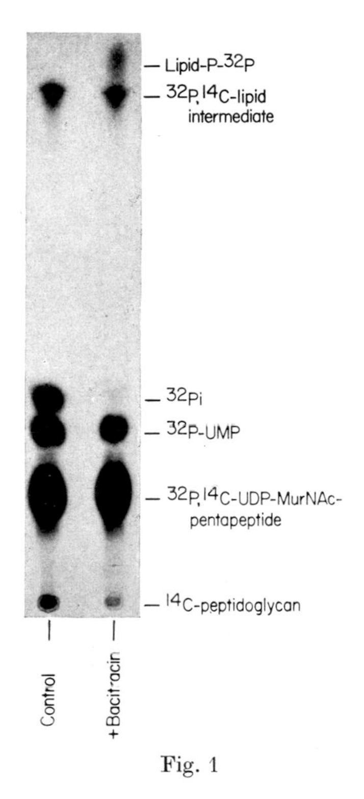

Fig. 1

If the substrate concentrations and the reaction velocity are increased, as was the case in the experiment in Fig. 1, each lipid phosphate molecule has to run through the cycle several times for full activity of the enzyme, and therefore, in comparison to the control, the amount of peptidoglycan synthesized in the presence of bacitracin is decreased, because in this case each lipid phosphate molecule can be utilized for peptidoglycan synthesis only once and is then trapped as lipid pyrophosphate.

The average number of cycles in which each lipid phosphate participated in the absence of the antibiotic is thus equal to the ratio of peptidoglycan synthesized without and with bacitracin or to the ratio of inorganic phosphate released without and lipid pyrophosphate accumulated with the antibiotic. The number of cycles under the conditions of the present experiment was approximately five.

This experiment therefore gives evidence that lipid pyrophosphate, first postulated by ANDERSON, MATSUHASHI, HASKIN and STROMINGER [2], is indeed an intermediate in the biosynthesis of the bacterial peptidoglycan. It also proves that the lipid carrier acts catalytically in the biosynthesis, participating in the reaction cycle repeatedly.

Fig. 2 shows how the inhibition of the hydrolysis of isolated ^{32}P-lipid pyrophosphate by the *M. lysodeikticus* enzyme depends upon the concentration of bacitracin. The substrate, i.e. lipid-P-^{32}P, was accumulated by bacitracin in a large scale reaction

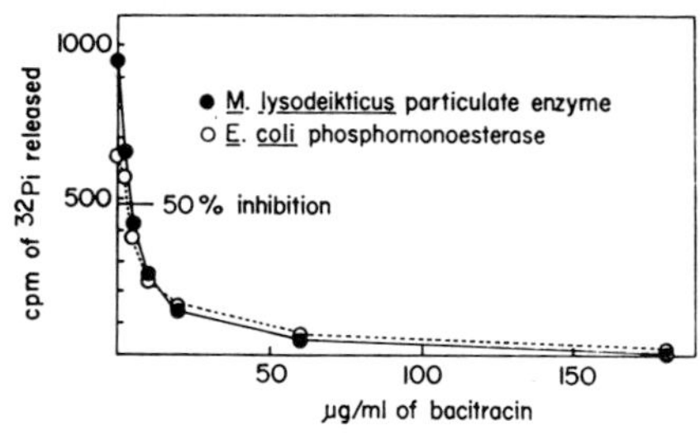

Fig. 2. From [1]

mixture similar to the one used in Fig. 1, isolated by extraction with n-butanol/pyridinium acetate, and purified by silicic acid column chromatography. The activity of the phosphatase was assayed by incubating the ^{32}P-lipid pyrophosphate with the particulate enzyme in the presence of deoxycholic acid and potassium ions at pH 8.5, extracting the excessive substrate with n-butanol/pyridinium acetate and counting the ^{32}P-inorganic phosphate left in the aqueous phase.

The concentration for 50% inhibition was approximately 4 µg/ml. The concentration required to inhibit growth of *M. lysodeikticus* was 3 µg/ml [3]. This experiment thus suggests that the inhibition of the hydrolysis of lipid pyrophosphate is the specific locus of action of bacitracin in inhibiting growth of cells of *M. lysodeikticus*.

As is shown in Fig. 2, lipid pyrophosphate is also hydrolyzed by *E. coli* phosphomonoesterase, and this hydrolysis is also inhibited by similar concentrations of bacitracin as needed for the inhibition of the hydrolysis by the particulate enzyme from *M. lysodeikticus*. On the other hand, bacitracin has no effect on the hydrolysis of such compounds as glucose-1-phosphate or p-nitrophenyl phosphate by the *E. coli* enzyme. The exact mechanism of the inhibition of the lipid pyrophosphatase by bacitracin is not known and remains an interesting problem.

References

1. Siewert, G., and J. L. Strominger: Proc. nat. Acad. Sci. (Wash.) **57**, 767 (1967).
2. Anderson, J. S., M. Matsuhashi, M. A. Haskin, and J. L. Strominger: Proc. nat. Acad. Sci. (Wash.) **53**, 881 (1965).
3. —, P. M. Meadow, M. A. Haskin, and J. L. Strominger: Arch. Biochem. **116**, 487 (1966).

Discussion

Strominger (Cambridge, Mass.): I should have said in my talk that one of the early observations that indicated that penicillin might inhibit the cross-linking was Dr. Martin's study [1] of the nature of the materials formed in *Proteus mirabilis* in the presence or absence of penicillin.

There are important physiological differences among microorganisms. The growth of *Staphylococcus aureus* is stopped by the addition of penicillin; cell wall synthesis stops. However, *Proteus mirabilis*, under appropriate conditions, as Dr. Martin and others have shown, continues to grow and multiply as round forms in the presence of penicillin, which are completely stable. The cause of the difference between these organisms is not presently known. It could be related to Dr. Martin's observations. If the carboxypeptidase is penicillin-resistant, the terminal alanine residue would be removed from the linear peptidoglycan strand in *Proteus*. Maybe this could impart some physiological advantage to the organism, so that cell wall synthesis could continue, and the organism could then continue to grow. It is an important enigma: Why in one case cell growth stops, and in the other cell growth continues in the presence of penicillin.

Westphal (Freiburg): When Dr. Martin spoke of maybe two centers in the same enzyme but only one to which penicillin is bound, I was thinking that we know that penicilloyl proteins are powerful antigens; one might use such a penicilloylated enzyme to produce antibodies. They would not be reactive against the site where penicillin acts, because this blocks. But if there is another site which acts on D-alanine-dipeptide, this would be an antienzyme only blocking this part. Then, one could take an enzyme without penicillin.

Helmreich (Würzburg): It is a remarkable achievement of Dr. Strominger that he can separate the lipid component from the protein component of a lipoprotein enzyme. I would like to ask if information is already available on the properties of the protein part. Is it a large protein? Does it have an unusual amino acid composition?

Strominger: We have concentrated so far on identifying the phospholipid cofactor. We do not know very much about the protein except that, as I said, it comes off the column in organic solvents, and it remains in solution without the phospholipid. But if you remove the solvent and try to put it back into an organic solvent, it will not dissolve. If you add the phosphatidyl glycerol, the solubility in the organic solvent is restored. We are also very interested in purifying the protein in order to find the basis for its lipid solubility.

Talalay has studied a steroid metabolizing protein from *Pseudomonas testosteroni*. One of the enzymes that is involved in steroid metabolism is soluble and stable in alcohol. He crystallized that enzyme and determined the amino acid composition, which is similar to that of any other protein. So, there was no obvious explanation of its unusual lipid solubility.

Egge (Marburg): Concerning the purification of the phospholipid of the enzyme: Have you done any studies on the composition of this phospholipid, and can you replace it by any other phosphatidic acid, from mammalian origin, for example?

Strominger: Cardiolipin from animal tissues is inactive in restoring the activity of the enzyme, whereas cardiolipin from bacterial sources is active. So we believe that there is some specificity for the fatty acids. We have not yet done a fatty acid analysis.

Sebald (Munich): Do you know where the phospholipid enzyme is localized inside the bacterial cell? Is it in the soluble part or in the membrane?

Strominger: It is in the membrane from which it is extracted by acidic butanol.

Westphal: You may mention how more general this carrier lipid is acting in bacteria, and one might suggest that some of these isoprenoid compounds up to C_{110} may be found in traces in the tissue of higher animals.

Strominger: There are several points. One is that at the same time as we isolated the lipid carrier in peptidoglycan synthesis, the groups of Robbins [2] and of Osborn [3] were working on the nature of the lipid carrier in O-antigen synthesis in *Salmonellae*. They identified it as a C_{55}-isoprenoid alcohol phosphate. A residual question is whether the two C_{55} alcohols are identical or not. There are 11 cis-trans double bonds in this molecule, and therefore the elucidation of the exact isomer is extremely difficult.

Since then, a variety of other polysaccharide syntheses in bacteria have been found which utilize an isoprenoid alcohol phosphate as a lipid carrier.

LENNARZ [4] has found an isoprenoid alcohol phosphomannose which is active in the extracellular synthesis of a mannoside. HEATH has found another example in *Acetobacter*, and NIKAIDO, and WRIGHT [5] also have found other examples.

We thought that they function in a transport mechanism. An enigma in studies of cell wall synthesis in the beginning was the fact that the precursors are soluble cytoplasmic substances, while the cell wall is an extracellular product on the other side of the permeability barrier, the membrane, to which the precursors are impermeable. We therefore believe the isoprenoid alcohol is serving as a carrier in the membrane for the transport of the activated intermediates from inside the cell to the outside.

To answer the question of Dr. WESTPHAL about the isoprenoid alcohol in plants and animals: We were, of course, interested in this possibility. It is a little difficult to find experimental evidence, for example, that dolichol in the liver, the C_{110} alcohol, might be involved in the synthesis of some polysaccharide which is on the outside of the membrane. We thought of looking for acidic derivatives of dolichol; the efforts were completely negative.

SCHWARZ (Tübingen): We recently analyzed the effects of penicillin on the morphogenesis of *E. coli.* and, as a control, the biochemical effects of the drug [SCHWARZ, U., A. ASMUS, and H. FRANK: J. molec. Biol. (in press)]. We found that very low concentrations of penicillin produced a measurable effect with respect to the rate of synthesis of peptidoglycan, and also to the fraction of surviving cells. However, the glycopeptide which was synthesized in the presence of the drug showed no expected excess of alanine, and also no decrease in the number of peptide bridges, compared with the control.

STROMINGER: I would need to see the details of the experiment to be sure that you could measure an inhibition of synthesis of a small amount of peptidoglycan in the presence of a large amount of peptidoglycan already there.

SCHWARZ: The interesting detail is that we have analyzed the glycopeptide which was synthesized in the presence of penicillin, not the total glycopeptide. The analyses have been done after penicillin G treatment of a mutant of *E. coli* which needs DAP for growth; the new glycopeptide was labelled with radioactive DAP.

STROMINGER: There may be particularly sensitive sites in the cell, for example septum formation, which may amount to just a fraction of total synthesis, although its inhibition would result in a defect in growth.

SCHWARZ: This may be true.

BÜCHER (Munich): Going back to the phosphatidyl glycerol: Do you know the fatty acid component?

STROMINGER: No. (Added in proof: It is mainly a C_{15}-methyl branched fatty acid).

Westphal: After you showed that cycloserine, which is a synthetic compound, acts on the D-alanine metabolism, I'm sure that in your mind you have synthesized a lot of new antibiotics which do not exist in nature but can be fabricated; for instance, against D-glutamic acid or D-glutamine.

Strominger: At the IUB-Meeting in New York, Russian scientists reported that they had synthesized the D-glutamic acid analogue of D-cycloserine:

```
                  H        H
                  |        |
HOOC—CH2—C————————C—NH2
                  |        |
                  |        |
                  O        C = O
                   \      /
                      N
                      H
```

I am not aware of anything they have reported about the antibacterial activity of this compound.

There is also a report in the literature that the D-leucine analogue inhibits the growth of a special strain of an organism which contains D-leucine in the cell wall.

References

1. Martin, H. H.: Folia microbiol. (Praha) **12,** 234 (1967).
— Abstr. VI. Int. Congr. Biochem., New York, **VI,** 518 (1964).
2. Wright, A., M. Dankert, P. Fennesy, and P. W. Robbins: Proc. nat. Acad. Sci. (Wash.) **57,** 1798 (1967).
3. Osborn, M. J., and J. M. Weiner: Fed. Proc. **26,** 70 (1967).
4. Scher, M., W. J. Lennarz, and C. C. Sweeley, Proc. nat. Acad. Sci. (Wash.) **59,** 1313 (1968).
5. Wright, A.: Fed Proc. **28**, 658 (1969).

IV. Respiratory Chain

Mechanisms and Inhibitors Acting on Electron Transport and Energy Conservation between NADH and the Cytochrome Chain

P. B. GARLAND, R. A. CLEGG, P. A. LIGHT, and C. I. RAGAN

Department of Biochemistry, University of Bristol, England

With 6 Figures

Introduction

The successful application of enzyme inhibitors to more complex systems such as the whole cell, organ or animal would, in an ideal world, be based on correct and detailed knowledge of the mechanism of inhibitor action at the molecular level. However, the absence of such detailed information need not bar the effective employment of inhibitors in the study of organised biological systems. Nor should it be forgotten that the majority of biologically interesting inhibitors have come to us through laboratories which were primarily concerned with toxicology or pharmacology at a level far removed from that which is currently called "molecular". These thoughts should therefore reassure the biologist who, intending to make use of inhibitors active in the NADH-cytochrome segment of the respiratory chain, and, having read with increasing dismay and confusion the literature on the subject, gives up the project. This particular segment of the respiratory chain is admittedly difficult and contentious, so much so that in 1966 SLATER [1] was moved to remark that "The last 4 years have seen a lively controversy between workers in this field on the nature of the NADH dehydrogenase of the respiratory chain. There have been some bitter recriminations and accusations of misrepresentations and misquotations". From which we can gather that the smoke of battle has somewhat observed the bystander's view. Since then there has been yet further dissent over the interpretation of experimental data. Fortunately the amount of such data has increased, and much of it is cold, hard and factual. By concentrating on experimental data of this sort, and by focussing our attention on the areas of general agreement, we hope that a useful account of the NADH-cytochrome segment will emerge. Towards this end we have organised our account along the lines of experimental approach rather than actual (and possibly disputed) conclusion. For whatever else is certain, the experimental approaches are real in that they exist. Furthermore, the greatest problems in research on highly integrated systems like cells appear to be technical, and by describing the experimental techniques used largely at the sub-cellular level of organization we may facilitate their application or modification for more complex systems.

The Mitochondrial Oxidation of NADH

NADH generated by intramitochondrial NAD-specific dehydrogenases such as those oxidizing L-malate (E.C.1.1.1.37), L_S-(+)-isocitrate (E.C.1.1.1.42), 2-oxoglutarate (E.C.1.2.4.2), pyruvate (E.C.1.2.4.1) and L-3-hydroxyacyl-CoA (E.C.1.1.1.35) is reoxidized by the respiratory chain with oxygen as the terminal acceptor. The midpotential of the NADH/NAD^+ couple at pH 7.0 is −320 mV, and the transfer of two electrons to oxygen at +815 mV involves a fall in free energy of approximately 51 kcal per mole of NADH oxidized. By contrast, the free energy change for the synthesis of ATP (at equal activities of ADP and ATP, and 10 mM phosphate, at pH 7.0) is +9.5 kcal/mole. It follows that the free energy change involved in the oxidation of a molecule of NADH by oxygen could be coupled to the synthesis of 51/9.5 = 5 molecules ATP. In fact the number is less than this, being 3 in mammalian systems, 2 in some but not all yeasts [3], 2 in *Micrococcus denitrificans* [4], 1 in *Ascaris lumbricoides* [5], and zero in a mutant of *Saccharamyces cerevisiae* [6]. The overall efficiency of this energy conserving process is therefore between a maximum of 60% and a minimum of zero, according to the species.

For electron transfer operating with 100% efficiency of energy conservation, 2 electrons would have to traverse an oxido-reduction potential rise of 210 mV in order to accomplish the synthesis of one molecule of ATP from ADP and P_i under the conditions described above. An important corollary of the relationship between free energy change (ΔG^o) and oxido-reduction potential change (ΔE_o), given by

$$\Delta G_o = nF \, \Delta E^o \tag{1}$$

where n is the number of electrons involved in the oxido-reduction, and F the Faraday constant (23 kcal/volt equivalent), is that oxido-reductions between carriers of similar potential could occur freely in either direction without the production or utilisation of energy.

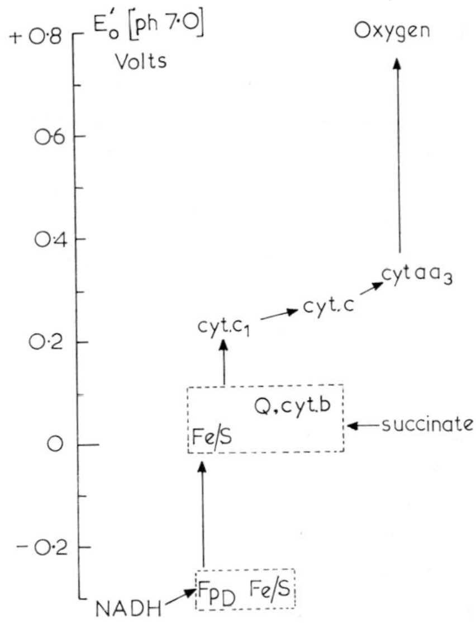

Fig. 1. Mid-potentials of respiratory carriers

This possibility is a thermodynamic one, and whether it occurs at significant rates in biological systems depends upon the presence of suitable enzymes.

Examination of the mid-potentials for the carriers of the mammalian respiratory chain reveals that there are three regions where the span between adjacent carriers is adequate for ATP synthesis, i.e., between (1) NADH and the collection of cytochrome b, ubiquinone, and a ferroprotein, (2) the afore-mentioned collection and cytochrome c_1 and c, (3) cyt. a and oxygen (Fig. 1). These three regions of energy conservation are known as sites I, II and III, respectively.

This brief survey illustrates the function of the NADH to cytochrome segment of the respiratory chain — namely, to transfer reducing equivalents from NADH to the cytochromes and, in doing so, to convert the energy available from the oxido-reduction into a form that can drive the otherwise unfavoured synthesis of ATP from ADP and P_i.

Biochemical Preparations Used in the Study of the NADH-Cytochrome Segment: The Fractionation Approach

The one undisputed fact concerning this segment is that the reductant is NADH. This implies the existence of an NADH dehydrogenase which catalyses the reduction of an unspecified oxidant by NADH. The unequivocal identification of the respiratory chain NADH dehydrogenase "must await the demonstration that it can react with the next member of the electron transport chain. This, of course, must await the clear cut identification of the next member of the electron transport chain [7]". In other words, the characterization of the NADH dehydrogenase requires the characterization of its acceptor which requires the characterization of the NADH dehydrogenase. Fortunately this apparent impasse is not insoluble; a similar situation existed with acyl-CoA dehydrogenases and their acceptor, ETF [8]. In addition, there are convincing data (reviewed by Mackler [9], Hatefi [10], King [11] and Singer [12]) that a flavoprotein isolated from mitochondria and assayed as an NADH: ferricyanide oxido-reductase corresponds to the NADH dehydrogenase proper of the respiratory chain.

The enzymes of electron transport and energy conservation are an integral part of the inner mitochondrial membrane, and it is inevitable that any procedure which succeeds in dislodging a protein from such an environment and bringing it into solution runs the risk of altering the protein's properties. It is therefore necessary to infer from experiments with membrane bound systems the *in situ* behaviour of the NADH dehydrogenase, and to use these behavioural properties as a yardstick for assessing the degree to which the solubilized NADH dehydrogenase is modified either by incomplete function or the appearance of new and non-physiological catalytic properties. Tables 1 and 2 compare the properties of a number of membrane-bound and soluble NADH dehydrogenases of varying complexity. It should be noted that as the fractionation proceeds, the nature of the terminal acceptor for NADH oxidation must inevitably change. Initially NADH is oxidized by oxygen, then, with the loss of cytochrome oxidase, by added cytochrome c. Next follows the use of coenzyme Q analogues, and finally, ferricyanide.

Table 1 illustrates the manner in which increasing purification of the NADH dehydrogenase results in the loss of other respiratory components. In all these cases the endogenous Q_{10} of the membrane fraction can be reduced by NADH, and this reduction is blocked by the inhibitors rotenone and amytal [10]. The same is true for the reduction of low concentrations of Q_{10} analogues [18] which, for reasons of solubility, are usually of shorter side chain length, (e.g. Q_2). Higher concentrations of added Q are reduced by NADH in a rotenone and amytal insensitive manner that probably has no physiological counterpart [18].

Table 2 compares the two main types of soluble NADH: ferricyanide reductase that have been described. There are, of course, differences amongst the three preparations of high molecular weight and also amongst the six preparations of lower molecular weight, and these are more comprehensively covered in the papers of Singer [12], King et al. [11], Mackler [9], Hatefi and Stempel [25], and Hatefi [10]. Nevertheless, the striking contrast between the two groups of enzyme is both noteworthy and agreed upon. It is also evident from Tables 1 and 2 that the least complex of the particulate systems (NADH Q reductase) is in many ways comparable with the more complex of the soluble systems, (e.g. the preparation of Singer [20]), and these features are summarized in Table 3.

The major differences between the two preparations are the losses of rotenone sensitive NADH-Q reductase activity and of lipid from the soluble fraction. It is possible that these two losses are related, since treatments that might be expected to alter the hydrophobic environment of the membrane-bound respiratory chain are known to block electron transfer in the same region as rotenone (see below). Thus the loss of lipid and Q_{10} occuring during the solubilization of the NADH dehydrogenase may result in the

Table 1. *NADH oxidation by particulate preparations of varying complexity*

Preparation	Scheme (Low potential flavoproteins; Site I: Rotenone, Amytal; High potential Flavins; Site II: Antimycin; Site III)	Comments
Mitochondria and mechanically derived particles	$NADH \rightleftharpoons Fp_D \rightarrow [Fe/S, Q_{10}, cyt\ b] \rightarrow c_1\ c \rightarrow aa_3 \rightarrow$ oxygen.	Phosphorylation sites absent in non-phosphorylating particles. The terminal acceptor is oxygen — hence "NADH oxidase"
Detergent salt fractionation	$Fp_D \dashrightarrow Q$; $Fp_D \dashrightarrow$ Ferricyanide; $Q_{10} \dashrightarrow Q$; $c_1 \dashrightarrow$ cyt c	
NADH — cyt c reductase	$NADH \rightleftharpoons Fp_D \rightarrow [Fe/S, Q_{10}, cyt\ b] \rightarrow c_1$	Non-phosphorylating
Detergent salt fractionation	$Fp_D \dashrightarrow Q$; $Fp_D \dashrightarrow$ Ferricyanide; $Q_{10} \dashrightarrow Q$; $c_1 \dashrightarrow$ cyt c	
NADH — Q reductase	$NADH \rightleftharpoons Fp_D \rightarrow [Fe/S, Q_{10}]$ $Fp_D \dashrightarrow Q$; $Fp_D \dashrightarrow$ Ferricyanide; $Q_{10} \dashrightarrow Q$	Non-phosphorylating

loss of the normal rotenone-sensitive NADH-Q reductase activity [29].

A further step in the fractionation of this region of the respiratory chain has recently been reported by HATEFI and STEMPEL [25], and arises from observations made by HATEFI et al. [28]. These authors reported in 1961 that reduction of the particulate NADH-cyt c reductase with NADH led to a fall in absorbance at 460 nm which was twice as great as would have been anticipated from reduction of the known amount of flavin present. Furthermore, titration of the NADH-cyt c reductase with NADH revealed that the absorbance change at 460 nm exhibited a biphasic response, indicating the presence of two distinct components that could be bleached at this wavelength by NADH. In the presence of amytal, an inhibitor of the reaction, only 50% of the maximal absorbance change at 460 nm was caused by NADH. A similar two-fold excess of the absorbance change at 460 nm over that attributable to flavin reduction is also observed in the particulate NADH-Q reductase [37] and the soluble NADH dehydrogenase of high molecular weight [10]. On the basis of these and other considerations HATEFI proposed [10, 37] that the immediate acceptor for the NADH dehydrogenase ferroflavoprotein was

---

Legend to Tab. 1

For details see the review by HATEFI [10]. Fp_D represents the ferroflavoprotein of the NADH dehydrogenase, Fe/S represents ferroprotein (non-heme, non-flavin, iron protein) of which there may be more than one species in that region of the respiratory chain within brackets, Q_{10} — the naturally occurring coenzyme Q of mammals, Q — ubiquinone of unspecified side chain length, cyt b, c, c_1, a and a_3 — the respective cytochrome. All intermediate carriers joined by solid arrows are an integral part of the particulate fraction, whereas the acceptors indicated by interrupted arrows must be added to the suspending medium. "High potential flavins" include membrane bound dehydrogenases such as succinate (E.C.1.3.99.1) and L-3-glycerol-phosphate (E.C.1.1.2.1.) dehydrogenases. The flavoproteins of fatty acid oxidation [13] and also Fp_{D_2} of CHANCE et al. [5, 14] are not membrane bound [15, 16]. Some low potential flavoproteins are also not tightly bound to the membrane [16, 17], and include lipoamide dehydrogenase (E.C.1.6.4.3). Carriers joined by reversible reaction arrows are considered to have *approximately* the same oxidoreduction potential, whereas in the reaction written irreversibly the reductant has a potential at least 200 mV more negative than the oxidant. The sequence of carriers in the collection [Fe/S, Q_{10}, cyt b] is discussed below.

Table 2. *NADH oxidation by soluble preparations of varying complexity*

Abbreviations as in Table 1. The electron paramagnetic resonance (EPR) spectroscopy signal at g = 1.94 refers to that elicited by reduction of the enzyme with NADH. Fp_D probably corresponds to fraction A of Hatefi and Stempel [25], Fe/S to fraction B

Preparation	Activities	M.W. (g protein/ mole FMN)	E.P.R. g = 1.94	Fe:FMN	Labile sulfide/Fe
High molecular weight NADH dehydrogenases (Ringler et al. [19]; Cremona and Kearney [20]; King et al. [11])	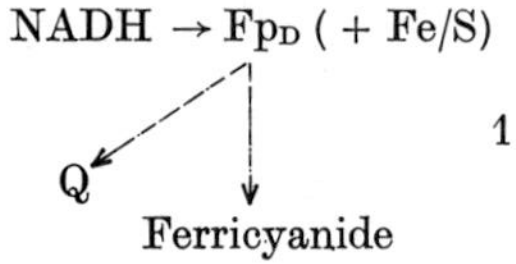 NADH → Fp_D (+ Fe/S) → Q → Ferricyanide	1.1×10^6 5×10^5 5×10^5	Present	17:1 10:1	1.5:1
Low molecular weight NADH dehydrogenases (Mahler et al. [21]; de Bernard [22]; Mackler [23]; King et al. [11]; Pharo et al. [24]; Hatefi and Stempel [25])	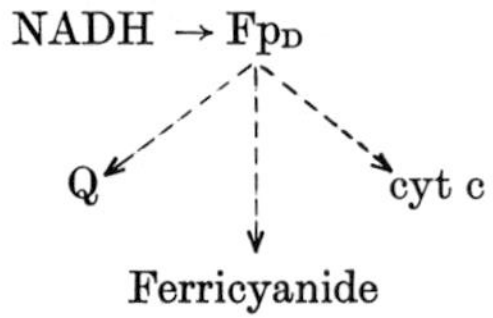 NADH → Fp_D ⇢ Q ⇢ cyt c ⇢ Ferricyanide	7—9 $\times 10^4$	Absent	4:1 2:1	1.5:1

another protein that contained iron — a ferroprotein. In 1967 HATEFI and STEMPEL [25] reported the isolation of two distinct soluble proteins from particulate NADH-Q reductase. One of

Table 3. *Comparison of the properties of the particulate NADH-Q reductase and soluble NADH dehydrogenase (high M.W.)*

Nature	NADH-Q reductase (HATEFI [10]) Particulate. Membrane bound	NADH dehydrogenase (SINGER [12, 26]) soluble
FMN (nmole/mg protein)	1.4	1.12
Fe:FMN	26	17.5
Labile sulfide:Fe	1:1	1.6:1
Lipid (mg/mg protein)	0.22	0
Q_{10} (nmole/mg protein)	4.3	0
NADH induced EPR signal at g = 1.94	Present	Present
NADH: Ferricyanide reductase		
Turnover number (30°, per FMN)	6.5×10^5	$8—15 \times 10^5$
K_m for NADH (μM)	105	108
NADH: cyt c. reductase	slight activity	slight activity
Rotenone sensitive NADH-Q reductase	Present	Absent

these (Fraction A) was a ferroflavoprotein containing labile sulphide, Fe and FMN in the ratio 4:4:1, and catalysed the reduction by NADH of ferricyanide, quinones and cytochrome c. Its molecular weight per mole of FMN was 66,000, and both in this and its catalytic properties it resembled the low molecular weight types of NADH dehydrogenase (Table 2). The other soluble protein (Fraction B) was a ferroprotein containing 30 mμatom Fe per mg, a similar amount of labile sulphide, and no flavin or heme. Fraction B could be reduced by NADH only in the presence of fraction A, and its reduced form could be reoxidized by Q_1 or Q_2. An oxido-reduction potential (pH 8.0) of about +10 mV has been calculated [16] from the data of HATEFI and STEMPEL for fraction B [25]. The reduced minus oxidized difference spectrum for fraction B exhibited troughs at approximately 460 and 380 nm. On the basis of these observations and of a reinvestigation of the particulate NADH-Q reductase by dual wavelength spectrophotometry [37], HATEFI has concluded that this segment of the respiratory chain occurs according to scheme (a):

[scheme a] NADH → Ferroflavoprotein → Ferroprotein → Q
(Fraction A) (Fraction B)
Rotenone
Amytal

According to this formulation, the soluble NADH dehydrogenases are either derived from fraction A (low molecular weight with a Fe:FMN ratio of 2:1 or 4:1) or from a complex of fractions A and B (high molecular weight with a Fe:FMN ratio of 10 or greater).

There are other formulations for this segment. SINGER [12] in 1966 considered that the high molecular weight NADH dehydrogenase was not a multienzyme enzyme complex, and considered the sequence to be (PALMER et al. [59]):

[scheme b] NADH → Ferroflavoprotein → Q
Rotenone
Amytal

In 1967, CHANCE et al. [14] proposed, on the basis largely of measurements of flavoprotein fluorescence, that the sequence was:

[scheme c] NADH → Fp_{D_1} → Fp_{D_2} → [Q, cyt b]
Rotenone
Amytal

where Fp_{D_1} and Fp_{D_2} were flavoproteins of respectively low (about −300 mV) and high (about zero mV) oxidoreduction potential involved sequentially in the NADH-cytochrome segment. The evidence supporting this scheme has either been partly withdrawn (HASSINEN and CHANCE [17]) or severely criticised (RAGAN and GARLAND [16]) on the grounds that both the fluorescent flavoproteins identified in the original study of rat liver mitochondria as Fp_{D_1} and Fp_{D_2} are not membrane bound, whereas NADH oxidase activity is.

Whatever the individual merits or otherwise of these different formulations for explaining the properties of solubilized and to that extent artificial systems, it is clear that a final assessment of their physiological significance will need to be made on the basis of studies with more intact systems whose full function of electron transport and energy conservation is retained.

Inhibitors of Electron Transport between NADH and the Cytochromes

The pathways of electron transport from succinate and NADH converge about the level of Q, and the inhibitors of greatest interest in the present context are those that inhibit the oxidation of NADH but not succinate. An ideal inhibitor would have absolute specificity, that is to say that it would inhibit one, and only one, enzyme over a considerable range of inhibitor concentration. In practice this happy state of affairs is rarely met with, and additional effects may occur (Table 4). A further complication arises from the fact that the likely target for an inhibitor is a protein, and proteins with similar functions but in diverse tissues or species can be sufficiently different to exhibit very dissimilar inhibitor sensitivities. This point is elegantly made by the studies of BUTOW and ZEYDEL [29] on an antimycin resistant mutant of *Torulopsis utilis*; mitochondria from the mutant were a hundred or more fold less sensitive towards antimycin than those from the wild type.

Table 4 lists those inhibitors that at suitable concentrations are effective against NADH but not succinate oxidation. Most of the listed compounds probably inhibit electron flow in the region indicated in scheme (d); although rhein [30] may act differently.

Table 4. *Inhibitors of the NADH to cytochrome segment of the respiratory chain — SMP stands for submitochondrial particles. Data taken from the references quoted*

Inhibitor	Preparation	Concentration and % inhibition	Other effects
Barbiturates [31, 32] (e.g. Amytal)	Rat liver mitochondria	2 mM 80—90	Lowers P:O ratio for succinate oxidation [33] Inhibits P_i-ATP exchange [34]
Rotenone [34—38]	Rat liver mitochondria [34]	25 μμmole/mg protein 95	Much higher concentrations (e.g. × 10^3 increase) inhibit succinate oxidation [39]
	Rat kidney mitochondria [34]	75 μμmole/mg protein 95	
	Ox heart mitochondria [40]	20 μμmole/mg protein 95	
	T. utilis mitochondria [3, 41]	10 μM 70—80	
Piericidin A [42, 43]	As for rotenone, except T. utilis [41]	As for rotenone, except T. utilis 90 μμmole/mg 90	As for rotenone [39]
Alkyl guanidines [44, 48] (e.g. hexyl guanidine)	Rat liver mitochondria	100 μM 80	Inhibition requires energy dependent uptake of the cationic inhibitor
	Ox heart SMP		No specific effect [18]

Table 4 (continued)

Steroids (e.g. costicosterone [49])	Pig heart SMP	50 μM	40	Progesterone also inhibits [50]
Detergents (e.g. Emasol-1130	Ox-heart SMP [51]	1% v/v	80	succinate oxidation 40% inhibited
Triton x-100)	Rat liver mitochondria [52]	50 μg/ml	95	succinate oxidation unaffected
Urea	Ox heart SMP [27, 53]	3 M	75	succinate oxidation 20% inhibited
Chloramphenicol	Rat liver mitochondria [54]	6 mM	90	succinate oxidation unaffected but P/O ratio lowered
Organic solvents [55]	iso-octane extraction (biphasic)	—	80	
O- and m-phenanthroline	Micrococcus denitrificans [56]	4.5 mM	60—80	
Dicyclohexylcarbodiimide [57]	Ox heart SMP	67 μM	50	Complex. Oligomycin-like action
Rhein [30] (1,8-dihydroxy-anthraquinone-3-carboxylic acid)	RLM and SMP	300 μM		Block not by-passed by menadione

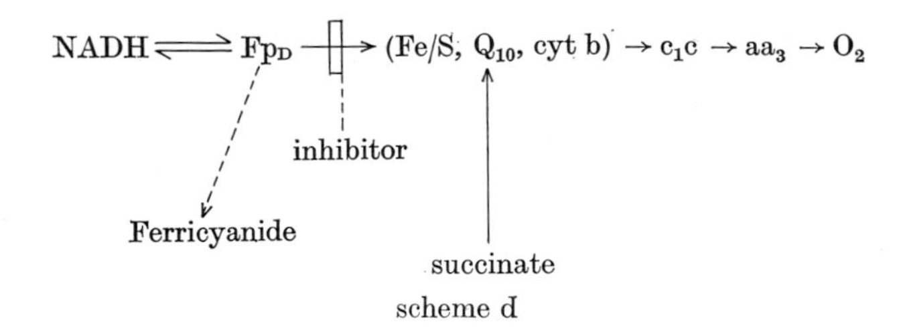

scheme d

Inhibitors of this type block the oxidation of intramitochondrial NADH, and they can be readily assayed by their effects on mitochondrial oxygen uptake in the presence of NAD-linked substrates Alternatively, NADH oxidation with submitochondrial particles can be measured spectrophotometrically as well as polarographically.

In general terms, all of these inhibitors block electron flow from NADH but not succinate to the cytochromes; and must therefore act at a region upstream of the convergence of the two pathways.

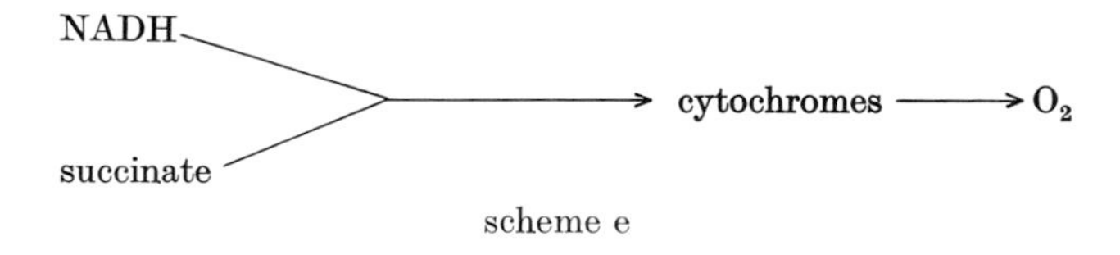

scheme e

Amytal, rotenone and piericidin A are the most comprehensively studied of these inhibitors, and spectroscopic, comparative, and binding studies indicate that all three act in the same region, namely, between the ferroflavoprotein (Fp_D) of the NADH dehydrogenase and the group composed of ferroprotein(s), Q_{10} and cytochrome b (scheme d).

A remarkable feature of the inhibition by rotenone [34] and piericidin A [40, 43] is the stoichiometry between inhibitor and mitochondrial protein. Furthermore, the partial effects of the two inhibitors are additive (Fig. 2). The exceedingly low amount of inhibitor (25 μμmole for rat liver; 20 μμmole for ox heart) needed to inhibit the NADH linked respiration of 1 mg mitochondrial protein is less than the corresponding mitochondrial content of any cytochrome or Q_{10}. The similarity between the mitochondrial FMN content (equated with Fp_D) and the amount of rotenone or piericidin A just required for maximal inhibition has led KLINGENBERG [58] to suggest that Fp_D is the target for these inhibitors. Unfortunately this attractive correlation breaks down in the case of *Torulopsis utilis* mitochondria, where the piericidin A titre is four times greater than the mitochondrial FMN content [41].

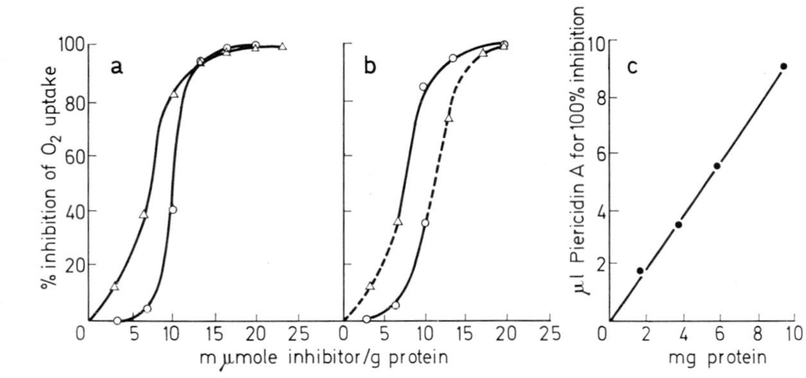

Fig. 2. Inhibition of respiration of rat liver mitochondria by rotenone and piericidin A. 3.0 or 6.0 mg mitochondrial protein were incubated in a final volume of 2.5 ml containing 200 μmole KCl, 50 μmole tris chloride pH 7.2, 2.5 μmole EDTA, 12.5 mμmole pentachlorophenol, 12.5 μmole malonate, 10 μmole L-glutamate, 10 μmole L-malate. In (a), piericidin A (o) and rotenone (Δ) alone was varied. In (b), both piericidin A (o and continuous line) and rotenone (Δ and interrupted line) were varied and inhibitor concentration refers to the total of both inhibitors. (c) stoichiometry. Piericidin A solution 25 μM

The Mechanism of Action of Inhibitors in the NADH-Cytochrome Segment

It is evident from Table 4 that a hydrophobic but otherwise relatively unspecified molecule is capable of disrupting electron transport in this region, and a number of authors [27, 59] have suggested that the site of action of not only these unspecific agents but also the more specific inhibitors (e.g. rotenone) is a lipid. The structures of rotenone, piericidin A, amytal, rhein, and alkylguanidine are shown in the *Appendix*.

The inhibitory effects of analogues of rotenone and piericidin A have also been reported. The rotenone structure appears to need the two methoxy groups and ring E for activity [38], whereas piericidin A loses activity if the ring hydroxyl is acetylated or the side chain is replaced by a carboxyl group [43]. The compounds with a reduced side chain are fully active [43].

The structural resemblance between piericidin A and coenzyme Q has led to the suggestion [42] that piericidin A acted at a site which normally involved Q. The resemblance is less marked with rotenone and virtually absent with amytal. An alternative possibility is that these inhibitors either dislocate or coordinate iron in a hydrophobic environment in a non-heme iron protein [60]. The much greater potency of the naturally occurring antibiotics (insecticides), rotenone and piericidin A, over any chemically-tailored iron chelating compound may reflect the effects of natural selection in screening out an inhibitor that recognised the protein structure at the target site. The specificity of a protein target site would also explain the relative ineffectiveness of hydrophobic iron chelating agents (e.g. antimycin A) that are potent inhibitors elsewhere in the respiratory chain [60].

Optical Techniques in the Study in the NADH-Cytochrome Segment

Inhibition of electron transport in the sequence between NADH and the cytochromes can be expected to cause reduction of those carriers on the NADH side of the site of inhibition and oxidation of those on the cytochrome side (Fig. 3).

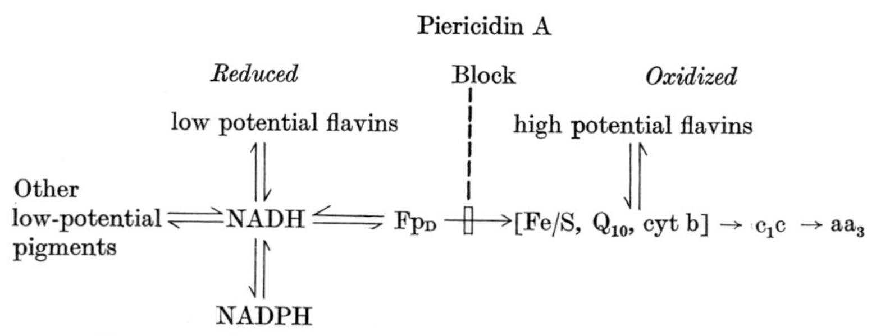

Fig. 3. Changes in the oxido-reduction state of carriers following inhibition of electron flow from NADH to the cytochromes. The low potential flavins include lipoamide dehydrogenase, and the high potential flavins include succinate and L-3-glycerophosphate dehydrogenase, ETF, and acyl-CoA dehydrogenases

Table 5. *Assays for studying oxido reduction carriers in biological systems*

Oxido-reduction carrier	Assay	Specificity or comment
NAD(P)	Fluorescence [64, 66] 366 → 450 nm. Reduced form fluorescent	not distinguished from NAD(P)
	Absorbance [61] 340 — 374 nm. Reduced λ_{max} at 340 nm	not distinguished from NAD(P)
	Extraction and enzymatic assay [71]	NAD and NADP distinguished
Flavoprotein (high and low potential)	Fluorescence [73] 436 → 520 nm. Oxidized form fluorescent	Specific for flavoprotein, but many flavoproteins have poor fluorescent yield
	Absorbance [61] 460—490 nm. Reduced λ_{min} at 440—460 nm	Confusion with Fe/S and possibly cytochrome [74]
	Extraction — not available	
Fe/S	Fluorescence 300 → 350 nm. Oxidized form fluorescent ?	Requires extensive further work
	Absorbance [29] 460—490 nm. Reduced λ_{min} at 460 nm	Variety in λ_{min} and spectra Confusion with Fp and cyt
	Extraction — not available	
	[EPR spectroscopy — expensive and relatively insensitive]	
Q_{10}	Absorbance 275—300 nm. Reduced λ_{min} at 270 nm	Technical problems in U-V
	Extraction and assay [72]	? other compounds
Cytochromes	Absorbance	α bands are characteristic

These changes in the oxidoreduction state can be followed with optical techniques that are applicable not only to subcellular fractions but also to intact cells and organs. Descriptions of the use of optical techniques in the study of whole tissues have been published [61—69] from the laboratories of Chance, Thorell, Lübbers and Bücher, and are suitable modifications of methods developed primarily for the study of suspensions of cells or particles. Table 5 lists the available techniques for the carriers of interest.

There are several points that must be considered when interpreting changes in oxido-reduction states following the addition of a respiratory inhibitor to a complex biological system:

(i) Oxido-reduction changes need not be confined to respiratory chain carriers, but can extend to components that can transfer reducing equivalents to and from the respiratory chain carriers at specific levels.

(ii) In the steady state prior to the addition of the inhibitor, a flow of electrons through the respiratory chains will cause varying degrees of reduction of carriers. In the case of two carriers that have spectroscopically common chromophores (e.g. flavoproteins) but locations above and below the inhibitor site, then inhibition of electron transfer will result in reduction of one carrier and oxidation of the other. The spectroscopically observed change is the sum of the individual changes, and can therefore exhibit complex kinetics and paradoxical directions. This particular difficulty can be avoided if the respiratory components are either fully oxidized (substrate deficient) or fully reduced (oxygen deficient) before adding the inhibitor. There is then only one possible change (reduction or oxidation, respectively) in each case, and the observations can be more confidently interpreted.

(iii) *The contribution of extramitochondrial components.* These are NAD, NADP, nonheme iron proteins, flavoproteins and hemeproteins in the extramitochondrial compartment of many cell types. The relationship between the oxidoreduction levels of these extramitochondrial components and that of their functional counterparts within the mitochondria is an outstanding problem, and one that can be investigated in the whole cell by the use of respiratory inhibitors.

(iv) *Other changes.* The inhibitor may react directly with a chromophoric compound causing a spectral change that is not directly related to the oxidoreduction changes following inhibition of respiration, e.g. the reaction between amytal and the microsomal hydroxylating pigment, P 450 [91].

Inhibition of the NADH-Cytochrome Segment by Thiol Reagents

Several types of inhibition occur, and the interpretations are contentious. In view of the widespread alternative targets for these agents in a system as complex as a whole cell, their effects will not be discussed. For details the reader should consult reviews by PULLMAN and SCHATZ [75], KING et al. [11], and the paper of MERSMAN et al. [76].

By-Passes or Shunts arround the Site of Rotenone and Amytal Inhibition

The addition of an artificial electron acceptor A to a rotenone or amytal blocked respiratory system could by-pass the block if A could accept electrons from above the block and donate electrons back to the respiratory chain below the block, e.g.

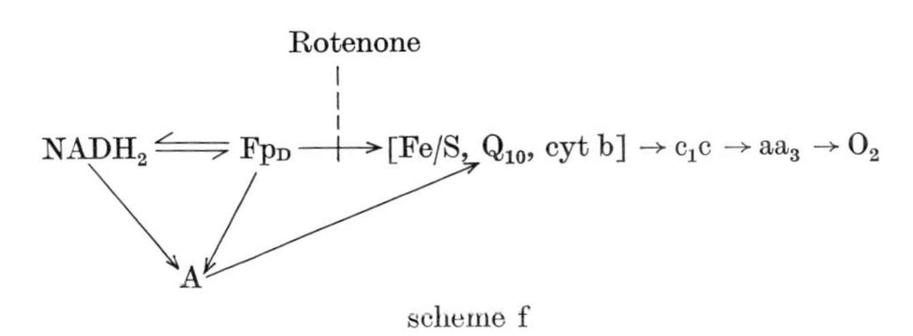

scheme f

An example of such a by-pass comes from the studies of CONOVER et al. [77—79] which showed that vitamin K_3 (menadione: 2-methyl-1,4-naphthoquinone) could be reduced by NADH and a flavoprotein (DT diaphorase), and then reoxidized by the respiratory chain at the level of the group Fe/S, Q_{10} and cyt b. The resultant electron flow was not coupled to energy conservation at the first site. This by-pass is sensitive to dicoumarol, an inhibitor of DT-diaphorase. An alternative by-pass, not involving DT diaphorase, can be established with WURSTER's blue [80].

Apart from these artificially established shunts, there is the possibility in an intact cell of the operation of hydrogen shuttles in such a way that reducing equivalents are transferred from intra- to extra-mitochondrial NAD, and thence to the respiratory chain at the level of the group Fe/S, Q_{10}, cyt b. The simplest case is illustrated by *Torulopsis utilis*, where intra- and extra-mitochondrial alcohol dehydrogenases (E.C.1.1.1.1) could catalyse the hydrogen shuttle, and an outward-looking (and additional) NADH dehydrogenase can catalyse a rotenone insensitive, non-phosphorylating oxidation of $NADH_2$ (Fig. 4). More complex schemes would

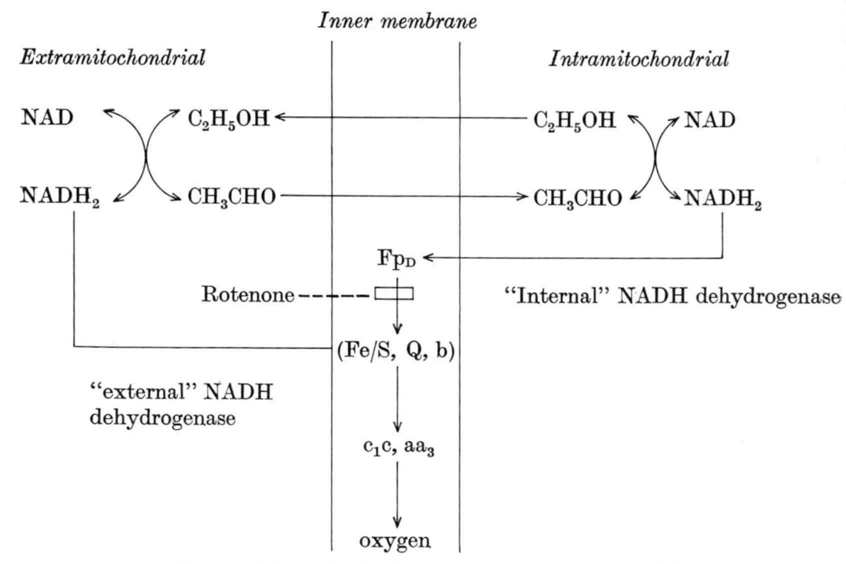

Fig. 4. A hypothetical rotenone by-pass in *T. utilis*

have to be constructed for mammalian mitochondria, and would include anion permeases such as those invoked by CHAPPELL (1969) [81]. Thermodynamically such a by-pass is entirely possible, the oxido-reduction potential of the cytoplasmic NAD^+/NADH couple being intermediate between that of intramitochondrial NAD and the group Fe/S, Q and cyt b.

In intact tissues oxidizing substrates via the tricarboxylic acid cycle, inhibition of NADH oxidation by an agent such as amytal would inhibit the cycle, and the amytal insensitive oxidation of succinate (which enters the respiratory chain below the inhibited site) would soon cease due to depletion of succinate. An exception to this type of behaviour occurs in liver tissue, which can oxidize fatty acids to acetoacetate independently of the tricarboxylic acid cycle. The oxidoreductions of β-oxidation are such that for each molecule of NAD that is reduced, a molecule of ETF is also reduced. ETF is reoxidized by the respiratory chain at a level (Fe/S, Q, cyt b) below that of amytal or rotenone inhibition:

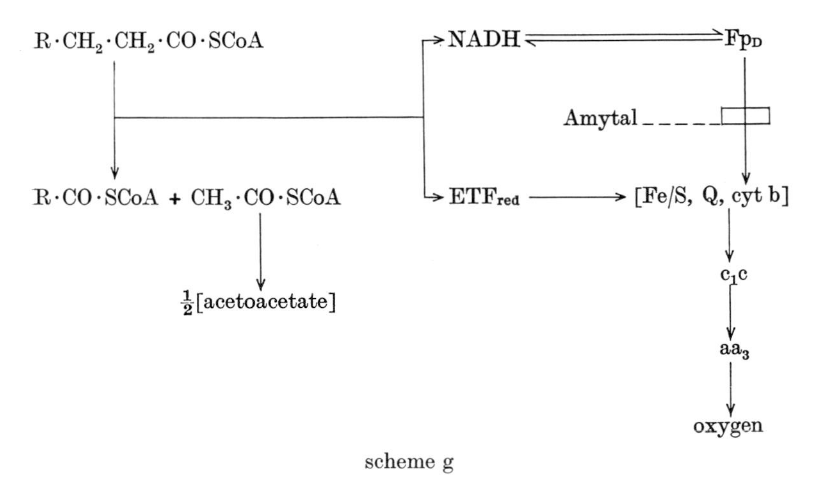

scheme g

Re-oxidation of half the NADH can occur by reduction of acetoacetate to D-3-hydroxybutyrate, and the remainder can be reoxidized by usage in reductive biosynthesis (e.g. gluconeogenesis) or as a result of incomplete inhibition at the amytal sensitive site (see SCHOLZ, SCHWARZ and BÜCHER [70]).

Energy Conservation at Site 1

There are several hypotheses concerning the mechanism of energy conservation, none are unequivocally proven or disproven, all have been discussed at length in recent reviews or symposium proceedings, and all will shortly be discussed again. Whatever the underlying mechanism, the outstanding fact in the present context is that energy conservation at Site I is readily reversible [82—84]. This is illustrated in Fig. 5, where a substrate of high potential (E_0 at pH 7 for the succinate/fumarate couple is +30 mV) can reduce NAD ($E_0 = -320$ mV) in a manner that utilizes one high energy phosphate bond per molecule of NAD reduced. It should therefore be possible in a more complex system to study the reverse electron flow in this region by making suitable choices for the high potential donor and low potential acceptor.

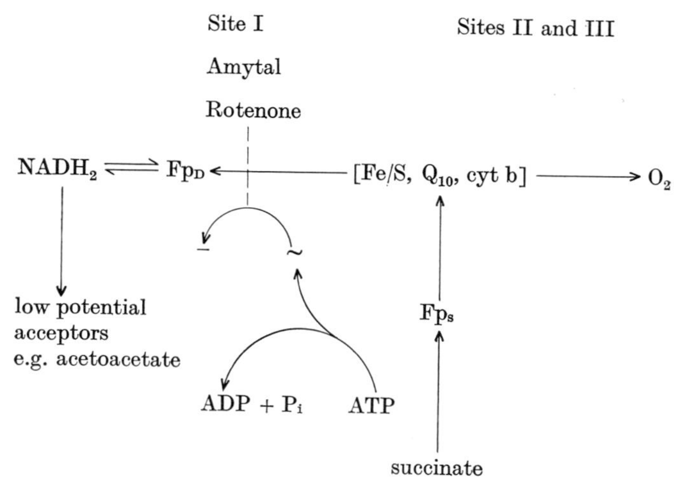

Fig. 5. Reversal of electron transport at site I. Fp_s is succinate dehydrogenase flavoprotein, "~" a high energy state or bond, "–" a low energy state or bond. ~ can be generated from sites II and III, or from ATP

Specific Inhibitors of Energy Conservation at Site 1 only

There probably are none. The various effects of substituted guanidines [44—48] on the NADH-cytochrome segment of intact mitochondria can be explained on the basis of an energy-dependent uptake [85] followed by a rotenone-like action.

Biological Approaches to the Mechanism of Inhibitor Action and Energy Conservation in the NADH-Cytochrome Segment

There are significant differences in the composition and function of this respiratory segment in *Saccharomyces carlsbergensis* and *S. cerevisiae* on the one hand and *Torulopsis utilis* on the other. These differences are summarized in Table 6, and it is evident from these data that there is a phosphorylating and rotenone sensitive segment in *T. utilis* and a non-phosphorylating rotenone insensitive seg-

Table 6. *Comparison of properties of mitochondria from ox heart and yeasts*

Property	Mitochondria or particles from			
	Ox heart	T. utilis	S. carlsbergensis	S. cerevisiae
Electron flow. Intramitochondrial NADH $\rightarrow O_2$	+	+	+	+
Sensitivity to rotenone and amytal	+	+	–	–
Sensitivity to piericidin A	+	+	–	N.T.
Energy conservation at site I	+	+	–	–
NADH elicited $g = 1.94$ signal	+	+	N.T.	–
Q species	Q_{10}	Q_7	Q_6	Q_6
Flavin of NADH oxidase	FMN	FMN and FAD	N.T.	FAD
Mersalyl-sensitive site between NADH and Fp_D	+	+	N.T.	–

+ means present; – means absent; and N.T., not tested. See Refs. [3, 41, 75, 88 and 89] for details.

ment in the *Saccharomyces*. Other differences are apparent, and it is tempting to seek correlations and implied causal relations between certain features. Unfortunately, this comparative approach suffers from the drawback that the number of differences found between the two types of yeasts is likely to increase with the intensity with which they are sought. The true significance of these differences is obscured by the possibility that they are generic differences that are otherwise unrelated to the presence or absence of energy conservation and rotenone sensitivity in the NADH-cytochrome segment.

The role of iron in energy conservation and electron transport between NADH and the cytochromes can be explored in microbial systems by the simple method of growing the organism under iron deficient conditions. Sato et al. [86] have demonstrated that the NADH-cytochrome segment of *Micrococcus denitrificans* resembles that of mammalian systems, in that there is rotenone and piericidin A sensitivity, a g = 1.94 EPR signal on the NADH side of the rotenone block, Q_{10} on the oxygen side of the rotenone block, and phosphorylation associated with electron transfer from NADH to Q. Iron deficient growth resulted in the loss of the g = 1.94 signal but not of site I phosphorylation or electron flow. Thus the apparent correlation between this EPR signal and the presence of Site I energy conservation established in comparative studies with yeasts (Table 6) breaks down with *Micrococcus denitrificans*. Surprisingly, the authors [86] did not comment on the rotenone sensitivity or otherwise of the iron-deficient preparation.

The effects of iron deficiency have also been studied in our own laboratory, using *T. utilis* grown in continuous culture [41]. This culture technique is particularly suitable for the study of the effects of nutrient deficiency, since the nutrient in question can be arranged to be rate-limiting for growth under strictly defined and steady-state conditions. The types of cells obtained from the chemostat and with any subsequent manipulations are shown in Fig. 6, and the properties of the mitochondria prepared from such cells are shown in Table 7.

It is evident from Table 6 that three of the four possible combinations of piericidin A sensitivity and Site I energy conservation have been achieved — both present, both absent, one absent with one present. Thus the correlations between these two

Table 7. *Properties of mitochondria derived from phenotypically modified T. utilis*

Property	Mitochondria derived from cell type				
	G	F/G	F	FR	FR_{CYCLO}
Electron flow. Intramitochondrial NADH $\rightarrow$ O_2	+	+	+	+	+
Sensitivity to piericidin A (100 μμmole/mg)	+	−	−	+	−
Energy conservation at site I	+	+	−	+	+
NADH elicited g = 1.94 EPR signal	+	N.T.	−	N.T.	N.T.

For methods see LIGHT et al. [41] + means present and normal (= G); − means absent; N.T. means not tested. EPR spectroscopy from studies of SCHLEYER and OHNISHI [90] using batch culture. Antimycin sensitivity and energy conservation at sites II and III was unaltered by iron-limited growth.

phenomena are broken, and it can be concluded that they are not, as proposed by others [3, 75], interdependent.

The conversion of F cells to FR cells can be achieved in 3 h under conditions of minimal cell growth (no carbon source). We conclude from this that the changes observed in the F cells are phenotypic, and that the conversion of F to FR cells represents an *in vivo* reconstitution of the Site I energy conservation mechanism.

This biological system clearly has considerable promise for studying the molecular basis of piericidin sensitivity and energy conservation at Site I.

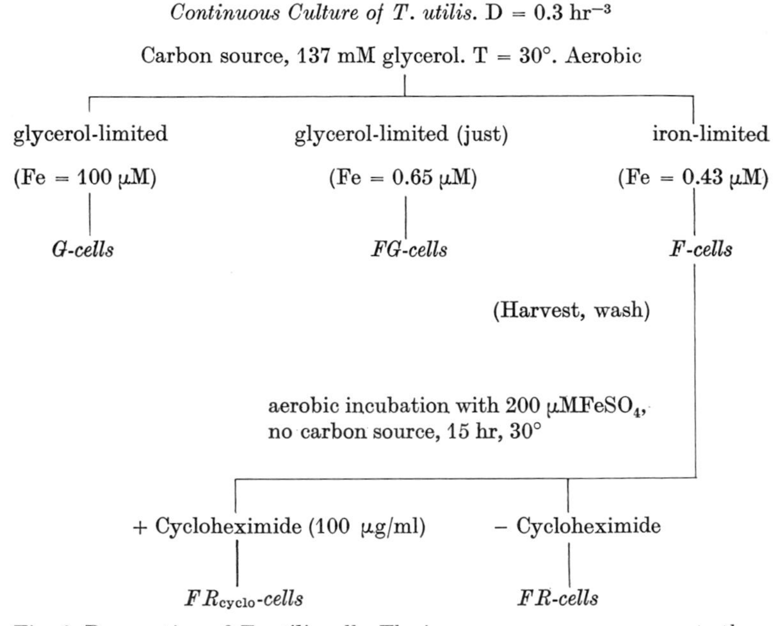

Fig. 6. Preparation of *T. utilis* cells. The iron assays are more accurate than that previously [41]. F and FG cells were grown in a chemostat constructed of non-ferrous materials [87]

Summary

The mechanisms of electron transport, energy conservation and inhibitor action in the respiratory chain leading from NADH to the cytochromes have been discussed. It should be apparent from this that the traditional biochemical approach of dissemble-and-reconstitute is meeting with only a limited success in this field, implying that there are structural considerations which are not yet fully understood. Nevertheless, studies of this type have provided a range of techniques and concepts that should assist the biologist in his study of more integrated systems.

The value of using all possible biological approaches to assist in the study of mitochondrial electron transport and energy conservation is stressed, and some examples of their successful use are given. The use of biological approaches that involve phenotypic and genotypic modifications of mitochondrial function is likely to become more widespread with the growing realisation that cells are much more able chemists than we are. In fact, we will go so far as to suggest that a future symposium of this distinguished society might be called "Cells — tools for inhibitor research".

Acknowledgements

Work reported from our laboratory was generously supported by the Medical Research Council, The Royal Society, Shell Ltd., The Wellcome Trust, and NATO Research Programme Grant No. 318.

References

1. SLATER, E. C.: In: Flavins and flavoproteins. (SLATER, E. C., Ed.) Biochim. biophys. Acta Library **8**, 487 (1966).
2. LEHNINGER, A. L.: The mitochondrion. New York: W. A. Benjamin Inc. 1965.
3. OHNISHI, T. O., G. SOTTOCASA et L. ERNSTER: Bull. Soc. Chim. biol. (Paris) **48**, 1189 (1966).
4. IMAI, K., A. ASANO, and R. SATO: Biochim. biophys. Acta **143**, 462 (1967).
5. CHANCE, B., W. D. BONNER, and B. STOREY: Ann. Rev. Plant Physiol. **19**, 295 (1968).
6. BECK, J. C., J. R. MATTOON, D. C. HAWTHORNE, and F. SHERMAN: Proc. nat. Acad. Sci. (Wash.) **60**, 186 (1968).
7. MASSEY, V., and C. VEEGER: Ann. Rev. Biochem. **32**, 379 (1963).
8. BEINERT, H.: In: The enzymes, **7**, 467. (BOYER, P., K. MYRBÄCK, and H. LARDY, Eds.) New York and London: Academic Press 1967.
9. MACKLER, B.: In: Flavins and flavoproteins. (SLATER, E. C., Ed.) Biochim. biophys. Acta Library **8**, 438 (1966).
10. HATEFI, Y.: In: Comprehensive biochemistry, **14**, 199. (FLORKIN, M., and E. H. STOTZ, Eds.) Amsterdam: Elsevier 1966.
11. KING, T. E., R. L. HOWARD, J. KETTMANN, B. M. HEGDEKAR, M. KUBOYAMA, K. S. NICKEL, and E. A. POSSEHL: In: Flavins and flavoproteins. (SLATER, E. C., Ed.) Biochim. biophys. Acta Library **8**, 477 (1966).
12. SINGER, T. P.: In: Comprehensive biochemistry, **14**, 127. (FLORKIN, M., and E. H. STOTZ, Eds.) Amsterdam: Elsevier 1966.
13. TUBBS, P. K., and P. B. GARLAND: Brit. med. Bull. **24**, 158 (1968).
14. CHANCE, B., L. ERNSTER, P. B. GARLAND, C.-P. LEE, P. A. LIGHT, T. OHNISHI, C. I. RAGAN, and D. WONG: Proc. nat. Acad. Sci. (Wash.) **57**, 1498 (1967).
15. HADDOCK, B. A., D. W. YATES, and P. B. GARLAND: (in preparation) (1969).

16. RAGAN, C. I., and P. B. GARLAND: Europ. J. Biochem. **10**, 399 (1969).
17. HASSINEN, I., and B. CHANCE: Biochem. biophys. Res. Commun. **31**, 895 (1968).
18. SCHATZ, G., and E. RACKER: J. biol. Chem. **241**, 1429 (1966).
19. CREMONA, T., and E. D. KEARNEY: J. biol. Chem. **239**, 2328 (1964).
20. RINGLER, R. L., S. MINAKAMI, and T. P. SINGER: J. biol. Chem. **238**, 801 (1963).
21. VERNON, L. P., H. R. MAHLER, and N. K. SARKAR: J. biol. Chem. **199**, 599 (1952).
22. DE BERNARD, B.: Biochim. biophys. Acta **23**, 510 (1957).
23. MACKLER, B.: Biochim. biophys. Acta **50**, 141 (1961).
24. PHARO, R. L., L. A. SORDAHL, S. R. VYAS, and D. R. SANADI: J. biol. Chem. **241**, 4771 (1966).
25. HATEFI, Y., and K. E. STEMPEL: Biochem. biophys. Res. Commun. **26**, 301 (1967).
26. SINGER, T. P.: In: Non-heme iron proteins, p. 349. (SAN PIETRO, A., Ed.) Yellow Springs, Ohio: The Antioch Press 1965.
27. REDFEARN, E. R., and T. E. KING: Nature (Lond.) **202**, 1313 (1964).
28. HATEFI, Y., P. JURTSHUK, and A. G. HAAVIK: Biochim. biophys. Acta **52**, 119 (1961).
29. BUTOW, R. A., and M. ZEYDEL: J. biol. Chem. **243**, 2545 (1968).
30. KEAN, E. A.: Arch. Biochem. **127**, 528 (1968).
31. QUASTEL, J. H., and A. H. M. WHEATLEY: Proc. roy. Soc. B **112**, 60 (1933).
32. ERNSTER, L., O. JALLING, H. LÖW, and O. LINDBERG: Exp. Cell Res. Suppl. **3**, 124 (1955).
33. PUMPHREY, A. M., and E. R. REDFEARN: Biochim. biophys. Acta **74**, 317 (1963).
34. ERNSTER, L., G. DALLNER, and G. F. AZZONE: J. biol. Chem. **238**, 1124 (1963).
35. LINDAHL, P. E., and K. E. ÖBERG: Exp. Cell Res. **23**, 228 (1961).
36. FUKAMI, J.: Chem. Abstr. **51**, 9068 (1957).
37. HATEFI, Y.: Proc. nat. Acad. Sci. (Wash.) **60**, 733 (1968).
38. BURGOS, J., and E. R. REDFEARN: Biochim. biophys. Acta **110**, 475 (1965).
39. TEETER, M. E., M. L. BAGINSKY, and Y. HATEFI: Biochim. biophys. Acta **172**, 331 (1969).
40. COLES, C. J., D. E. GRIFFITHS, D. W. HUTCHINSON, and A. J. SWEETMAN: Biochem. biophys. Res. Commun. **31**, 877 (1968).
41. LIGHT, P. ANN, C. I. RAGAN, R. A. CLEGG, and P. B. GARLAND: FEBS Letters **1**, 4 (1968).
42. HALL, C., M. WU, F. L. CRANE, N. TAKAHASHI, S. TAMURA, and K. FOLKERS: Fed. Proc. **25**, 530 (1966).
43. JENG, M., C. HALL, F. L. CRANE, N. TAKAHASHI, S. TAMURA, and K. FOLKERS: Biochemistry **7**, 1311 (1968).
44. HOLLUNGER, G.: Acta pharmacol. (Kbh.) **11** (suppl. 1) (1955).
45. CHANCE, B., and G. HOLLUNGER: Fed. Proc. **20**, 50 (1961).

46. PRESSMAN, B. C.: Fed. Proc. **20**, 51 (1961).
47. CHAPPELL, J. B.: J. biol. Chem. **238**, 410 (1963).
48. CHANCE, B., G. HOLLUNGER, and B. HAGIHARA: Biochem. biophys. Res. Commun. 8, 185 (1962).
49. JENSEN, P. K.: Nature (Lond.) **184**, 451 (1959).
50. YIELDING, K. L., G. M. TOMPKINS, J. S. MUNDAY, and I. J. COWLEY: J. biol. Chem. **235**, 3413 (1960).
51. REDFEARN, E. R., A. M. PUMPHREY, and G. H. FYNN: Biochim. biophys. Acta **44**, 404 (1960).
52. CHAPPELL, J. B.: Biochem. J. **90**, 225 (1964).
53. REDFEARN, E. R., P. A. WHITTAKER, and J. BURGOS: In: Oxidases and related redox systems, Vol. 2, p. 943. (KING, T. E., H. S. MASON, and M. MORRISON, Eds.) New York: John Wiley & Sons Inc. 1965.
54. FREEMAN, K. B., and D. HALDAR: Biochem. biophys. Res. Commun. **28**, 8 (1967).
55. DUEL, D., E. C. SLATER, and L. VELDSTRA: Biochim. biophys. Acta **27**, 133 (1958).
56. IMAI, K., A. ASANO, and R. SATO: J. Biochem. (Tokyo) **63**, 207 (1968)
57. BEYER, R. E., D. L. CRANKSHAW, and J. M. KUNER: Biochem. biophys. Res. Commun. **28**, 758 (1967).
58. KLINGENBERG, M.: In: Flavins and flavoproteins. (SLATER, E. C., Ed.) Biochim. biophys. Acta Library 8, 522 (1966).
59. PALMER, G., D. J. HORGAN, H. TISDALE, T. P. SINGER, and H. BEINERT: J. biol. Chem. **243**, 844 (1968).
60. TAPPEL, A. L.: Biochem. Pharmacol. **3**, 289 (1960).
61. CHANCE, B.: Science **120**, 767 (1954).
62. LÜBBERS, D. W., u. W. NIESEL: Pflügers Arch. ges. Physiol. **268**, 286 (1959).
63. THORELL, B., and B. CHANCE: Exp. Cell Res. **20**, 43 (1960).
64. CHANCE, B., and V. LEGALLAIS: I.E.E.E. Transactions, Vol. BME-10, p. 42 (1963).
65. NIESEL, W., D. W. LÜBBERS, D. SCHNEEWOLF, J. RICHTER, and W. BOTTICHER: Rev. Sci. Inst. **35**, 578 (1964).
66. CHANCE, B., B. SCHOENER, K. KREJCI, W. RÜSSMANN, W. WESEMANN, H. SCHNITGER und TH. BÜCHER: Biochem. Z. **341**, 325 (1965).
67. —, J. R. WILLIAMSON, D. JAMIESON und B. SCHOENER: Biochem. Z. **341**, 357 (1965).
68. THORELL, B., B. CHANCE, and V. LEGALLAIS: J. Cell Biol. **26**, 741 (1965).
69. BRAUSER, B.: Z. anal. Chem. **237**, 8 (1968).
70. SCHOLZ, R., F. SCHWARZ und TH. BÜCHER: Z. klin. Chem. **4**, 24 (1966).
71. KLINGENBERG, M., u. W. SLENCZKA: Biochem. Z. **331**, 486 (1959).
72. KRÖGER, A., u. M. KLINGENBERG: Biochem. Z. **344**, 317 (1963).
73. CHANCE, B., and B. SCHOENER: In: Flavins and flavoproteins, p. 510. (SLATER, E. C., Ed.) Amsterdam: Elsevier 1966.
74. — In: Flavins and flavoproteins, p. 496. (SLATER, E. C., Ed.) Amsterdam: Elsevier 1966.
75. PULLMAN, M. E., and G. SCHATZ: Ann. Rev. Biochem. **36**, 539 (1967).

76. Mersmann, H., J. Luthy, and T. P. Singer: Biochem. biophys. Res. Commun. **25**, 43 (1966).
77. Conover, T. E., and L. Ernster: Biochim. biophys. Acta **58**, 189 (1962).
78. —, L. Danielson, and L. Ernster: Biochim. biophys. Acta **67**, 254 (1963).
79. —, and L. Ernster: Biochim. biophys. Acta **67**, 268 (1963).
80. Mustafa, M. G., M. L. Cowger, R. F. Labbe, and T. E. King: J. biol. Chem. **243**, 1908 (1968).
81. Chappell, J. B.: Biochem. J. (1969) (in press).
82. Chance, B., and G. Hollunger: Nature (Lond.) **185**, 666 (1960).
83. — — J. biol. Chem. **236**, 1534 (1961).
84. Klingenberg, M.: Angew. Chem. internat. Edit. **3**, 54 (1964).
85. Mitchell, P.: Chemiosmotic coupling in oxidative and photosynthetic phosphorylation. Bodmin: Glynn Research Ltd. 1966.
86. Imai, K., A. Asano, and R. Sato: J. Biochem. **63**, 219 (1968).
87. Light, P. Ann: Ph. D. Thesis, University of Bristol 1969.
88. Ohnishi, T., E. Racker, H. Schleyer, and B. Chance: Proceedings Flavoproteins Symposium, Osaka, Japan (August 1967) (in press).
89. Sharp, C. W., B. Mackler, H. C. Douglas, G. Palmer, and S. P. Felton: Arch. Biochem. **122**, 810 (1967).
90. Schleyer, H., and T. Ohnishi: Fed. Proc. **28**, 885 (1969).
91. Schenkman, J. B., H. Remmer, and R. W. Estabrook: J. molec. Pharmacol. **3**, 113 (1967).

Fuscin, an Inhibitor of NADH Dehydrogenase

P. M. VIGNAIS

Laboratoire de Biochimie, Centre d'Etudes Nucléaires, Grenoble, France

I wish to say a few words about a respiratory inhibitor named *Fuscin* which blocks the transfer of electrons in the respiratory chain at the level of the first site as rotenone and amytal do [1, 2]. I also take this opportunity to express my thanks to Professor D. H. R. BARTON (Chemistry Department, Imperial College of Science and Technology, London SW-7) for generous gift of *Fuscin*.

Fuscin is a quinonoid compound the structure of which is shown in the *Appendix*. In rat liver mitochondria it blocks NAD-linked oxidations while leaving oxidation of succinate relatively unaffected. It prevents the reduction of cytochrome *b* by NADH (and also the reversal of electron flow from succinate to NAD^+).

Fuscin is a respiratory inhibitor which has no uncoupling effect at the inhibitory concentrations used ($3 \cdot 10^{-5}$ M gives 50% inhibition of the respiration of rat liver mitochondria on glutamate).

The site of action of fuscin is close to the rotenone sensitive site but is not exactly the same since it is not by-passed by menadione (the same thing was reported for rhein inhibition). The sensitivity of rat liver mitochondria to fuscin is much less than to rotenone (some 500 times less) since about 10 nmoles/mg of protein are required for 50% inhibition of glutamate oxidation.

Fuscin, like rotenone, inhibits NADH-CoQ reductase in fragments of beef heart mitochondria but not the soluble form.

We have also tested the effect of fuscin on yeast mitochondria: *Torulopsis utilis* and *S. cerevisiae*. With yeast mitochondria the substrates used to reduce NAD^+ of the respiratory chain was the mixture: pyruvate + malate. The following observations were made:

— In contrast to mammalian mitochondria, in yeast mitochondria (from *T. utilis*) oxidation of succinate was inhibited by fuscin and was more sensitive to fuscin than NADH oxidation: 10 nmoles fuscin/mg of protein bring about an inhibition of 50% of succinate oxidation; 4 to 5 times more are needed to get 50% inhibition of the respiration on pyruvate + malate. It may be of interest to note that contrary to rotenone, fuscin acts as an inhibitor of electron transport in the same range of concentrations on mammalian or on yeast mitochondria (with yeast mitochondria the amount of rotenone necessary to inhibit respiration is some 600 times greater than for rat liver mitochondria).

— Mitochondria from *S. cerevisiae* which lack the first coupling site and are insensitive to rotenone are still sensitive to fuscin (when using pyruvate + malate as substrates).

— Iron-deficient mitochondria from *T. utilis* which have lost their rotenone sensitivity are still inhibited by fuscin.

In conclusion, fuscin may constitute a tool to study the difference in composition of the respiratory chain in mammalian and in yeast mitochondria.

References

1. VIGNAIS, P. M., et J. DEMAILLE: Action de la fuscine sur l'oxydation phosphorylante. 3rd F.E.B.S. Meeting — Warsaw (1966) M-75.
2. DEMAILLE, J., P. M. VIGNAIS, and P. V. VIGNAIS: Europ. J. Biochem. (submitted for publication).

On the Possible Role of Cytochrome B-Type Pigments in Redox Relations Between Mitochondria and Endoplasmic Reticulum

H. Sies and B. Brauser

Institut für Physiologische Chemie und Physikalische Biochemie der Universität München

With 3 Figures

Inhibitors of the NADH dehydrogenase site can be usefully applied to the study of the respiratory organisation within living cells in whole organs. For an experimental model thereof, the hemoglobin-free perfused rat liver, we shall comment on the problem of the redox state of cytochrome b-type pigments, and, related to this, the interplay between mitochondria and endoplasmic reticulum.

Dual-wavelength transmission spectrophotometry [1] and surface fluorimetry of reduced pyridine nucleotides is performed in a peripheral area of the left lower liver lobe (Fig. 1). Oxygen concentration is measured in the perfusion fluid entering and leaving the liver.

The function of cytochrome *b*, located within the mitochondria, and that of cytochrome b_5, located in the microsomal fraction, is still controversial [2, 3]; b_5, in an amount $^1/_4$ of that in microsomes, has been also found in the outer mitochondrial membrane [4]. As known from the studies with isolated mitochondria (cf. presentation by Garland et al. [5]), cytochrome *b* becomes oxidized in the presence of NADH dehydrogenase inhibitors, while in the presence of antimycin A, an inhibitor acting on the oxygen side of cytochrome *b* (cf. review of Kaniuga, Bryla and Slater [6]), this pigment becomes fully reduced [7].

When rotenone is added to a perfused liver of a fed rat, the optical density difference between 564 and 575 nm, representing cytochrome *b* (see below), shows the expected decrease, i.e. oxidation of *b*, (left part of Fig. 2). When related to the reduction caused by antimycin A, the redox state of cytochrome *b* in the normoxic steady state is calculated to be 20 to 30%, indicating a largely ADP-controlled state [7] for this preparation [8]. Similarly, an ADP-controlled state was concluded from readout of cytochrome *b* in resting muscle [9].

In contrast, rotenone does not cause an oxidation of *b* in the perfused liver of a rat starved for 24 h, suggesting state 2 condi-

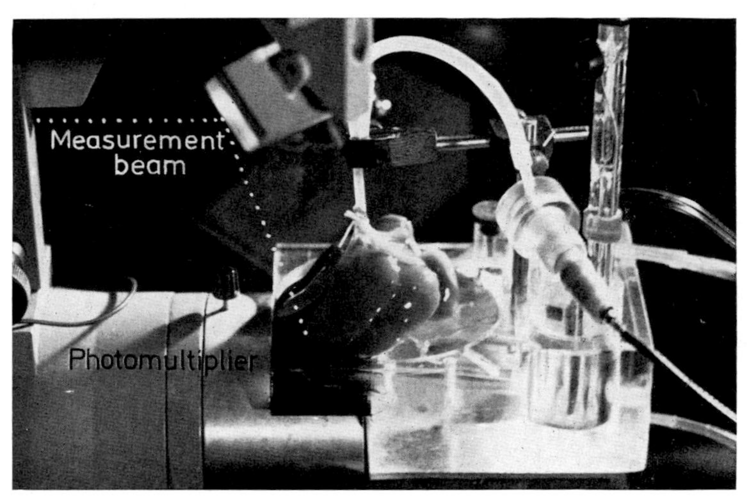

Fig. 1. Transmission spectrophotometry of hemoglobin-free perfused rat liver with a dual-wavelength technique [1] by use of a Rapidspektroskop with dual-wavelength attachment (Howaldt-Werke, Kiel). Measurement beam, providing wavelength-modulated light, passes through the liver lobe to the photomultiplier to record the optical density difference between to adjustable wavelengths. 564 and 575 nm are used for cytochrome *b*. Compensation for spectral characteristics of the apparatus is provided by a reference beam (not shown) which is reflected from a magnesia plate.

Perfusion fluid — dextran 40[1]-modified Krebs-Henseleit solution, pH 7.4, temperature 33 °C — passes through the liver by way of portal vein and vena cava sup. at speed of 25 ml/min. Perfusion fluid is equilibrated with gas mixture of 91.5% O_2, 5% CO_2, and 3.5% CO in a rotating cylinder oxygenator; in another such apparatus, oxygen is replaced by argon to allow rapid normoxia-anoxia transitions. Teflon-shielded Ag-Pt (20 μm)-microelectrodes inserted in the perfusion fluid entering and leaving the liver measure oxygen concentration. Fluorescence of reduced pyridine nucleotides (prim., 366 nm; sec., $>$ 420 nm) is monitored (not shown) from the liver surface directly adjacent to the absorption beam

[1] Kindly supplied by Knoll Co., Ludwigshafen.

tions. Lactate addition (6 mM) causes a reduction of cytochrome *b* (in the absence of rotenone) to the level in normoxic steady state; an accompanying increase in oxygen consumption has been attributed to gluconeogenesis [10] which is under study with isotope label techniques [11].

There is an antimycin-insensitive portion, about one half, of the normoxia-anoxia transition in the cytochrome *b* trace, unlike the isolated mitochondria [7]. The number of possible interpretations is limited by the observation that this anoxia increment is inducible with phenobarbital (Fig. 2, right part). The induction is

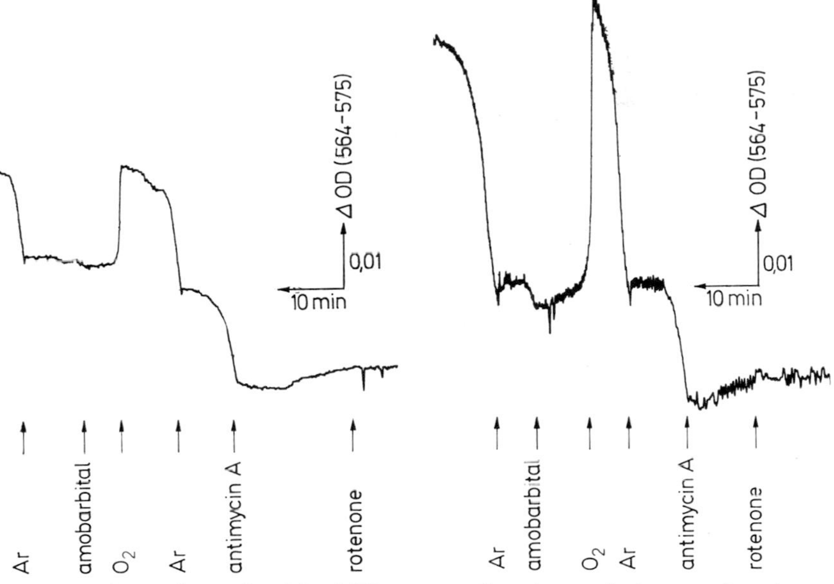

Fig. 2. Original records of the $\Delta OD_{[564-575nm]}$ from two perfusion experiments performed under identical conditions (female Wistar II rats of same age, 100 g, fed on stock diet). Record on right is from a liver of a rat treated with phenobarbital 0.1 g/kg i.p. for 3 days. Record on left is from untreated control animal. Normoxic steady state respiration: 1.6 mAtoms O/h per liver. Time from right to left.

Rotenone and antimycin A_1 dissolved in dimethylsulfoxide were added by continuous injection through a pipe of 0.1 mm diameter into the entering perfusion fluid, yielding a final concentration of 17 and 39 μM, respectively. An aqueous solution sodium amobarbital was added to final concentration of 0.4 mM. Anoxia was applied as described in Fig. 1

known to represent a proliferation of the microsomal mixed function oxygenation system [12, 13] with the cytochrome P-450 as the terminal oxidase, without influencing the cytochrome b_5 content [13, 14]. The anoxia increment at 564—575 nm, measured after two days of induction rises parallel to the P-450 content [15]. However, in spectra of P-450 particles [16], $\Delta OD_{(564-575\ nm)}$ in the reduced-CO minus oxidized spectrum can account for just $^1/_5$ of the observed increment; also, spectra of liver slices [17] do not show evidence for P-450 as a cause of a prominent α-peak. Hemoglobin traces (< 10 n Moles/g fresh) as a cause for the antimycin-insensitive portion are excluded due to the presence of 3.5 vol.% carbon monoxide, and for kinetic reasons [8].

Another candidate would be the cytochrome b_5. Since this pigment is not inducible by phenobarbital, an explanation of the antimycin-insensitive anoxia increment would have to be based on redox changes of this pigment: cytochrome b_5, mainly reduced in the normal rat liver [18], would be more oxidized in the induced liver. If this were the case, supply of reducing equivalents from NADH via b_5 to P-450 (instead of from NADPH to P-450) could become operational. In fact, when amobarbital, a substrate of the hydroxylating system, is added to the rotenone- and antimycin-supplemented induced liver, the 564 minus 575 nm trace (Fig. 2), and the 450 minus 463 nm trace (Fig. 3) indicate a reduction of "b_5" and P-450, respectively, whereas the fluorescence trace (Fig. 3) indicates an oxidation of reduced pyridine nucleotides. These experiments, therefore, support the hypothesis [17] that b_5 can mediate electron flow to P-450 (compare also [19]).

However, a definite conclusion must await direct identification of the participation of b_5 or of a so far unknown b-type component. The possibility that P-450 by itself is the cause of the antimycin-insensitive anoxia increment must be seriously considered (compare the rise in P-450 reduction after amobarbital addition in Fig. 3). Moreover, small artifacts must be expected from peak shifts due to antimycin [20]. Recently, it has been reported [21] that the amount of b_5 can be augmented by 20% following phenobarbital treatment, an observation conflicting with the work cited above [13, 14].

With respect to the interplay between mitochondria and endoplasmic reticulum, additional information has been gained with the use of amobarbital which acts both as an inhibitor of the NADH dehydrogenase and as a substrate of the microsomal mixed function oxygenation system. This inhibitor must pass through the micro-

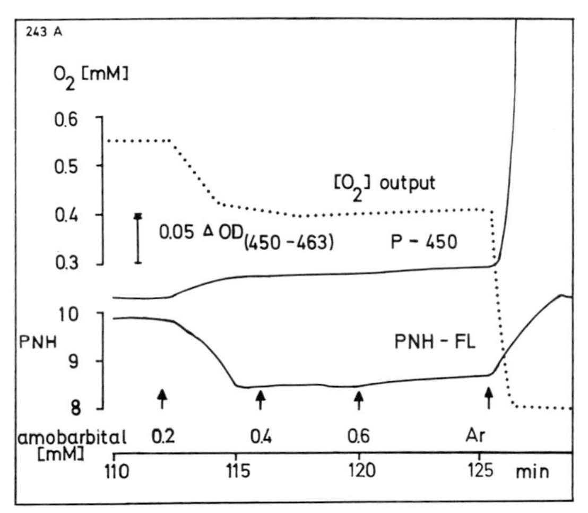

Fig. 3. Amobarbital effect on rotenone- and antimycin-supplemented liver of a phenobarbital-treated rat (as in Fig. 2, right part). Reduced pyridine nucleotide fluorescence (arbitrary units) decreases while cytochrome P-450 absorption (middle trace) increases; compare 564—575 nm trace in Fig. 2. Oxygen consumption rises concomitantly by 37%, indicated by a fall of $(O_2)_{output}$

somal shield which surrounds the mitochondria [4, 15] in order to reach the NADH dehydrogenase site. The addition of small amobarbital amounts, which inhibit in normal livers, causes a respira-

Table 1. *Response of overall respiration in hemoglobin-free perfused rat liver to low concentration of NADH dehydrogenase site inhibitors and its dependence on phenobarbital induction*

Respiration in normoxic steady state: 1.6 mAtoms 0 per hour per liver (= 100%)

	Controls	Phenobarbital-treated for 3 days (0.1 g/kg, i.p.)
Amobarbital, 0.2 mM	88%	122%
Rotenone, 2.5 μM	89%	86%

tory increase in induced livers. The stimulation can comprise one third of total liver respiration (compare Fig. 3 in Ref. [15]). Rotenone, in contrast, exerts an inhibitory action which appears unaffected by the induction (Table 1).

These findings emphasize that following the application of inhibitors to complex systems, inverse effects like inhibition and stimulation can be observed, depending on the state of the sites of attack.

References

1. BRAUSER, B.: Z. analyt. Chem. **237**, 8 (1968).
2. KLINGENBERG, M.: In: SINGER, T. P., Ed., Biological oxidations, p. 3. New York, London, Sydney: Interscience Publ. 1968.
3. STRITTMATTER, P.: In: SINGER, T. P., Ed., Biological oxidations, p. 171. New York, London, Sydney: Interscience Publ. 1968.
4. SOTTOCASA, G. L., B. KUYLENSTIERNA, L. ERNSTER, and A. BERGSTRAND: J. Cell Biol. **32**, 415 (1967).
5. GARLAND, P. B., R. A. CLEGG, P. A. LIGHT, and C. I. RAGAN: *this volume, p.* 217.
6. KANIUGA, Z., J. BRYLA, and E. C. SLATER: *this volume, p.* 282.
7. CHANCE, B., and G. R. WILLIAMS: J. biol. Chem. **217**, 409 (1955).
8. Paper in preparation.
9. CHANCE, B., and A. WEBER: J. Physiol. (Lond.) **169**, 263 (1963).
10. ZEHNER, J.: Thesis, Faculty of Medicine, University of Munich 1969.
11. MÜLLHOFER, G., O. KUNTZEN, S. HESSE, and TH. BÜCHER: FEBS Letters **4**, 33 (1969).
12. REMMER, H.: Arch. exp. Path. Pharmak. **235**, 279 (1959).
13. ERNSTER, L., and S. ORRENIUS: Fed. Proc. **24**, 1190 (1965).
14. ULLRICH, V.: Z. physiol. Chem. **350**, 357 (1969).
15. BRAUSER, B., H. SIES, and TH. BÜCHER: FEBS Letters **2**, 170 (1969).
16. MIYAKE, Y., J. L. GAYLOR, and H. S. MASON: J. biol. Chem. **243**, 5788 (1968).
17. ESTABROOK, R. W., A. HILDEBRANDT, H. REMMER, J. B. SCHENKMAN, O. ROSENTHAL und D. Y. COOPER: In: HESS, B., u. HJ. STAUDINGER, Eds., 19. Mosbacher Colloquium „Biochemie des Sauerstoffs", p. 142. Berlin-Heidelberg-New York: Springer 1968.
18. LÜBBERS, D. W., M. KESSLER, R. SCHOLZ und TH. BÜCHER: Biochem. Z. **341**, 346 (1965).
19. KRISCH, K., u. H. STAUDINGER: Biochem. Z. **334**, 312 (1961).
20. PUMPHREY, A. M.: J. biol. Chem. **237**, 2384 (1962).
21. HEWICK, D. S., and J. R. FOUTS: Fed. Proc. **28**, Abstract No. 1265 (1969).

Discussion

O. Wieland (Munich): Dr. Garland, you discussed the situation of fatty acid oxidation which could be possible even when NADH oxidation is blocked. It is well-known from many groups that during fatty acid oxidation NADH increases in mitochondria. Do you think that this would be also a physiological mechanism: blocking of flavoprotein oxidation by intermediates such as ATP and other metabolites?

Garland (Bristol): I think you asked whether or not during fatty acid oxidation, which is producing electrons both at the ETF and at the NADH level, there is anything which makes NAD more reduced than one might expect. The flow of extra electrons at this level (b, UQ, from ETF) is not enough in itself to cause an extra reduction of NAD in rat liver mitochondria. Dr. König showed this at Bristol by using two substrates, one of which was NAD-linked, namely isocitrate, and the other of which was flavin-linked, namely succinate. The oxidation rates of the two could be followed independently; the isocitrate with the CO_2-electrode, and the succinate from the oxygen uptake rate corrected for the isocitrate oxidation rate. Under these conditions, succinate was unable to inhibit isocitrate oxidation, or to cause state 4-like reduction of NAD. One could get the succinate-inhibition of NADH oxidation on this pathway only when putting the mitochondria in a state that we call state three and a half; namely, we cut back the rate of respiration by using atractylate. The path of electron flow in fatty acid oxidation (scheme g) is therefore in itself not enough to explain the extensive reduction of NADH. Maybe there is something that affects the phosphorylation potential in this region which poises site I rather more in the steady state towards NAD reduction than oxidation [König, T., D. G. Nicholls, and P. B. Garland: Biochem. J. **114,** 589 (1969)].

Lardy (Madison, Wisc.): Dr. Garland, you place the site of piericidin inhibition before the non-heme iron component of the chain, but Beinert, Singer, and Palmer find that the non-heme iron of the NADH dehydrogenase is reduced just as rapidly and extensively in the presence of inhibitors such as piericidin and rotenone as in their absence.

Garland: Scheme *a* is the Hatefi scheme [37] which takes account of the possibility that the high M. W. NADH dehydrogenase as isolated by many workers contains a ferroflavoprotein of low potential and additional amounts of non-heme iron protein which may be removed as the enzyme is further purified.

This point has been more recently substantiated by Mackler who, using immunodiffusion, showed that the Singer enzyme is in fact two proteins. If this ferroflavoprotein species is responsible for the $g = 1.94$ signal, it still does not exclude that an additional non-heme iron species may act as an intermediate in the reduction of Q. If this were so, and if the inhibitors acted as in scheme *a*, one should be able to observe oxidation changes in any species on the oxygen side of the inhibitor site. Hatefi has observed just this in complex I [37], as we also were able to observe in mitochondria [14, 16]. So, for these reasons I am unable to discard the HATEFI interpretation.

LARDY: However, BEINERT can differentiate these non-heme irons. For instance, there are slight differences in the g-values: g = 1.96 for the one that is involved with the NADH dehydrogenase, and 1.90 for one that is involved beyond Q. BEINERT feels strongly that rotenone does not interfere with the first one, as you also indicate, but I think he believes that there is no evidence for a second one before Q in the NADH pathway.

GARLAND: There is no conclusive evidence either way, with the possible exception that HATEFI and STEMPEL [25] produced two fractions, A and B, from NADH-Q-reductase. Their behavior was this: A was reducible by NADH, and was oxidizable by B, and B was oxidizable by Q.

Regarding the g = 1.94 EPR signal: in iron-limited Micrococcus denitrificans and iron-limited Torulopsis utilis, this signal disappears altogether, but the electron flow is unaltered [86, 90]. I don't know what the g = 1.94 signal means in terms of evidence for the carriers here; but nevertheless, the signal does not appear to be an obligatory aspect of the NADH dehydrogenase.

LARDY: Is there a phosphorylation site?

GARLAND: There is in Micrococcus denitrificans, where the iron-limited preparation still phosphorylates at site I, but the g = 1.94 signal is absent [86].

LARDY: I think this is an important point.

ALBRACHT (Amsterdam): I should like to comment on the problem whether there exists an Fe/S protein between NADH dehydrogenase and coenzyme Q. In heart muscle preparation, when Q_{10} is taken out, non-heme iron cannot be observed any more by reduction with NADH; so I don't think that there is non-heme iron between the rotenone-sensitive site and the Q_{10}. Furthermore, I isolated the NADH dehydrogenase which is essentially free of reductive activity due to such a non-heme iron and contains no Q_{10}, but recombines very good with Q in a bc_1-complex in a rotenone-sensitive way.

LARDY: Dr. GARLAND, when you grow yeast under conditions where iron intake is controlled so as to give rotenone-sensitive cells that do not have a phosphorylation at site I, how does this affect the amount of coenzyme Q?

GARLAND: We have not assayed the Q under these conditions.

STAUDINGER (Giessen): Dr. SIES, if your assumption that there is electron flow from cytochrome b_5 to P-450 is correct, you should observe a reduction of P-450 at appropriate wavelengths in the presence of carbon monoxide.

SIES (Munich): In fact, we see a reduction of the cytochrome P-450 after substrate addition (cf. Fig. 3) which parallels the reduction of the b-type pigment in question, and the oxidation of the reduced pyridine nucleotides in the rotenone- and antimycin-supplemented system.

STAUDINGER: This is not obtained with isolated microsomes.

LARDY: Dr. GARLAND showed a slide in which he alluded to some question about the site of phosphorylation in the vicinity of cytochrome oxidase. Earlier data of CHANCE [Advanc. Enzymol. **17**, 65 (1956)] indicate that it is between the cytochromes *c* and *a*. There is some evidence in some microorganisms that it may be completely in the aa_3-complex. Have either the Amsterdam, Munich, or Bristol schools any further data on where site III is?

GARLAND: I have none, but I suspect Prof. SLATER has.

SLATER: I agree with Dr. GARLAND that site III must be between aa_3 and oxygen, and certainly not between *c* and *a* where CHANCE wanted to put it because of the crossover.

LARDY: Because of the standard potentials, or for other reasons?

SLATER: Because of the position of the equilibrium between the respiratory chain and the ATP, ADP, P_i system in State 4. I do not think that the findings of a crossover between *c* and *a* under certain conditions, as CHANCE reported many years ago, has any relevance to the position of the phosphorylation site.

LARDY: Yes, but aa_3 is very much oxidized in State 4, and this increases the energy span between *c* and aa_3.

Applications of Oligomycin and Related Inhibitors in Bioenergetics

E. C. SLATER and H. F. TER WELLE

Laboratory of Biochemistry, B. C. P. Jansen Institute, University of Amsterdam, Amsterdam (The Netherlands)

With 14 Figures

Introduction

Oligomycin is a fungicide made by *Streptomyces diastatochromogenes* and related strains [1]. It owes its name to the fact that few

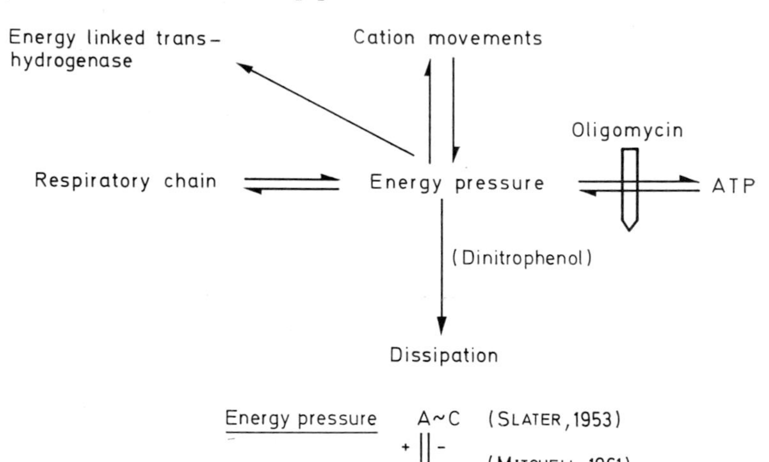

Fig. 1. General description of conservation and utilization of energy in the respiratory chain

fungi are sensitive. Its place in the arsenal of inhibitors used in bioenergetics is made clear by Fig. 1. As first shown by LARDY [2], it specifically inhibits the utilization for the synthesis of ATP of the energy conserved by operation of the mitochondrial respiratory chain. The primarily conserved energy is called 'energy pressure', since in the absence of reactions leading to its utilization or dissipation, the redox reactions of the respiratory chain are in equilibrium with this energy. When this equilibrium is reached, there is no net transfer of electrons or hydrogen atoms along the chain to oxygen, i.e. respiration is inhibited. On the addition of ADP and P_i, respiration proceeds until the concentration of ATP rises to a value corresponding to a phosphate potential of about 16 kcal/mole [3]. Oligomycin inhibits respiration in the presence of P_i and ADP, not by a direct effect on the respiratory chain, but by inhibiting the utilization of the energy pressure for the synthesis of ATP.

Oligomycin has no effect on the utilization of this energy for the energy-linked transhydrogenase or for the active transport of ions into the mitochondria, or on its dissipation. Indeed, the existence of other energy-utilizing reactions, predicted as long ago as 1953, had to await the arrival of oligomycin on the scene before they could be established. This was first done by ERNSTER [4] and SNOSWELL [5] for the reversal of electron transfer in one phosphorylation site driven by the energy pressure built up in another site — the so-called reversal of the respiratory chain, earlier discovered by CHANCE [6].

When the respiratory chain is inhibited, e.g. by antimycin or cyanide, all the energy-requiring processes shown in Fig. 1 may be driven by ATP. In this case, the reactions are oligomycin-sensitive.

Oligomycin preparations are a mixture of three structurally related unsaturated alcohols (oligomycin A, B and C) of molecular weight between 400 and 480 [1, 7, 8[1]]. Rutamycin, a related compound, may be used instead of oligomycin [9]. Oligomycin C is somewhat less active than the other compounds [8]. The chemical structures are unknown.

Effects of Oligomycin on Intact Mitochondria

Fig. 2 shows the effect of a low concentration of oligomycin on the respiration of rat-liver mitochondria, with succinate as sub-

[1] CHAMBERLIN *et al.* [75] have recently reported much higher molecular weights, namely 776, 772, and 804 (minimum values) for rutamycin, and oligomycins A and B, respectively.

strate in the presence of phosphate and rotenone [10]. The ADP-stimulated respiration is progressively inhibited by oligomycin, until a rate is reached that is about the same as in the absence of

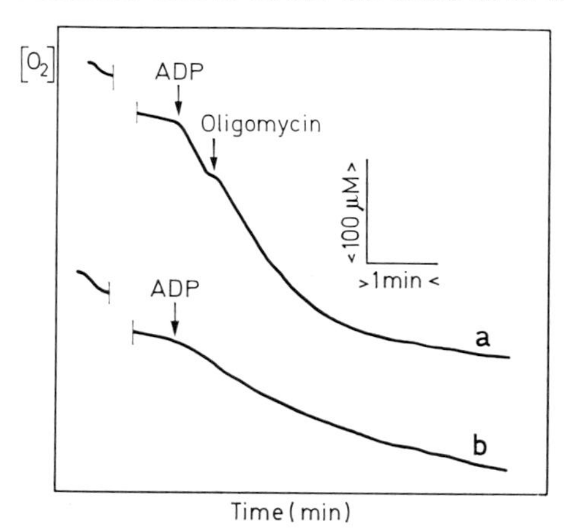

Fig. 2. Inhibition of State-3 respiration of rat-liver mitochondria by oligomycin. Succinate as substrate in the presence of rotenone. A. ADP and oligomycin (0.15 µg/mg protein) added as indicated. B. Oligomycin (0.15 µg/mg protein) added 3 min before ADP. O_2 concentration measured with Clark electrode. From Ter Welle [10]

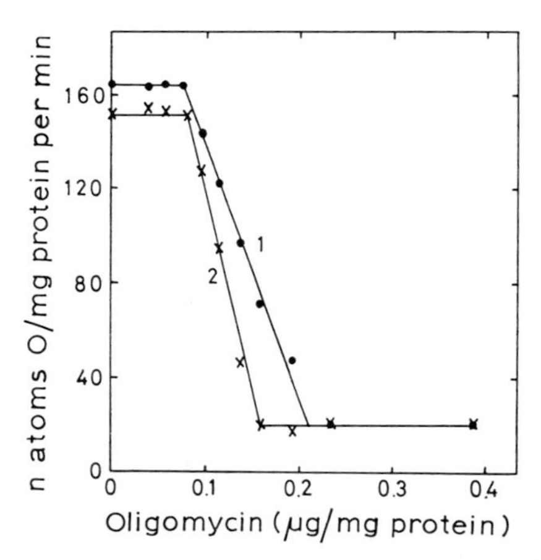

Fig. 3. Oligomycin inhibition curves for succinate oxidation by rat-liver mitochondria in the presence of rotenone. Oligomycin added to mitochondria 2 min before adding ADP. Curve 1, initial velocity; Curve 2, velocity 3 min after adding ADP. From Ter Welle [10]

ADP. For the first half min after addition of oligomycin, no inhibition is seen. When oligomycin is added 3 min before the reaction is started by the addition of ADP, inhibition is immediate but also increases with time.

Fig. 3 shows the effect of different concentrations of oligomycin. In this experiment, ADP was added 2 min after the oligomycin. Curve 1 gives the respiratory rate immediately after adding the ADP, Curve 2, 3 min later. Three features are noteworthy: (1) the sigmoidal inhibition curve; (2) the low concentration of

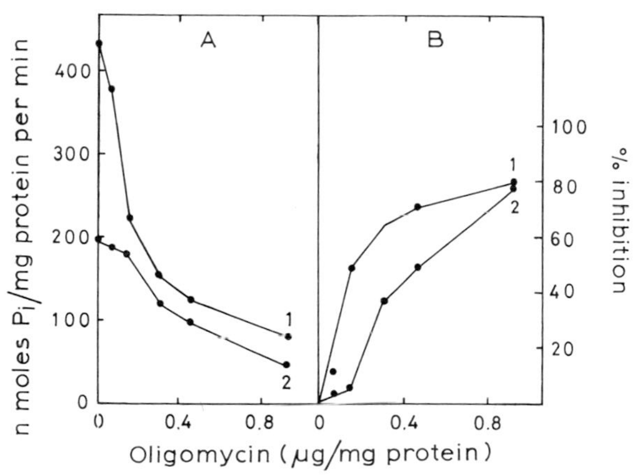

Fig. 4. Effect of oligomycin on dinitrophenol-induced ATPase of rat-liver mitochondria. Mitochondria pre-incubated with oligomycin for 2 min. Curve 1, 0.1 mM 2,4-dinitrophenol; Curve 2, 0.016 mM 2,4-dinitrophenol. From TER WELLE [10]

oligomycin required for maximal inhibition (0.15 to 0.2 μg/mg protein); (3) the oligomycin-insensitive respiration. The latter is due to the fact that it is impossible to make mitochondria without some so-called 'leaks' of the energy pressure. These 'leaks' may be due to structural damage, the presence of endogenous uncouplers, or the utilization of the energy for ion transport. In general, the smallness of the oligomycin-insensitive respiration is a good measure of the intactness of the mitochondria [11].

The uncoupler-induced hydrolysis of added ATP, which is represented in Fig. 1 by the building up of 'energy pressure' with ATP, followed by dissipation of the pressure, is also inhibited by oligomycin. This inhibition also does not set in immediately on adding the oligomycin [12]. The inhibition curve with an optimal concentration of dinitrophenol (Fig. 4, Curve 1) shows little if any sigmoidicity. In consequence, 0.1 μg oligomycin/mg protein, that has no effect on the respiration, inhibits the ATPase, even though much more oligomycin is required to inhibit maximally the dinitrophenol-induced ATPase than the respiration. A sigmoidal inhibition curve is found with sub-optimal concentrations of dinitrophenol (Curve 2).

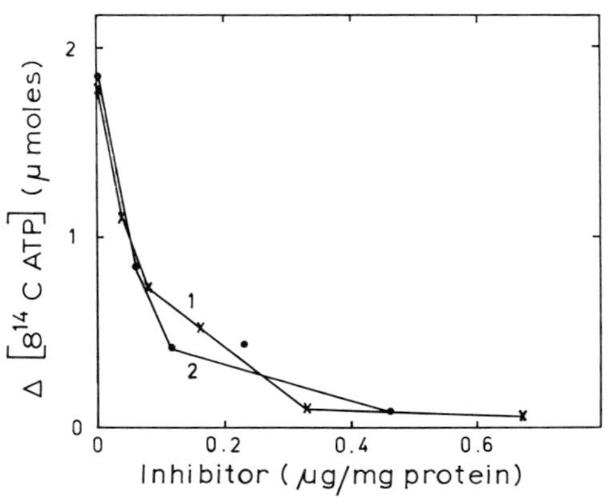

Fig. 5. Effect of aurovertin and oligomycin on the ADP-ATP exchange reaction of rat-liver mitochondria. Curve 1, aurovertin; Curve 2, oligomycin. From TER WELLE [10]

Oligomycin inhibits also the P_i-ATP and ADP-ATP exchange reactions. Fig. 5 shows that a hyperbolic and not a sigmoidal inhibition curve is obtained with the ADP-ATP exchange reaction. GROOT [13] has found the same with the P_i-ATP exchange reaction.

The differences in shape of the inhibition curves with intact mitochondria found in these reactions are not understood, and are at present being further studied in our laboratory. The direction in which we are thinking will become obvious after the following paper.

Effects of Oligomycin on Sub-Mitochondrial Particles

Oligomycin, in concentrations lower than 0.1 μg/mg protein, that have no effect on mitochondrial respiration, also has no effect on the P:O ratio. In larger amounts, the ratio is lowered because of the presence of the oligomycin-resistant respiration. LEE and ERNSTER [14] found a different behaviour with certain types of sub-mitochondrial particles. Although phosphorylation is inhibited by higher concentrations of oligomycin, just as in intact mitochondria, lower concentrations stimulate. This is illustrated by an experiment of TER WELLE [10] given in Curve 3 of Fig. 6. Despite an inhibition of the respiration, which is much less than with intact mitochondria because of structural damage, phosphorylation

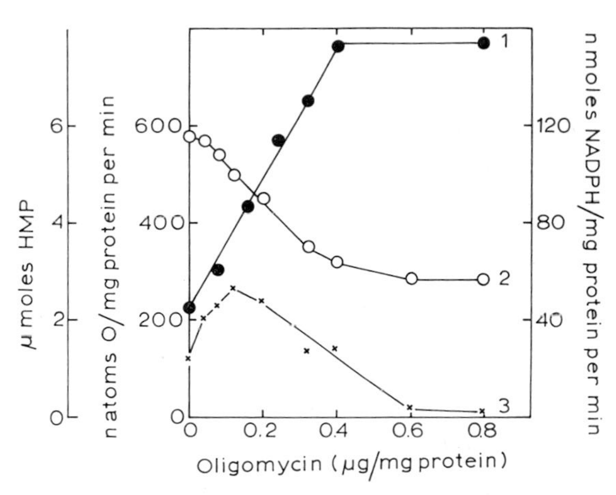

Fig. 6. Effect of oligomycin on energy-dependent transhydrogenase (Curve 1), O_2 uptake (Curve 2) and synthesis of hexose monophosphate (Curve 3) by EDTA particles. Succinate as substrate in the presence of rotenone. From TER WELLE [10]

is stimulated by low concentrations of oligomycin. Also in agreement with LEE and ERNSTER [14], this experiment shows the stimulation by oligomycin of the energy-dependent transhydrogenase (Curve 1) catalysed by these particles. The only point on which TER WELLE [10] disagrees with LEE and ERNSTER [14] is the fact that, in his experiments, the optimum oligomycin concentration is less for oxidative phosphorylation than for the transhydrogenase. ATP-utilizing reactions in these particles are also stimulated by low and inhibited by high concentrations of oligomycin.

The particles used in these experiments are deficient in, but not lacking, certain phosphorylating factors. The P:O ratio may be stimulated not only by adding oligomycin, but also by adding F_1, a cold-labile protein isolated and thoroughly studied by Racker and co-workers [15, 16]. The effects of F_1 and oligomycin are additive [17]. Racker has shown that oligomycin has no effect on particles made completely deficient in F_1 [18]. We may conclude that the oligomycin-*stimulating* effect is seen only in particles partly deficient in certain phosphorylating factors, and it may be that oligomycin promotes a membrane conformation favouring the mutual accessibility of the different components of the phosphorylating system.

Use of Oligomycin in Reconstituting Oxidative Phosphorylation

Since all ATP-utilizing reactions in F_1-deficient particles are stimulated by the addition of F_1, there is good reason to believe that F_1 is the terminal enzyme in the phosphorylating sequence

Table 1. *Differences in properties between isolated F_1 and terminal phosphorylating enzyme in mitochondria*

F_1	Terminal enzyme in mitochondria
Catalyses hydrolysis of ATP in absence of uncoupler	Catalyses hydrolysis of ATP only in presence of uncoupler
ATPase insensitive to oligomycin	ATPase sensitive to oligomycin
Cold labile	Cold stable

leading to the synthesis of ATP. However, there are important differences between the properties of isolated F_1 and those to be expected of the terminal enzyme. These are listed in Table 1. The oligomycin sensitivity of the ATPase in the mitochondria has been an important tool in the hands of Racker and his co-workers in reconstructing the membrane-bound F_1 system. When F_1 is bound to a specific membrane fraction, now called TUA-CF_o [T, U and A for trypsin, urea and ammonia used in preparation of particles from which the preparation is made, C for cholate used to treat the particles, F for factor, o (not zero) for oligomycin] [19], the ATPase is inhibited, but may be restored by addition of phospholipid. The restored activity is oligomycin sensitive and cold stable. An additional factor, called F_c by RACKER [19, 20] and OSCP (oligomycin sensitivity conferring protein) by MACLENNAN and TZAGOLOFF [21], is necessary for binding of F_1 to CF_0. Cations are also involved in the binding [20]. F_c appears to be identical with F_5, a coupling factor required in addition to F_1 for maximal activity in submitochondrial particles [22]. This is understandable if F_1 is the terminal enzyme of oxidative phosphorylation and F_5 is necessary for binding of F_1 to the membrane.

A second form of F_1, called $F_1 \cdot X$ because it contains a second factor, has been isolated by VALLEJOS et al. [23]. In the presence of $F_1 \cdot X$, oligomycin no longer stimulates oxidative phosphorylation. GROOT and MEIJER [24] have shown that the X is identical

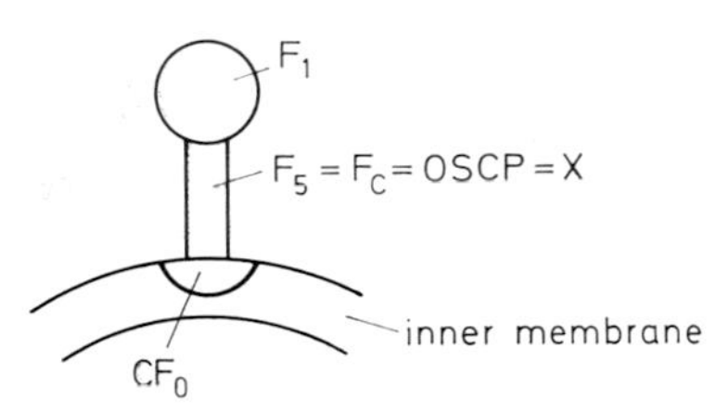

Fig. 7. Speculative representation of oligomycin-sensitive ATPase complex

with OSCP. Thus, $F_1 \cdot X$ would appear to be the membrane-free part of the oligomycin-sensitive ATPase complex, made up of F_1, F_5 and membrane. Indeed, it is very tempting, as MACLENNAN and ASAI [25] have done, but probably premature, to identify F_5 with the stalk of the tripartite structure seen in electron micrographs of negatively stained disrupted mitochondria [26] (see Fig. 7). The 'knobs' have previously been identified with F_1 [27]. The status of three other coupling factors proposed by RACKER [17] — F_2, F_3 and F_4 — is doubtful. CF_0 probably contains the oligomycin-binding site (see below).

SCHATZ [28] has shown that the ATPase activity of mitochondria isolated from the 'petite' mutant of *Saccharomyces cerevisiae* is insensitive to oligomycin and is cold labile. F_1 isolated from these mitochondria is indistinguishable from the enzyme isolated from mitochondria of wild-type yeast, and it becomes cold stable and oligomycin sensitive when bound to F_1-deficient submitochondrial particles of heart. It appears, then, that these mutants have an impaired linkage of F_1 to the inner mitochondrial membrane. It would be interesting to know if it is F_5 or CF_0 that is lacking.

Use of Oligomycin in Determining Whether an Energy-Requiring Process in Mitochondria Involves ATP

As already mentioned, one of the main uses of oligomycin is to determine whether an energy-requiring process is driven by the primarily conserved energy pressure or by ATP. In both cases dinitrophenol will inhibit, either by dissipating the energy pressure or, indirectly, by causing hydrolysis of the ATP. Oligomycin will have different effects depending upon whether or not ATP is necessary for the energy-utilizing reactions and whether respiration or ATP is the source of the energy. If it is respiration, inhibition by oligomycin indicates that conversion of the primarily conserved energy to ATP is necessary. If respiration is inhibited and the process is driven by added ATP, oligomycin will not inhibit. In the presence of dinitrophenol, oligomycin will have no effect when respiration is the energy source, and it will stimulate the reaction when ATP is the energy source, since it will prevent the breakdown of ATP.

Table 2. *Use of oligomycin in determining whether an energy-requiring process in mitochondria involves ATP*

Energy source	Uncoupler	Effect of oligomycin when energy-requiring process	
		Involves ATP	Does not involve ATP
Respiration	Absent	Inhibits	Does not inhibit
	Present	No effect	No effect
ATP	Absent	No effect	Inhibits
	Present	Stimulates	No effect

If, on the other hand, the energy-requiring process is driven by the primarily conserved energy, without conversion to ATP, it will not be inhibited by oligomycin when respiration is the source of the energy, but will be when ATP is. In neither case will oligomycin be able to overcome the inhibitory effect of dinitrophenol. These conclusions are summarized in Table 2.

An example of an energy-requiring reaction not involving ATP is the reduction of NAD^+ by succinate (Table 3). The source of energy for this endergonic reaction is the oxidation of succinate by O_2. The reaction is insensitive to oligomycin but inhibited by dinitrophenol. In the experiment shown in Table 4, the reduction of NAD^+ was measured by linking it with the synthesis of glutamate

Table 3. *Effect of oligomycin and dinitrophenol on the succinate-induced reduction of NAD^+ in rabbit-heart mitochondria* (from SNOSWELL [5])

Expt.	Addition	NAD^+ (µmole/g protein)	NADH
1	None	4.5	0.8
	Succinate	1.0	3.2
	Succinate, oligomycin	0.9	3.0
2	None	3.8	0.9
	Dinitrophenol (0.1 mM)	5.3	0.2
	Succinate	0.9	2.5
	Succinate, dinitrophenol	5.3	0.2

Table 4. *Synthesis of glutamate with ATP as energy source* (from TAGER and SLATER [29])

Addition	Δ Glu (µmoles)
Succinate	2.3
Succinate + oligomycin	5.6
Succinate + antimycin	0.7
Succinate + antimycin + oligomycin	0.5
Succinate + antimycin + ATP	1.6
Succinate + antimycin + ATP + oligomycin	0.5

from α-oxoglutarate and NH_3. The reaction is insensitive to oligomycin when succinate oxidation is the source of energy, but is sensitive to oligomycin when ATP is the energy source. Thus ATP cannot be used directly but its energy must first be converted into the form in which energy is primarily conserved by operation of the respiratory chain.

When mitochondria are treated with arsenate, they are no longer able to oxidize succinate rapidly, in the presence of uncoupler. ATP restores the oxidation. AZZONE and ERNSTER [30] concluded that this is due to a requirement for energy for initiation of succinate oxidation. However, when it was found [31, 32] that the effect of ATP is not inhibited by oligomycin, it was clear that, in these experiments, ATP acts directly and not *via* the respiratory chain. Probably, it acts by removing an inhibitor formed during the pre-incubation [31, 32].

Another example of a mitochondrial energy-requiring process involving ATP is the activation of fatty acid oxidation. Fig. 8

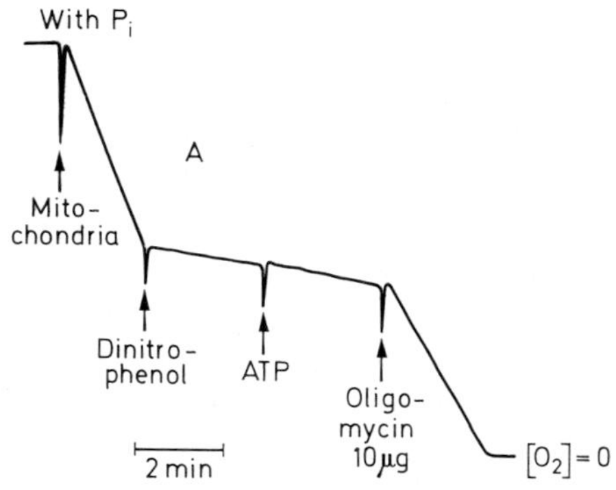

Fig. 8. Effect of dinitrophenol, ATP and oligomycin on palmitate oxidation by rat-liver mitochondria. 30 mM P_i, 0.1 mM dinitrophenol, 12 mg mitochondrial protein, 5 mM ATP. From VAN DEN BERGH [33]

shows an experiment of VAN DEN BERGH [33] demonstrating the inhibition of fatty acid oxidation by dinitrophenol and the restoration by the addition of both ATP and oligomycin.

Use of Oligomycin in Studies with Intact Cells

In intact cells, oligomycin will not stop all ATP synthesis, since neither the phosphorylation linked with glycolysis nor the substrate-linked phosphorylation linked with α-oxoglutarate oxidation is inhibited. Figs. 9—12 show some experiments carried out to determine whether the beating of cultured heart cells is driven by ATP or is more directly linked with respiration [34]. The beating rate is inhibited by dinitrophenol and partly restored with ATP (Fig. 9). However, it is not affected by oligomycin (Fig. 10) nor by iodoacetate (Fig. 11). Iodoacetate followed by oligomycin or oligomycin followed by iodoacetate is necessary. Inhibition by dinitrophenol is restored by oligomycin (Fig. 12). These results clearly show that ATP, formed either by glycolysis or respiration,

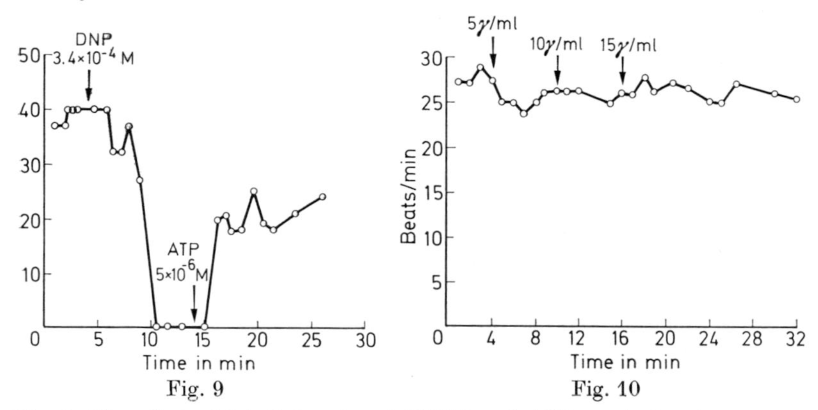

Fig. 9

Fig. 10

Fig. 9. The effect of 2,4-dinitrophenol (DNP) and ATP on the beating rate of cultured heart cells. From HARARY and SLATER [34]

Fig. 10. Effect of oligomycin on the beating rate of cultured heart cells. From HARARY and SLATER [34]

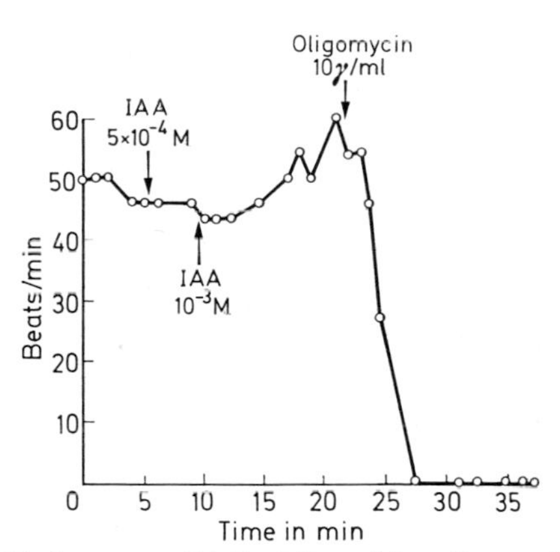

Fig. 11. Effect of iodoacetate (IAA), followed by oligomycin on the beating rate of cultured heart cells. From HARARY and SLATER [34]

is necessary for the heart beat. Direct analyses of the ATP present in the heart cells after the various treatments (Table 5) show that either dinitrophenol, or oligomycin + iodoacetate is necessary to lower the concentration of ATP appreciably [35]. When oligomycin is added in the presence of dinitrophenol, the ATP formed by glycolysis is prevented from being broken down by the dinitrophenol-induced ATPase (see Fig. 13).

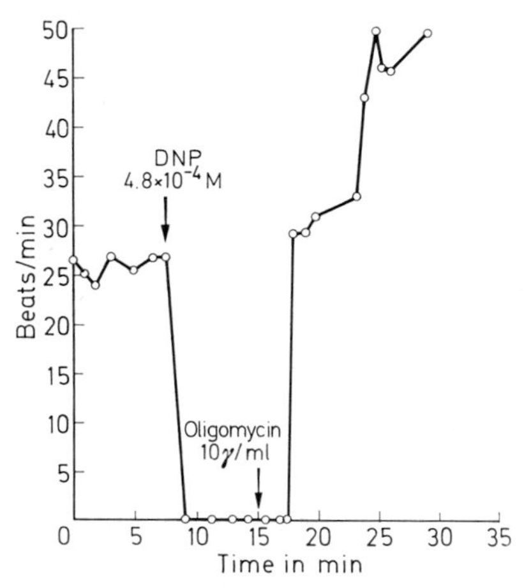

Fig. 12. Effect of oligomycin on the beating rate of 2,4-dinitrophenol-inhibited cultured heart cells. From Harary and Slater [34]

Table 5. *Effect of inhibitors on ATP level in cultured heart cells* (from Seraydarian et al. [35])

Conditions	ATP (μmoles/g protein)	
	Control	Expt.
Iodoacetate	52	52
Oligomycin	66	57
Iodoacetate + oligomycin	57	40
Oligomycin + iodoacetate	49	26
Dinitrophenol	44	29
Dinitrophenol + oligomycin	43	43

Considerable ATP is still formed even in the presence of dinitrophenol or of iodoacetate + oligomycin, but the amount is apparently insufficient to support spontaneous contraction. The cells still respond electrically, unless they are almost completely deprived of ATP by prolonged incubation with a high concentration of oligomycin [35].

Oligomycin can also be used to study the capacity of intact cells to use respiratory energy directly without converting it into ATP. This may be determined by measuring the inhibition of respiration by oligomycin. This was first done by VAN ROSSUM [36], who found the surprisingly low value of 20% for rat-liver slices. TOBIN and SLATER [37] found inhibitions of the same order with frog muscle and rat diaphragm, brain and kidney. Other workers have reported similar values for various tissues. Ascites tumour cells appear to be an exception, since up to 85% inhibition has been reported [38, 39]. Oligomycin has a greater effect on rat-brain slices in the presence of added K^+, and in fact virtually abolishes

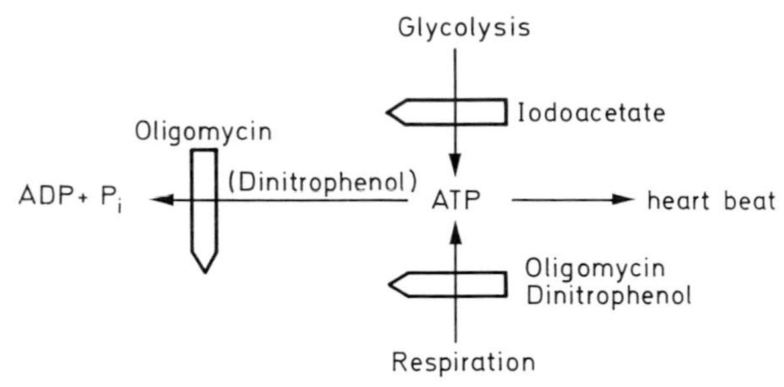

Fig. 13. Schematic representation of paths of synthesis and breakdown of ATP utilized in beating heart

the stimulation by K^+ [40, 37]. This is to be expected if the K^+-induced respiration is due to an increased supply of ADP to the mitochondria.

In concentrations similar to those that inhibit mitochondrial respiration, oligomycin stimulates glycolysis [41, 37], which is to be expected if phosphorylation of ADP by the mitochondria is inhibited. Incidentally, this stimulation is clear evidence that oligomycin is acting, in these preparations, on the mitochondria and not on the cell-membrane ($Na^+ + K^+$)-stimulated ATPase as suggested by WHITTAM [42]. An inhibition of the utilization of ATP would cause high ATP/ADP ratios and an inhibition of glycolysis. It is true that oligomycin can inhibit the ($Na^+ + K^+$)-stimulated ATPase [43—46], but only at concentrations about 100 times greater than those needed to inhibit mitochondrial ATPase [46]. Oligomycin can also be used to measure the contamination with 'microsomes' of preparations of mitochondria or the ($Na^+ + K^+$)-stimulated ATPase since the Mg^{2+}-stimulated ATPase of microsomes is insensitive to oligomycin.

The slight inhibition of the respiration of tissue preparations by oligomycin does not necessarily mean that, in the absence of oligomycin, only small amounts of ATP are formed. Under these conditions, there will be competition between the various energy-requiring reactions, and the phosphorylation reaction might well compete successfully. The oligomycin-insensitive respiration does, however, give a measure in the intact cells of the capacity of the systems to use or dissipate respiratory energy without converting it into ATP. It is a slight over-estimate since it will include the substrate-level phosphorylation step. Two molecules of ATP are formed by this reaction for every molecule of glucose oxidized.

The restoration by oligomycin of the beating of isolated heart cells stopped by dinitrophenol and the stimulation of glycolysis by brain slices show that oligomycin is able readily to penetrate the intact cell.

A Cautionary Word

The lack of inhibition by oligomycin of an energy-requiring process is insufficient evidence for a direct utilization of the primarily conserved energy, even in experiments with isolated mitochondria. Oligomycin does not inhibit ATP production completely [47], since it leaves substrate-linked phosphorylation linked with the oxidation of α-oxoglutarate intact, and, owing to 'leaks', it does not stop the operation of the respiratory chain completely. On the other hand, it will stop any loss by endogenous ATPase of the residual ATP formed by the substrate-linked phosphorylation. The production of ATP in the presence of oligomycin will be increased by the addition of uncoupler which will stimulate the respiration. Thus, in the presence of oligomycin and uncoupler, there can be a considerable production of ATP (*via* GTP). VAN DEN BERGH [48] showed that, under these conditions, fatty acids are rapidly activated by the GTP and oxidized, provided that phosphate is not present (phosphate inhibits the activation by GTP). Previously, the lack of inhibition by oligomycin of fatty acid oxidation had led to the suggestion that fatty acids may be oxidized without the intervention of nucleoside triphosphates [49].

Similarly, the lack of inhibition by oligomycin of protein synthesis in isolated mitochondria, first reported by BRONK [50], is insufficient evidence that the energy for this process is directly derived from respiration, since GTP (and ATP formed from it) synthesized in the presence of oligomycin is probably sufficient to drive the very small amount of protein synthesis observed *in vitro*. If arsenite is added in order to inhibit the substrate-linked phosphorylation, oligomycin inhibits protein synthesis [51]. The inhibition by dinitrophenol in the absence of arsenite but presence of oligomycin is stronger support for a role of the primarily conserved energy, but even so the role may be quite indirect [52].

The critical experiments necessary to demonstrate the direct utilization of the primarily conserved energy are to show that when the energy source is ATP (added in experiments with isolated mitochondria, produced by glycolysis in experiments with the intact cell) the process is inhibited by oligomycin, and that oligomycin does not relieve the inhibitory effects of uncouplers. One example in which this is clearly not the case is furnished by the experiments with beating heart cells already mentioned. A second is the work of GALEOTTI, KOVÁČ and HESS [53] on respiratory adaptation in yeast, carried out under such conditions that most of the energy is provided by fermentation. Although respiratory adaptation was inhibited by uncouplers, it was scarcely affected by oligomycin, nor did oligomycin relieve inhibition by uncouplers. GALEOTTI et al. [53] conclude that the uncouplers are, in this case, interfering with membrane processes in general.

The general picture that has emerged from work in the last 5 years in this field is that, although the primarily conserved energy may be used directly in many mitochondrial energy-requiring processes, other mitochondrial reactions and all extra-mitochondrial reactions require that it first be converted to ATP.

Compounds with Action Similar to that of Oligomycin

Dicyclohexylcarbodiimide (DCCD). BEECHEY et al. [54—56] introduced N,N′-dicyclohexylcarbodiimide as an inhibitor of mitochondrial oxidative phosphorylation, resembling oligomycin in its action. It is necessary to incubate 15 h at 0° to obtain inhibition with concentrations of the order of 1 nmole/mg protein.

Although it is the only one of the compounds to be considered in this talk whose structure is known, this has not been as yet of great help since the chemistry of the inhibition is not known. KOVÁČ et al. [57] found DCCD more useful than oligomycin in studies with intact yeast cells, since it penetrates the yeast cell under conditions where oligomycin does not. Like oligomycin with animal cells, DCCD inhibits yeast respiration only partially (about 30%). It has an advantage over oligomycin in resisting washing with phospholipids after being bound to sub-mito-

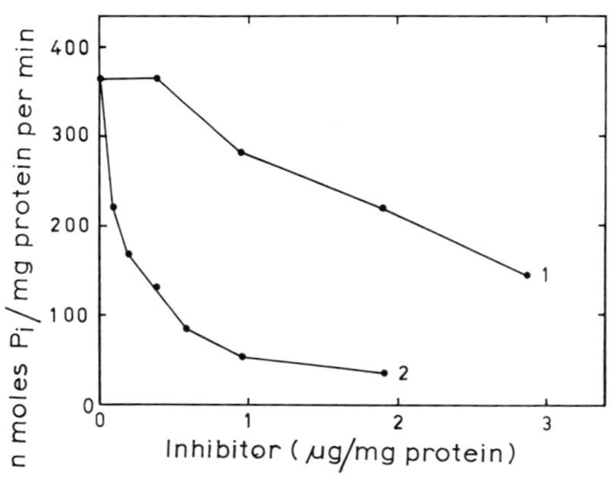

Fig. 14. Effect of aurovertin (Curve 1) and oligomycin (Curve 2) on dinitrophenol-induced ATPase of rat-liver mitochondria. From TER WELLE [10]

chondrial particles [20, 54—56], so that it can be used to label the oligomycin-binding site. This is on the TUA particles and not on F_c [20]. Like oligomycin it stimulates phosphorylation [18] and the energy-linked transhydrogenase [56] in sub-mitochondrial particles in the presence of F_1. High concentrations of DCCD inhibit other reactions [58—60].

Aurovertin. Aurovertin is made by the mould *Calcarisporium arbuscula Preiss*. The name is derived from its yellow colour and the mistaken belief that it was formed by a strain of *Verticillium* [61]. Its molecular formula is $C_{25}H_{32}O_9$ (cf. oligomycin A, $C_{28}H_{46}O_4$) [62][2]. It was introduced as an inhibitor of oxidative phosphorylation by LARDY [63, 64], who showed that it gives a titration curve

[2] See footnote, p. 259.

identical with that of oligomycin for inhibition of respiration and the ATP-P_i and P_i-H_2O exchange reactions. This is also the case with the ATP-ADP exchange reaction (Fig. 5). However, the dinitrophenol-induced ATPase is much less susceptible to aurovertin [64]; see also Fig. 14). Other ATP-driven reactions are little inhibited by aurovertin [64—68].

The lack of effect of aurovertin on the dinitrophenol-induced ATPase may also be demonstrated by measuring the P:O ratio for the oxidation of α-oxoglutarate in the presence of malonate and dinitrophenol. Oligomycin gives the expected increase, but aurovertin has no effect (Table 6) [10].

Table 6. *Effect of oligomycin and aurovertin on P:O ratio with α-oxoglutarate as substrate in presence of 2,4-dinitrophenol* (from TER WELLE [10])

Addition	P:O
None	0.01
Oligomycin (0.66 μg/mg protein)	0.44
Aurovertin (3.3 μg/mg protein)	0.04

Aurovertin, unlike oligomycin and DCCD, does not stimulate oxidative phosphorylation and related reactions in sub-mitochondrial particles [10, 68], but inhibits the oligomycin-stimulated phosphorylation [69].

Dio-9. Dio-9 is Holland's contribution to this arsenal. Nothing is known about its chemistry. Following Lardy's example, some years ago we undertook an investigation of toxic antibiotics on the shelf of the Royal Netherlands Fermentation Industries. One of these looked promising and it was investigated in detail by GUILLORY [70, 71]. In the presence of phosphate it acts as an inhibitor of mitochondrial phosphorylation; in the absence of phosphate it is an uncoupler.

However, the main interest in Dio-9 lies in its effect on photosynthetic phosphorylation in chloroplasts [72]. It appears to have the same effect on the chloroplast as oligomycin has on the mitochondrion. Photosynthetic phosphorylation in chloroplasts is not inhibited by oligomycin, but it is in chromatophores [73].

None of the inhibitors described are effective against oxidative phosphorylation catalysed by fragments of bacterial protoplast membranes. Pandit-Hovenkamp and Eilermann (unpublished observations) have found that desaspidin, a compound known for its uncoupling activity on photosynthetic phosphorylation in chloroplasts, inhibits oxidative phosphorylation and the ADP-stimulated respiration [74] in *Azotobacter* particles.

References

1. Masamune, S., J. M. Sehgal, E. E. van Tamelen, F. M. Strong, and W. H. Peterson: J. Amer. chem. Soc. **80**, 6092 (1958).
2. Lardy, H. A., D. Johnson, and W. McMurray: Arch. Biochem. **78**, 587 (1958).
3. Slater, E. C.: Proc. 5th Meeting Fed. Europ. Biochem. Socs., Prague 1968 (in press).
4. Ernster, L.: In: Goodwin, T. W., and O. Lindberg (Ed.), Biol. Struct. and Function, p. 139. New York: Academic Press 1961.
5. Snoswell, A. M.: Biochim. biophys. Acta **52**, 216 (1961).
6. Chance, B.: In: Enzymes: Units of biological structure and function, p. 447. Gaebler, O. H., Ed. New York: Academic Press 1956.
7. Visser, J., D. E. Weinauer, R. C. Davis, W. H. Peterson, W. Nazarewicz, and H. Ordway: J. biochem. microbiol. Technol. Engng. **2**, 31 (1960).
8. Lardy, H. A., P. Witonsky, and D. Johnson: Biochemistry **4**, 552 (1965).
9. Thompson, R. Q., M. M. Hoehn, and C. E. Higgens: Antimicrobial agents and chemotherapy, p. 47. Detroit (Michigan): Amer. Soc. Microbiologists 1961.
10. Ter Welle, H. F.: Ph.D. Thesis, Amsterdam 1968.
11. Huijing, F., and E. C. Slater: J. Biochem. (Tokyo) **49**, 493 (1961).
12. Slater, E. C.: Bull. Soc. Chim. biol. (Paris) **48**, 1151 (1966).
13. Groot, G. S. P.: Biochim. biophys. Acta (in press).
14. Lee, C.-P., and L. Ernster: Biochem. biophys. Res. Commun. **18**, 523 (1965).
15. Pullman, M. E., H. S. Penefsky, A. Datta, and E. Racker: J. biol. Chem. **235**, 3322 (1960).
16. Penefsky, H. S., M. E. Pullman, A. Datta, and E. Racker: J. biol. Chem. **235**, 3330 (1960).
17. Fessenden, J. M., and E. Racker: J. biol. Chem. **241**, 2483 (1966).
18. Racker, E., and L. L. Horstman: J. biol. Chem. **242**, 2547 (1967).
19. Bulos, B., and E. Racker: J. biol. Chem. **243**, 3901 (1968).
20. — — J. biol. Chem. **243**, 3891 (1968).
21. MacLennan, D. H., and A. Tzagoloff: Biochemistry **7**, 1603 (1968).
22. Fessenden-Raden, J. M., and E. Racker: Fed. Proc. **29**, 297 (1968).
23. Vallejos, R. H., S. G. van den Bergh, and E. C. Slater: Biochim. biophys. Acta **153**, 509 (1968).

24. GROOT, G. S. P., and A. J. MEIJER: Biochim. biophys. Acta (in press).
25. MACLENNAN, D. H., and J. ASAI: Biochem. biophys. Res. Commun. **33**, 441 (1968).
26. FERNÁNDEZ-MORÁN, H., T. ODA, P. V. BLAIR, and D. E. GREEN: J. Cell Biol. **22**, 63 (1964).
27. RACKER, E., D. D. TYLER, R. W. ESTABROOK, T. E. CONOVER, D. F. PARSONS, and B. CHANCE: In: Oxidases and related redox systems, Vol. 2, p. 1077. KING, T. E., H. S. MASON, and M. MORRISON Eds. New York: Wiley 1965.
28. SCHATZ, G.: J. biol. Chem. **243**, 2192 (1968).
29. TAGER, J. M., and E. C. SLATER: Biochim. biophys. Acta **77**, 227, 246 (1963).
30. AZZONE, G. F., and L. ERNSTER: J. biol. Chem. **236**, 1518 (1961).
31. CHAPPELL, J. B.: In: GOODWIN, T. W., and O. LINDBERG, Eds., Biol. Struct. and Function, Vol. 2, p. 71. New York: Academic Press.
32. SLATER, E. C., and A. KEMP JR.: Biochem. J. **84**, 65P (1962).
33. VAN DEN BERGH, S. G.: Biochim. biophys. Acta **98**, 442 (1965).
34. HARARY, I., and E. C. SLATER: Biochim. biophys. Acta **99**, 227 (1965).
35. SERAYDARIAN, M. W., I. HARARY, and E. SATO: Biochim. biophys. Acta **162**, 414 (1968).
36. VAN ROSSUM, G. D. V.: Biochim. biophys. Acta **82**, 556 (1964).
37. TOBIN, R. B., and E. C. SLATER: Biochim. biophys. Acta **105**, 214 (1965).
38. DALLNER, G., and L. ERNSTER: Exp. Cell Res. **27**, 372 (1962).
39. MINAKAMI, S., and H. YOSHIKAWA: Biochim. biophys. Acta **74**, 793 (1963).
40. —, K. KAKINUMA, and H. YOSHIKAWA: Biochim. biophys. Acta **78**, 808 (1963).
41. WU, R.: Biochim. biophys. Acta **82**, 212 (1964).
42. WHITTAM, R., K. P. WHEELER, and A. BLAKE: Nature (Lond.) **203**, 720 (1964).
43. GLYNN, I. M.: Biochem. J. **84**, 75P (1962).
44. JÄRNEFELT, J.: Biochim. biophys. Acta **59**, 643 (1962).
45. JÖBSIS, F. F., and H. J. VREMAN: Biochim. biophys. Acta **73**, 346 (1963).
46. VAN GRONINGEN, H. E. M., and E. C. SLATER: Biochim. biophys. Acta **73**, 527 (1963).
47. SLATER, E. C., and A. KEMP JR.: Nature (Lond.) **204**, 1268 (1964).
48. VAN DEN BERGH, S. G.: Biochim. biophys. Acta **96**, 517 (1965).
49. WOJTCZAK, L., H. ZALUSKA, and Z. DRAHOTA: Biochim. biophys. Acta **98**, 8 (1965).
50. BRONK, J. R.: Proc. nat. Acad. Sci. (Wash.) **50**, 524 (1963).
51. KROON, A. M.: Protein synthesis in mitochondria, M. D. Thesis, Hoorn 1966.
52. — Biochim. biophys. Acta **91**, 145 (1964).
53. GALEOTTI, T., L. KOVÁČ, and B. HESS: Nature (Lond.) **218**, 194 (1968).
54. BEECHEY, R. B., C. T. HOLLOWAY, I. G. KNIGHT, and A. M. ROBERTON: Biochem. biophys. Res. Commun. **23**, 75 (1966).

55. —, A. M. ROBERTON, C. T. HOLLOWAY, and I. G. KNIGHT: Biochemistry **6**, 3867 (1967).
56. ROBERTON, A. M., C. T. HOLLOWAY, I. G. KNIGHT, and R. B. BEECHEY: Biochem. J. **108**, 445 (1968).
57. KOVÁČ, L., T. GALEOTTI, and B. HESS: Biochim. biophys. Acta **153**, 715 (1968).
58. SCHATZ, G., H. S. PENEFSKY, and E. RACKER: J. biol. Chem. **242**, 2552 (1967).
59. PENEFSKY, H. S.: J. biol. Chem. **242**, 5789 (1967).
60. BEYER, R. E., D. L. CRANKSHAW, and J. M. KUNER: Biochem. biophys. Res. Commun. **28**, 758 (1967).
61. BALDWIN, C. L., L. C. WEAVER, R. M. BROOKER, T. N. JACOBSEN, C. E. OSBORNE JR., and H. A. NASH: Lloydia **27**, 88 (1964).
62. BEECHEY, R. B., V. WILLIAMS, C. T. HOLLOWAY, I. G. KNIGHT, and A. M. ROBERTON: Biochem. biophys. Res. Commun. **26**, 339 (1967).
63. LARDY, H. A.: In: GOODWIN, T. W., and O. LINDBERG, Eds., Vol. 2, p. 265. New York: Academic Press 1961.
64. —, J. L. CONNELLY, and D. JOHNSON: Biochemistry **3**, 1961 (1964).
65. CONNELLY, J. L., and H. A. LARDY: Biochemistry **3**, 1969 (1964).
66. LENAZ, G.: Biochim. biophys. Res. Commun. **21**, 170 (1965).
67. BIELAWSKI, J., and A. L. LEHNINGER: J. biol. Chem. **241**, 4316 (1966).
68. ERNSTER, L., C. P. LEE, and S. JANDA: In: Biochemistry of mitochondria, p. 29. SLATER, E. C., Z. KANIUGA, and L. WOJTCZAK, Eds. London: Academic Press, and Polish Scientific Publishers, Warsaw, 1967.
69. LEE, C.-P., and L. ERNSTER: Europ. J. Biochem. **3**, 391 (1968).
70. GUILLORY, R. J.: Biochim. biophys. Acta **89**, 197 (1964).
71. FISHER, R. B., and R. J. GUILLORY: Biochim. biophys. Acta **162**, 182 (1968).
72. McCARTY, R. E., R. J. GUILLORY, and E. RACKER: J. biol. Chem. **240**, PC 4822 (1965).
73. BALTSCHEFFSKY, H., and M. BALTSCHEFFSKY: Acta chem. scand. **14**, 257 (1960).
74. PANDIT-HOVENKAMP, H. G., and L. J. M. EILERMANN: Abstr. Fifth Meeting Fed. Europ. Biochem. Socs., p. 50, Prague 1968.
75. CHAMBERLIN, J. W., M. GORMAN, and A. AGTARAP: Biochem. biophys. Res. Commun. **34**, 448 (1969)

Inhibition of Mitochondrial Oxidative Phosphorylation by Aurovertin

HENRY LARDY and CHEN-HO CHIEU LIN

Institute for Enzyme Research, University of Wisconsin

Aurovertin inhibits oxidative phosphorylation in mitochondria in much the same way as oligomycin. Oligomycin and aurovertin, applied in amounts less than those maximally effective, have additive effects on the inhibition of oxidative phosphorylation, ^{32}P-P_i-ATP exchange, and the exchange of ^{18}O between P_i and water in rat liver mitochondria [1]. Aurovertin is, however, much less effective than oligomycin in inhibiting mitochondrial ATPase induced by various uncoupling agents [1, 2]. It was of great interest to find [1] that the ATPase extracted from rat liver mitochondria [3] was inhibited by aurovertin but not by oligomycin.

Aurovertin is a yellow compound that exhibits no fluorescence in either aqueous or nonpolar solvents. CHANCE and LARDY (unpublished experiments) found that aurovertin forms a fluorescing complex with mitochondria from many tissues of several different species. In our laboratory Mrs. C.-H. LIN and I have found that the solubilized liver ATPase also forms a fluorescing complex with aurovertin as does the pure F_1 coupling factor isolated from beef heart mitochondria by PULLMAN, PENEFSKY, DATTA and RACKER [4].

The aurovertin-coupling factor 1 complex is formed in a ratio of 1 mole aurovertin to 1 mole of F_1 (molecular weight 284,000). The dissociation constant of this complex varies from 8×10^{-7} M in Tris buffer to 3×10^{-7} M in phosphate buffer. The stoichiometry of complex formation is not altered by the buffer species, but the fluorescence yield is considerably higher in Tris than it is in phosphate. The addition of ATP to the aurovertin-F_1 complex in P_i buffer enhances the fluorescence yield without altering the stoichiometry of binding. ATP diminishes the fluorescence yield of the aurovertin-F_1 complex in Tris buffer, again without influencing the stoichiometry of the complex. It thus appears that the F_1 protein can exist in at least three different conformations, as evidenced by the fluorescence intensity of the aurovertin-F_1 complex and the respective influences of buffers and ATP. Adenosine monophosphate and highly purified samples of adenosine diphosphate do *not* influence the fluorescence yield of the aurovertin-F_1 complex.

Fractionation studies have disclosed no other mitochondrial component that forms such a fluorescing complex. Quantitative studies indicate that, if the fluorescence yield of the F_1-aurovertin complex in mitochondria were the same as that of the isolated enzyme, the amount of fluorescence observed would correspond to an F_1 content of 4.5% in beef heart mitochondria. This is probably a minimum value because some mitochondrial proteins appear to quench the fluorescence of the pure F_1-aurovertin complex.

References

1. Lardy, H. A., J. L. Connelly, and D. Johnson: Biochemistry **3**, 1961 (1964).
2. — In: Biological structure and function. II, p. 265. New York: Academic Press 1961.
3. —, and H. Wellman: J. biol. Chem. **201**, 357 (1953).
4. Pullman, M., H. S. Penefsky, A. Datta, and E. Racker: J. biol. Chem. **235**, 3322 (1960).

Discussion

Klingenberg (Munich): One problem in the study of the effects of aurovertin and oligomycin is the permeability of these substances to the mitochondria. There is indication that oligomycin is rather slowly permeating, and that aurovertin is rather rapidly permeating.

Lardy (Madison, Wisc.): Possibly the size has some influence. Aurovertin has half the size of oligomycin.

Slater (Amsterdam): I doubt very much if permeability is the whole explanation of the oligomycin lag, because no matter how long you preincubate, after you start the respiration, you still find an increasing inhibition with time.

Klingenberg: In submitochondrial particles, there should be no time ag of the oligomycin effect, since oligomycin does not need to penetrate the barrier from the outside to its site of action.

SLATER: I am intrigued that oligomycin has twice the molecular weight as that ascribed to it in the literature. Aurovertin and oligomycin are exactly equivalent as inhibitors on a weight basis; this would mean that oligomycin would be more active on a molecular weight basis.

LARDY: The molecular weights of all oligomycins, including rutamycin, are in the vicinity of 800 [CHAMBERLIN et al.: Biochem. biophys. Res. Commun. **34**, 448 (1969); PROUTY et al.: Biochem. biophys. Res. Commun. **34**, 511 (1969)]. Apparently, BEECHEY was observing only fragments of the native molecule.

BÜCHER (Munich): May I ask Dr. VIGNAIS whether fuscin also permeates in the whole cell? Would you think it is applicable to the whole organ?

VIGNAIS (Grenoble): I cannot answer.

LARDY: It would be nice if we could induce Boehringer to produce these antibiotics that most drug houses lose an interest in because they are not marketable. (BÜCHER, added in proof: In the meantime, Boehringer began to organize an inhibitor program.)

BÜCHER: I would like to express our sincere thanks to Professor SLATER, not only because he came here, but also because he has done so much for European biochemistry.

Inhibitors Around the Antimycin-Sensitive Site in the Respiratory Chain

Z. Kaniuga, J. Bryła, and E. C. Slater

Department of Biochemistry, Warsaw University (Poland) and Laboratory of Biochemistry, B.C.P. Jansen Institute, University of Amsterdam (The Netherlands)

With 5 Figures

The region of the respiratory chain between cytochromes *b* and c_1 is affected by several compounds in such a way as to lead to inhibition of electron transport. The site of action of these inhibitors is usually called the "antimycin-sensitive" site because antimycin [1] is the most firmly bound. Three main classes of inhibitors will be considered here: (i) antimycin, (ii) alkyl derivatives of 4-hydroxyquinoline-N-oxide and (iii) alkyl derivatives of 3-hydroxy-1,4-naphthoquinone. Their application in studies on the structure and function of the respiratory chain has been manyfold: (a) in elucidation of the sequence of the components [58], (b) in reconstitution of the respiratory chain [39], (c) in oxidative phosphorylation [59] especially in estimating the sites of phosphorylation and (d) in studies on the reversal of the respiratory chain [33, 41].

Common features of the majority of these inhibitors are: (i) strong inhibition of the electron transport at very low concentration; (ii) relatively strong binding to the site of inhibition; (iii) probably the same site of action; (iv) sigmoidal inhibition curves with antimycin and HOQNO in particulate preparations and linear or hyperbolic with soluble preparations, e.g. Complex III; (v) reversal of the inhibition by serum albumin, some other proteins

Abbreviations: HOQNO, 4-hydroxyquinoline-N-oxide; DNQ, 2-hydroxy 3-(3′,7′-dimethyloctyl)-1,4-naphthoquinone; CNQ, 2-hydroxy-3-cyclohexyl-1,4-naphthoquinone; SN 5949, 2-hydroxy-3(2′-methyloctyl)-1,4-naphthoquinone; CCCP, carbonyl cyanide *m*-chlorophenylhydrazone; BAL, 2,3-dimercaptopropanol.

and lipophilic compounds and in coupled mitochondria also by uncoupling agents. Antimycin and HOQNO are known to modify the spectral properties of cytochrome *b* and to inhibit the cleavage of Complex III into cytochromes *b* and c_1 promoted by bile salts.

This review will be devoted to three aspects of the inhibition of electron transport in the cytochrome $b - c_1$ region of the respiratory chain: (i) the structure and inhibitory properties of the inhibitors, (ii) reversal of the inhibition and (iii) mechanism of the inhibition. Since the interaction between antimycin and the respiratory chain has been studied in greater detail [7—9, 34—36] a possible mechanism of action of this inhibitor will be discussed.

Structure and Inhibitory Properties

The inhibitors acting on the antimycin-sensitive site in the respiratory chain display some similarities in structure (see *Appendix*), *viz.* an aromatic ring with a phenolic hydroxyl group, an alkyl side chain, and the lipophilic nature [67]. In general, the inhibitory power of these compounds increases with increase in the lipophilic character of the side chain [3, 29, 43].

Antimycin A. Antimycin A is the name given to an antibiotic complex that consists of at least four compounds of closely related structure. Compounds of this series are produced by a number of species of microorganism of the genus *Streptomyces*. The basic structure of the antibiotic, determined in STRONG's laboratory [16, 66], consists of an acyl- and alkyl-substituted dilactone ring linked *via* an amide bond to 3-formamidosalicylic acid. Antimycins A_1 and A_3 differ only by two methylene carbons in the alkyl substituent of the dilactone ring. On the basis of the inhibitory activity of various derivatives of antimycin A_3 toward electron transport in the respiratory chain it may be concluded that the substituted dilactone ring, the phenolic hydroxyl group and an N-carbonyl group individually and collectively are indispensible for inhibitory activities of antimycin A [51]. From the experiments of DICKIE et al. [16] with synthetic analogues of antimycin A it appears that in addition to conferring lipid solubility, the dilactone ring and its substituted alkyl groups may function in providing a proper fit between the inhibitor and its binding site on the enzyme.

In the early studies of POTTER and REIF [47] and THORN [68] the stoichiometry between the amount of inhibitor required and the amount of enzyme preparation was established. It was concluded that the inhibition of the respiratory chain by antimycin results from binding to one of the components of the chain. Indeed, CHANCE [10] and ESTABROOK [18] observed that almost stoichiometric amounts of antimycin to cytochrome inhibit oxidation in heart-muscle preparations. Moreover, RIESKE and ZAUGG [52] found that both cleavage and the QH_2-cytochrome *c* reductase activity of Complex III is completely inhibited when the antimycin/cytochrome c_1 ratio is 1. On the basis of spectrophotometric studies the site of antimycin action between cytochrome *b* and c_1 was localized by KEILIN and HARTREE [38], CHANCE and WILLIAMS [13] and ESTABROOK [17].

Antimycin displays a characteristic sigmoidal inhibition curve with particulate preparations [10, 18, 47, 68] and linear or hyperbolic curves with soluble preparations containing the antimycin-sensitive site, *viz.* NADH-cytochrome *c* reductase [23] and Complex III [9, 52—54]. It is striking that only one of the components of the respiratory chain, cytochrome *b*, is known to be modified in the presence of antimycin. As shown first by CHANCE [11] and confirmed by others [15, 40, 48, 55, 61, 63] antimycin increases both the rate and extent of reduction of cytochrome *b* in submitochondrial particles and causes a small shift toward the red of the maxima of both the α- and γ-bands.

2-alkyl-4-hydroxyquinoline-N-oxide. The streptomycin antagonist, 2-heptyl-4-hydroxyquinoline-N-oxide, was found by LIGHTBOWN and JACKSON [43] also to be a potent inhibitor of the succinate and NADH oxidase chains. Maximum activity of substituted quinoline-N-oxides both in antagonizing the inhibitory action of dihydrostreptomycin and inhibiting the electron transport was obtained with a 2-alkyl chain length of nine carbons. Loss of both activities resulted when the heptyl side chain was moved from the 2- to the 6-position. Removal of the oxygen atom from the nitrogen resulted in loss of both activities, and introduction of a bromine atom in the 3-position increased the inhibitory effect as well as antagonistic activity. The relative inhibitory activities of the 2-*n*-nonyl, 2-*n*-undecyl, 2-*n*-heptyl-3-bromo and 2-*n*-heptyl derivatives are 3:3:2.5:1, respectively.

The site of inhibition by HOQNO and its modification of the spectral properties of cytochrome *b* were reported by LIGHTBOWN and JACKSON [43] and CHANCE [11]. HOQNO appears to act at the same site in the respiratory chain as antimycin, since their effects are additive [45]. The inhibition curve is sigmoidal in particulate preparations [27] and hyperbolic with soluble NADH-cytochrome *c* reductase [23]. The main use of this compound is with bacterial preparations since, unlike antimycin, it inhibits the respiratory chain in bacterial protoplast membranes.

2-hydroxy-3-alkylnaphthoquinones. A number of alkylhydroxy-naphthoquinones, originally studied for their antimalarial activity [70], have been shown to be potent inhibitors of the mitochondrial respiratory chain [3, 17, 26, 28—30, 49] also acting at a locus between cytochromes b and c_1 [17]. From the data of BALL et al. [3] and HOWLAND [29] it may be concluded that the inhibitory activity of different hydroxynaphthoquinones on mitochondrial electron transport depends only on the nature of the alkyl side chain substituted in the 3-position of the naphthoquinone nucleus. The greatest inhibitory action on succinate oxidation is displayed by compounds containing 9 or 10 carbon atoms in the side chain, i.e. SN 5949 [3] and DNQ [29], respectively. Decrease in the inhibitory activity results from shortening the side chain as well as from the introduction of a 2′, 3′ double bond or a hydroxyl group in the side chain.

Inhibition of succinate oxidation by hydroxynaphthoquinones declines with increasing pH [3, 29, 30] at least within the region 7.0 to 8.0, probably due to decreasing lipid solubility upon ionization of the 2-hydroxyl group [29]. Thus, less of the inhibitor would reach the lipophilic portion of the mitochondrial membrane, where its action presumably occurs. A similar pH-dependence was observed for antimycin [18]. In intact mitochondria inorganic phosphate is required for maximum inhibition, appearing to facilitate the penetration of the inhibitor to the site of action [29].

Another important property of hydroxynaphthoquinones is their uncoupling action on oxidative phosphorylation. β-unsaturation in the side chain renders the quinone inactive as an inhibitor although it remains effective as an uncoupler. Since all the naphthoquinones examined [30], both saturated and unsaturated at the β-position, are uncouplers, it is clear that the character of the side chain does not influence the ability to uncouple, which is more likely related to the hydroxyl group in the 2-position.

One group of hydroxynaphthoquinones, including DNQ, CNQ and hydrolapachol, appears to have the characteristic of inhibitors of oxidative phosphorylation acting in much the same manner as oligomycin, inhibiting ATP synthesis and preventing the stimulation of respiration by phosphate acceptor [27].

Some naphthoquinones appear also to give a sigmoidal inhibition curve [29].

The inhibitory activity of the compounds acting at the antimycin-sensitive site are compared in Table 1.

Table 1. *Inhibitory activity of inhibitors acting at the antimycin-sensitive site of mitochondrial preparations*

Inhibitor	Concentration for 50% inhibition (nmoles/mg of protein)			
	Rat-liver mitochondria	Ref.	Heart-muscle preparation	Ref.
Antimycin	0.05	[18]	0.15	[18]
HOQNO				
Heptyl	0.09	[27]	2.2	[43]
Nonyl	—		1.2—1.6	
Naphthoquinones				
DNQ	0.06	[29]	—	
Hydrolapachol	6.56		—	

Antimycin [4, 19, 46, 64], HOQNO [2, 4, 39, 62] and SN 5949 [20] inhibit light-induced phosphorylation in chloroplasts and chromatophores.

Reversal of the Inhibition

Antimycin and derivatives of HOQNO and naphthoquinone are known to be tightly bound to the respiratory chain, and have been classified as pseudoirreversible inhibitors [49]. In the case of antimycin, this binding is so strong that at a molar ratio of inhibitor to cytochrome c_1 of 1:1 the cleavage of Complex III is completely inhibited [54]. Since the reversibility of binding of the inhibitor is a very useful tool in studies on the mechanism of its action, methods for reversal of the inhibition induced by all the inhibitors have been elaborated. Three methods will be considered here: (i) by uncoupling agents (in mitochondria only); (ii) displacement of the inhibitors by various proteins or lipophilic substances, and (iii) removal of the inhibitor, *in casu* antimycin, by extraction with diethyl ether.

Reversal by uncoupling agents. It was suggested by HÜLSMANN [25] that certain respiratory inhibitors might react at the same location in the energy-transfer apparatus as uncoupling agents, the difference residing in the relative rates of dissociation of the complex between the inhibitor or uncoupler and a component of the energy-transfer apparatus. In accordance with this suggestion, the reversal of the effect of several inhibitors by means of uncoupling agents has been taken to mean that the action of these

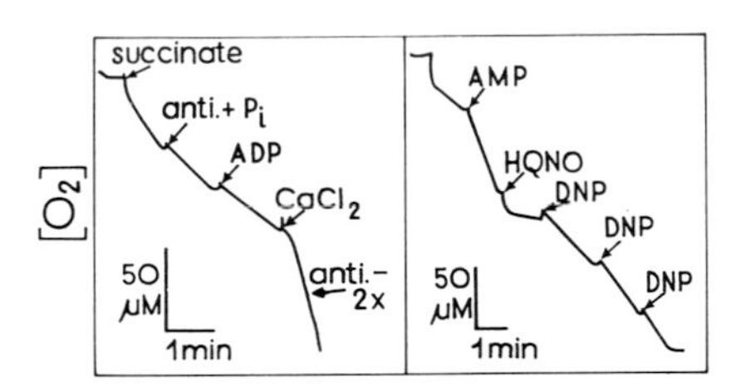

Fig. 1. Release of antimycin inhibition by calcium and of HOQNO inhibition by 2,4-dinitrophenol. From HOWLAND [28, 26]

inhibitors is, at least in part, concerned with energy-conserving reactions [12]. HOWLAND [26, 27, 29, 30] in a series of papers showed that inhibition by alkylhydroxynaphthoquinones, alkylhydroxyquinoline-N-oxide and antimycin may be reversed in this way.

Fig. 1 shows the release of inhibition by antimycin and HOQNO of succinate oxidation in rat-liver mitochondria by dinitrophenol and calcium, respectively. Antimycin inhibition is also released by CCCP and gramicidin [31]. It should be added that inhibition is reversible only within extremely narrow limits of antimycin concentration (giving not more than 60% inhibition), inhibition by even a small excess being irreversible. HOWLAND [26, 29] demonstrated also that inhibition of succinate oxidation by hydrolapachol is released completely by CCCP and 2,4-dibromophenol and partly by 2,4-dinitrophenol. CCCP also releases inhibition by isolapachol, CNQ and DNQ [29].

It was suggested [31] that the reversal of the inhibition indicates a requirement for the active translocation of the inhibitor to its intramitochondrial site of action. Uncouplers, by discharging the high-energy state of mitochondria might prevent them from maintaining a high internal inhibitor concentration and give rise to the observed release of inhibition. The requirement for active translocation would be expected to disappear with a high inhibitor concentration, a condition under which uncouplers do not, in fact, give rise to release. However, the recent suggestion by VAN DAM and SLATER [14] that anionic uncouplers act by virtue of their energy-linked translocation across the mitochondrial membrane should be taken into consideration. According to this idea, uncouplers may interfere with respiratory inhibition by competing directly with anionic inhibitors for entry, thus resulting in a lower intramitochondrial inhibitor concentration and the diminished inhibition which is observed. All the inhibitors considered here are anions bearing a phenolic hydroxyl group [67].

Reversal by proteins and lipophilic compounds. POTTER and REIF [49] first observed that addition of serum albumin to antimycin- or SN 5949-inhibited preparations reactivates succinate oxidase activity. THORN [68] demonstrated reversal of antimycin inhibition of succinate oxidase activity in heart-muscle preparation when an antimycin-free preparation was added to an antimycin-inhibited. Moreover, he showed that the antimycin-binding site in heart-muscle preparations is not affected by BAL [56] or *p*-aminophenylarsenoxide treatment [57], indicating that different sites are involved in the action of these inhibitors.

Similarly, antimycin inhibition can be reversed by a protein from chicken liver [50], and inhibition by hydrolapachol and other naphthoquinones by bovine serum albumin [29].

In all these experiments reactivation was explained as due to redistribution of the inhibitor from its site of action to binding sites on the added proteins.

Reversal of antimycin, quinoline-N-oxide and naphthoquinones inhibition has also been demonstrated for lipophilic substances. Thus HENDLIN and COOK [24] observed the release of naphthoquinone inhibition by a number of lipophilic compounds, including ubiquinone, tocopherol and squalene. In the experiments of TAKEMORI and KING [65] Q-2 released the inhibition of succinate-cytochrome *c* reductase activity by antimycin, 2-heptyl-HOQNO and 2-(9-cyclohexyl-*n*-nonyl)-naphthoquinone with a reactivation of 51, 100 and 76%, respectively. In this case reversal required a large excess of the lipophilic material over the inhibitor. This, as well as the lack of specificity suggests that the added lipid may either take up the inhibitor into solution and effectively reduce its concentration or displace the inhibitor in the lipid phase of the mitochondria.

Reversal by ether extraction. A useful procedure for reversal of antimycin inhibition is that described by KANIUGA, GARDAS and BRYLA

Table 2. *Reversal by extraction with diethyl ether of antimycin inhibition of the succinate oxidase activity of heart-muscle preparation*

For extraction procedure, see Ref. [36].

Sample	Activity	
	µatoms 0/min per mg protein	%
Control	0.545	100
Inhibited[a]	0.031	6
Extracted	0.560	103
Inhibited[a] and extracted	0.462	85

[a] 0.38 nmole antimycin per mg protein.

[36, 37]. When an antimycin-inhibited heart-muscle preparation is extracted with diethyl ether, oxidation of succinate is completely restored, provided soluble cytochrome *c* is present during the enzymic assay (Table 2). Extraction with ether of antimycin-treated Complex III [9] results in reactivation of both QH_2-cytochrome *c* reductase activity (in comparison with the ether-extracted control) and cleavage of the Complex III promoted by bile salts. This is in contrast to the extraction of antimycin from Complex III with acetone or taurocholate since even though most of the antimycin was extracted by taurocholate, its inhibitory effect on the cleavage was retained [53].

Although extraction by ether leads to almost complete restoration of the enzyme activity, it releases only about one-half of the antimycin, independent of the degree of the inhibition (Table 3).

This suggests that amounts of antimycin sufficient to inhibit the respiratory chain are not bound more firmly than larger amounts. This conclusion is shown more directly by the redistribution ex-

Table 3. *Release of antimycin bound to heart-muscle preparation and Complex III by extraction with diethyl ether* (from BRYŁA et al. [9])

Expt.	Preparation	Protein (mg)	Added antimycin (nmoles)	Inhibition of activity (%)	Extracted antimycin	
					nmoles	%
1	Heart-muscle	24.5	15.3	0	6.5	42
			31.1	30	15.0	48
			32.7	98	13.8	42
2	Cholate[a]-treated	113.0	40.0	93	36.4	81
3	Complex III	10.2	24.5	87	21.4	87

[a] 13.3 mg cholate per mg heart-muscle preparation.

Table 4. *Extraction of antimycin after preincubation of heart-muscle preparation treated with various amounts of antimycin with untreated preparation*

Heart-muscle preparation containing 50.6 mg protein was incubated with the indicated amounts of antimycin and then either extracted with ether or preincubated with 2.5 ml of the untreated preparation (C) for 5 min and then extracted with ether. The other symbols, A_0, A_{10}, A_{90} refer to preparations inhibited by 0, 10 and 90%, respectively (from BRYŁA et al. [9]).

Preparation	Antimycin added (nmoles)	Inhibition of succinate oxidase (%)	Antimycin extracted	
			nmoles	%
A_0	3.1	0	1.5	49
A_{10}	8.2	10	4.2	51
A_{90}	14.1	90	7.7	54
A_0 + C	3.1	0	1.4	45
A_{10} + C	8.2	0	3.5	42
A_{90} + C	14.1	22	7.3	51

periment (cf. [68]) shown in Table 4. The amount of antimycin extractable by ether remains the same even when antimycin is redistributed between an antimycin-inhibited preparation and an untreated, resulting in a decline of inhibition from 90% to 22%.

Moreover, the antimycin remaining after ether extraction is re-distributed when an ether-extracted antimycin preparation is preincubated with an untreated preparation. About one-half of the antimycin is now extractable by ether (Table 5). Even more significantly, allowing a suspension of ether-extracted antimycin-treated preparation to stand resulted in one-half of the antimycin becoming extractable with ether (Table 5, Expt. 2b).

Table 5. *Re-distribution of antimycin between ether-extracted antimycin-treated preparation and uninhibited preparation*

Heart-muscle preparation (71 mg in Expt. 1 and 158 mg in Expt. 2), treated with 0.24 nmole antimycin per mg protein, was extracted with ether (preparation E). The amounts of antimycin remaining in the E were determined by extraction with ether-ethanol (see ref. [36]). The extractability with ether was determined after 5 min preincubation of E with an untreated preparation. 71 mg and 157 mg protein of preparations E in Expts. 1 and 2, respectively, were mixed with 131 mg and 158 mg protein of control preparations (C) in Expts. 1 and 2, respectively. The extractability with ether of E was determined either without (Expt. 2a) or after re-suspension in phosphate buffer and standing for 30 min at 0° before the repeated extraction with ether (Expts. 1 and 2b) (from Bryła et al. [9]).

Expt.	Antimycin extracted with	Amounts of antimycin extracted from E		E + C	
		nmoles	%	nmoles	%
1	Ether-ethanol	14.3	100	14.3	100
	Ether	8.4	58	7.4	51
2a	Ether-ethanol	18.8	100		
	Ether	2.4	13		
b	Ether-ethanol	16.7	100	17.2	103
	Ether	9.5	56	9.5	55

These results indicate that there are two types of antimycin-binding sites in particulate preparations, differing in accessibility to ether. Both sites are saturated simultaneously and with the same amount of antimycin, and the binding constants are equal. Thus, even on standing, antimycin remaining bound to the ether-inaccessible site is redistributed to the ether-accessible site in the same preparation.

Treatment with cholate makes antimycin bound to the ether-inaccessible site also extractable (Table 3). This effect of cholate was found with as little as 1 mg per mg protein, much less than is necessary to change the sigmoidal titration curve to a linear (see following section). Antimycin bound to Complex III is also extractable with ether (Table 3). However, redistribution studies by THORN's [68] procedure showed that Complex III binds antimycin more firmly than heart-muscle preparations (9; cf. ref. [53]).

Transformation of the Sigmoidal Inhibition Curve into a Linear

As already mentioned, the extraction with ether of either cholate-solubilized particulate preparations or soluble Complex III released more than 80% of the added antimycin (Table 3) and the antimycin titration curve of the Complex III is linear. Thus, it appeared interesting to study the effect of cholate on the nature of the inhibition curve of the particulate preparation.

As can be seen from Fig. 2A when increasing amounts of cholate are added to a particulate heart-muscle preparation, the inhibition curve becomes less sigmoidal. When the concentration of cholate is 4.6% (14 mg/mg of protein), it is almost linear[1]. However, the amount of antimycin required for almost complete inhibition is unaffected. The effect of cholate in transforming the sigmoidal inhibition curve towards a linear is reversed by removal of the cholate by dialysis, as shown in part B of this figure. Dialysis does not remove all the cholate, and the solution still appears clear after 8 h dialysis. However, light-scattering measurements summarized in part C show that return of a sigmoidal inhibition curve is associated with increased average particle weight.

Treatment of a particulate preparation with deoxycholate results also in the transformation of the sigmoid curve into a linear or hyperbolic. As it is seen from Fig. 3 this phenomenon is observed for both antimycin and HOQNO.

Treatment of the heart-muscle preparation with cholate also changes the effect of antimycin on the reducibility of cytochrome *b*.

[1] Because of the very high binding constant of antimycin, the curve relating inhibition to total antimycin (bound and free) is practically linear. If it were possible to plot the concentration of free antimycin, the curve would presumably be hyperbolic.

As can be seen from Fig. 4, treatment with cholate sufficient almost completely to abolish the sigmoidal curve of the enzymic activity makes the cytochrome *b* non-reducible with succinate, in spite of

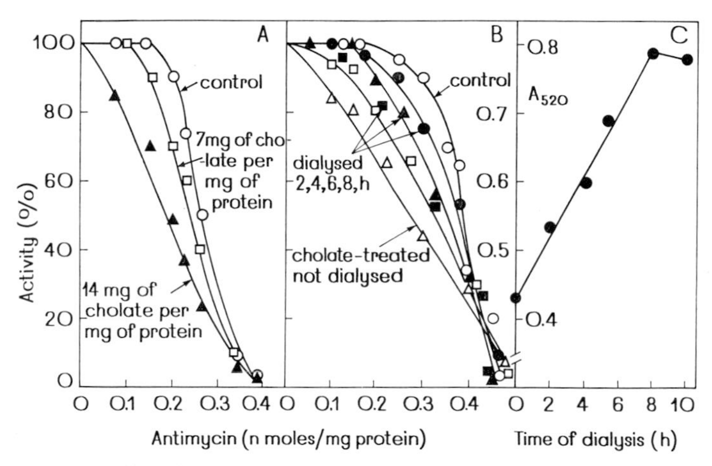

Fig. 2A—C. The effect of cholate on the inhibition by antimycin of the succinate-cytochrome *c* reductase activity of heart-muscle preparation. A. Titration curves of the succinate-cytochrome *c* reductase of heart-muscle preparation. B. The effect of dialysis time. C. Light-scattering after dialysis. The activity of the preparations is expressed as μmoles of succinate oxidized per min and mg of protein. In A: o —— o, control preparation, activity = 0.117; □ —— □, preparation treated with 7 mg cholate/mg protein (26 mg cholate/ml), activity = 0.235; Δ —— Δ, preparation treated with 14 mg cholate/mg protein (46 mg cholate/ml), activity = 0.104. Antimycin was added after treatment with cholate. In B and C: the preparation treated with 14 mg cholate/mg protein (53 mg cholate/ml) was dialysed against 10 mM Tris-HCl buffer (pH 8.0). Every 2 h, samples were taken and light-scattering and inhibition by antimycin of enzymic activity were measured. In B: o —— o, control preparation, activity = 0.085; Δ —— Δ, preparation treated with cholate and not dialysed, activity = 0.075; □, ■, Δ, o, cholate-treated preparations after 2, 4, 6 and 8 h of dialysis, respectively. Activity = 0.072, 0.074, 0.071 and 0.077, respectively. The samples assayed for light-scattering (C) were diluted to 1.2 mg protein/ml. From Bryła et al. [8]

the fact that the succinate-cytochrome *c* reductase activity is unaffected. This confirms Pumphrey's observations [48]. Antimycin restores the reducibility somewhat, the activity curve, however, being linear in contrast to the sigmoidal curve

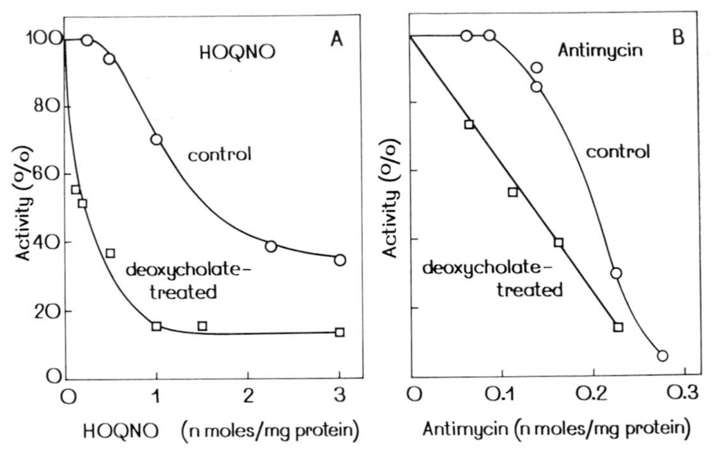

Fig. 3. The effect of deoxycholate on the inhibition by HOQNO (A) and by antimycin (B) of the succinate-cytochrome *c* reductase activity of heart-muscle preparation. The activity is expressed as in Fig. 2. o —— o, control preparation, containing 7.2 mg protein per ml, activity = 0.074; □ —— □, preparation treated with 11.7 mg deoxycholate per mg protein (45.6 mg deoxycholate/ml), activity = 0.077

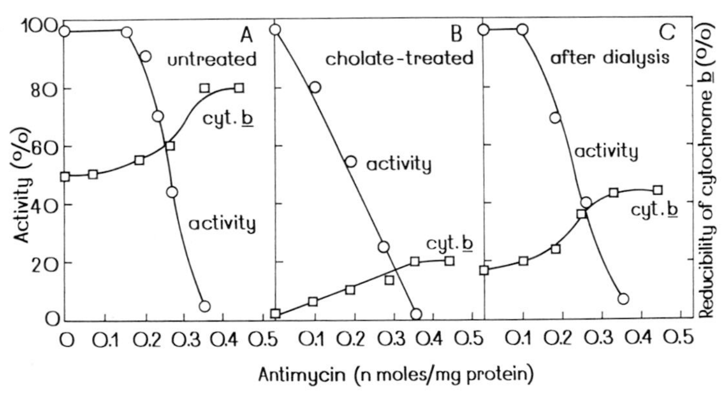

Fig. 4. The effect of antimycin on the reducibility of cytochrome *b* by succinate in cholate-treated heart-muscle preparation before and after dialysis. Activity is expressed as in Fig. 2. o —— o, activity of the succinate-cytochrome *c* reductase, activity = 0.070; □ —— □, cytochrome *b* reduced by succinate. The amount of cytochrome *b* reduced by dithionite was taken as 100%. A, untreated preparation; B, preparation treated with 14.2 mg cholate/mg protein (69 mg cholate/ml), activity = 0.068; C, preparation treated with cholate as in B, incubated with antimycin as indicated and dialysed for 6 h against 10 mM Tris-HCl buffer (pH 8.0). From Bryła et al.

obtained for the intact preparation. Dialysis of the cholate-treated preparation, either before adding the antimycin (cf. Fig. 2B) or in the presence of antimycin [8], restores both reducibility with succinate in the absence of antimycin and the sigmoidal curve of the reducibility of the cytochrome *b* in the presence of increasing amounts of antimycin, as shown in part C of Fig. 4.

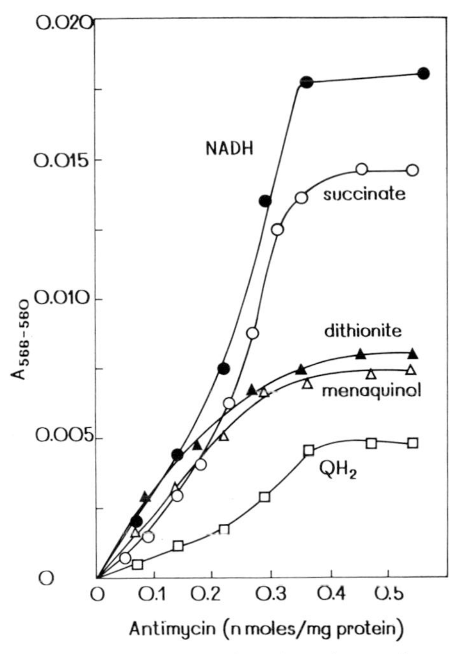

Fig. 5. The effect of concentration of antimycin on the magnitude of the spectral shift of cytochrome *b* reduced by different substrates. ●——●, 1 mM NADH; o——o, 10 mM succinate; □——□, 1 mM QH_2-2; Δ——Δ, 1 mM menaquinol-O; ▲——▲, dithionite. Antimycin (as indicated) was added to the preparation previously treated with substrates. From BRYŁA et al. [8]. 9.5 mg protein in the sample

Moreover, it is interesting that the effect of antimycin on the displacement to the red of the α-band of ferrocytochrome *b* depends on the substrate used for reduction of the cytochrome *b*. As shown in Fig. 5 the effect of antimycin is described by a sigmoidal curve in the presence of NADH, QH_2 and succinate, but not with menaquinol-O or dithionite.

Mechanism of Inhibition by Antimycin

The following effects of antimycin on the heart-muscle preparation are described by sigmoidal curves: (1) inhibition of succinate oxidase or succinate-cytochrome *c* reductase; (2) stimulation of reducibility of cytochrome *b*; (3) displacement to the red of the α-band of cytochrome *b*. The sigmoidal curves are replaced by linear by treatment with cholate and are restored by removal of the cholate, either before or after the addition of antimycin. Three explanations of the sigmoidal curves may be considered.

(1) The preparation contains two antimycin-binding sites, one with the higher affinity for antimycin not concerned in the catalytic activity, and a 'catalytic site' with lower affinity [47]. Thorn [68] has already pointed out that the shape of the curve relating activity to concentration of a preparation at fixed antimycin concentration is against this explanation. It is also not supported by the fact that small amounts of antimycin are extracted by ether to the same extent as larger amounts. Nor does it account for the hyperbolic curves describing the effect of antimycin on the shift of the α-band of cytochrome *b* reduced by menaquinol-O or dithionite. Finally, the very high slope of the inhibition curve (equivalent to 100% inhibition with about 0.03 μmole/mg protein) makes this explanation very unlikely, since the concentration of cytochrome c_1 in heart-muscle mitochondria is about 0.25 nmole/mg protein (59a).

(2) An antimycin-sensitive factor necessary for electron transport is either present in large excess [47] or reacts rapidly in comparison with other components of the electron-transport chain [68, 18]. This explanation is difficult to reconcile with the linear inhibition curves obtained after cholate treatment.

(3) Inhibition by antimycin is a co-operative phenomenon similar to those proposed for allosteric inhibitors by Monod et al. [44] and Koshland et al. [42]. This is the explanation that we favour. The specific allosteric model of Monod et al. [44], as extended below to particulate systems, provides a suitable framework for a consideration of the effects of antimycin, but other models could also be used.

It is proposed that in particulate preparations the respiratory chain, or at least the segment involved in the QH_2-cytochrome *c* reductase activity, exists in two enzymically active conformation states, the R and the T,b oth oligomeric (or polymeric). The protomer contains two *b* sub-units, one c_1 and may be others (see [5]) and one antimycin-sensitive site. If electron transfer in the respiratory chain favours the T state, and antimycin combines more firmly with the R state, a sigmoidal inhibition curve would be expected. This would be replaced by a linear curve if the polymeric or oligomeric structure is dispersed by cholate in the same way as urea abolishes allosteric effects in aspartate carbamyltransferase (EC 2.1.3.2) [21]. The linear inhibition curves obtained with Complex III [9, 52—54] are also to be expected since the Complex III appears to be entirely in the form of the monomer [69]. It seems justified then to call antimycin an allosteric inhibitor.

The allosteric effect of antimycin should be clearly distinguished from its effect on the 'conformation stability' of the monomer Complex III, investigated in detail by RIESKE et al. [5, 52—54]. The stabilizing effect of antimycin on the conformation of the monomer is manifested by its inhibition of splitting of Complex III into components by cholate-ammonium sulphate or guanidine [52, 53], its protection against proteolysis of the Complex III by trypsin [54] and the smaller number of titratable-SH groups in the presence of antimycin [5].

It is of particular interest that the sigmoidal curves relating the effects of antimycin on cytochrome *b* in non-phosphorylating particulate preparations are seen with the natural hydrogen donors: succinate, NADH or the analogue of a natural donor (QH_2-2), but not with menaquinol-0 or dithionite, which probably reduce cytochrome *b* directly.

The increased rate and extent of reduction of cytochrome *b* by antimycin [11] is more likely explained by its allosteric effect. Thus, one might imagine that in the oligomer in the T state only one of the two *b* sub-units is reduced during electron transport from QH_2-2 to cytochrome c_1 (cf. [15]), but that in the R state both are rapidly reducible. The displacement by antimycin of the absorption peaks of ferrocytochrome *b* may be due to a different hydrophobic environment around the haem in the two states. In this respect it is interesting to recall PUMPHREY's observation [48] that cholate displaces the absorption peak in the opposite direction from antimycin. Cholate has a second effect opposite to that of antimycin, namely it prevents the reduction of cytochrome *b* without, however, inhibiting the succinate-cytochrome *c* reductase activity.

The fact that the same amount of antimycin is required for complete inhibition before and after treatment with cholate can only be explained on the basis of the model proposed if the monomer, obtained by cholate treatment, is entirely in the R form. This is understandable if T is a constrained state that can be only stabilized in an oligomeric structure. In agreement with this conclusion is the finding that Complex III binds antimycin much more firmly than particulate preparations. Complex III may be considered as a preparation of the R monomer [9].

The suggestion that in the particulate preparation antimycin interacts with the multi-enzyme system in a co-operative fashion is consistent with the possibility that electron transport *via* the natural carriers causes a conformational change in an oligomeric or polymeric complex. The possible role of conformational changes in energy conservation has been discussed by BOYER [6], GREEN [22], CHANCE (11a) and SLATER [60].

References

1. AHMAD, K., H. G. SCHNEIDER, and F. M. STRONG: Arch. Biochem. **28**, 281 (1950).
2. ARNON, D. I., H. Y. TSUJIMOTO, and B. H. McSWAIN: Proc. nat. Acad. Sci. (Wash.) **51**, 1274 (1964).
3. BALL, E. G., C. B. ANFINSEN, and O. COOPER: J. biol. Chem. **168**, 257 (1947).
4. BALTSCHEFFSKY, H.: Acta chem. scand. **14**, 264 (1960).
5. BAUM, H., H. I. SILMAN, J. S. RIESKE, and S. H. LIPTON: J. biol. Chem. **242**, 4876 (1967).
6. BOYER, P.: In: KING, T. E., H. S. MASON, and M. MORRISON: Oxidases and related redox systems, Vol. 2, p. 984. New York: Wiley 1965.
7. BRYŁA, J., and Z. KANIUGA: Biochim. biophys. Acta **153**, 910 (1968).
8. — —, and E. C. SLATER: Biochim. biophys. Acta (in press).
9. — — — Biochim. biophys. Acta (in press).
10. CHANCE, B.: Nature (Lond.) **169**, 215 (1952).
11. — J. biol. Chem. **233**, 1223 (1958).
11a. —, C. P. LEE, and L. MELA: Fed. Proc. **26**, 1341 (1967).
12. —, G. HOLLUNGER, and B. HAGIHARA: Biochem. biophys. Res. Commun. **8**, 180 (1962).
13. —, and G. R. WILLIAMS: Advanc. Enzymol. **17**, 65 (1956).

14. van Dam, K., and E. C. Slater: Proc. nat. Acad. Sci. (Wash.) **58**, 2015 (1967).
15. Deul, D. H., and M. B. Thorn: Biochim. biophys. Acta **59**, 426 (1962).
16. Dickie, J. P., M. B. Loomans, T. M. Farley, and F. M. Strong: J. med. Chem. **6**, 424 (1963).
17. Estabrook, R. W.: J. biol. Chem. **230**, 735 (1958).
18. — Biochim. biophys. Acta **60**, 236 (1962).
19. Fewson, C. A., C. C. Black, and M. Gibbs: Plant Physiol. **78**, 680 (1963).
20. Geller, D. M., and F. Lipmann: J. biol. Chem. **235**, 2478 (1960).
21. Gerhart, I. C., and A. B. Pardee: Cold Spr. Harb. Symp. quant. Biol. **28**, 491 (1963).
22. Harris, R. A., J. T. Penniston, I. Assai, and D. E. Green: Proc. nat. Acad. Sci. (Wash.) **59**, 830 (1968).
23. Hatefi, Y., A. G. Haavik, and P. Jurtschuk: Biochim. biophys. Acta **52**, 106 (1961).
24. Hendlin, D., and F. Cook: Biochim. biophys. Res. Commun. **2**, 71 (1960).
25. Hülsmann, W. C.: Over het mechanisme van de ademhalingsketen-fosforylering. M. D. Thesis, Amsterdam 1958.
26. Howland, J. L.: Biochim. biophys. Acta **73**, 665 (1963).
27. — Biochim. biophys. Acta **77**, 419 (1963).
28. — Biochim. biophys. Acta **77**, 659 (1963).
29. — Biochim. biophys. Acta **105**, 205 (1965).
30. — Biochim. biophys. Acta **131**, 247 (1967).
31. — Biochim. biophys. Acta **153**, 309 (1968).
33. Kaniuga, Z., and J. Bryła: Post. Biochem. **12**, 451 (1966).
34. — — Abstr. 5th Meeting Fed. Europ. Biochem. Socs., p. 293, Prague 1968.
35. — —, and E. C. Slater: Proc. 6th Meeting Fed. Europ. Biochem. Socs., Madrid 1969 (in press).
36. —, A. Gardas, and J. Bryła: Biochim. biophys. Acta (Amst.) **153**, 60 (1968).
37. —, J. Bryła, A. Gardas, and I. Chmielewska: Abstr. 3rd Meeting Fed. Europ. Biochem. Socs., Warsaw 1966, p. 140. London and Warsaw: Academic Press and Polish Scientific Publishers 1966.
38. Keilin, D., and E. F. Hartree: Nature (Lond.) **176**, 200 (1955).
39. King, T. E.: Advanc. Enzymol. **28**, 218 (1966).
40. Kirschbaum, I., and W. W. Wainio: Biochim. biophys. Acta **113**, 27 (1963).
41. Klingenberg, M.: Angew. Chem. **75**, 900 (1963).
42. Koshland, D. F., Jr., G. Nemethy, and D. Filmer: Biochemistry **5**, 365 (1966).
43. Lightbown, J. W., and F. L. Jackson: Biochem. J. **63**, 130 (1956).
44. Monod, J., J. Wyman, and J. P. Changeux: J. molec. Biol. **12**, 88 (1965).
45. Nijs, P.: Biochim. biophys. Acta **143**, 454 (1967).
46. Nishimura, M.: Biochim. biophys. Acta **66**, 17 (1963).
47. Potter, V. R., and A. E. Reif: J. biol. Chem. **194**, 287 (1952).

48. PUMPHREY, A. M.: J. biol. Chem. **237**, 2384 (1962).
49. REIF, A. E., and V. R. POTTER: J. biol. Chem. **205**, 279 (1953).
50. REPORTER, M.: Biochemistry **5**, 2416 (1966).
51. RIESKE, J. S.: In: GOTTLIEB, D., and P. D. SHAW: Antibiotics, Vol. 1, p. 542. Berlin-Heidelberg-New York: Springer 1967.
52. —, and W. S. ZAUGG: Biochem. biophys. Res. Commun. 8, 421 (1962).
53. —, S. H. LIPTON, H. BAUM, and H. I. SILMAN: J. biol. Chem. **242**, 4888 (1967).
54. —, H. BAUM, C. D. STONER, and S. H. LIPTON: J. biol. Chem. **242**, 4854 (1967).
55. SHORE, I. B., and W. W. WAINIO: J. biol. Chem. **240**, 3165 (1965).
56. SLATER, E. C.: Biochem. J. **45**, 14 (1949).
57. — Biochem. J. **45**, 130 (1949).
58. — Advanc. Enzymol. **20**, 147 (1958).
59. — In: FLORKIN, M., and E. M. STOTZ, Comprehensive biochemistry, Vol. 14, p. 327. Amsterdam: Elsevier 1966.
59a. — In: SLATER, E. C., Z. KANIUGA, and L. WOJTCZAK: Biochemistry of mitochondria, p. 1. London and Warsaw: Academic Press and Polish Scientific Publishers 1967.
60. — Proc. 5th Meeting Fed. Europ. Biochem. Socs., Prague 1968 (in press).
61. —, and J. P. COLPA-BOONSTRA: In: FALK, I. E., R. LEMBERG, and R. K. MORTON: Haematin enzymes, Vol. 2, p. 575. London: Pergamon Press 1961.
62. SMITH, L., and M. BALTSCHEFFSKY: J. biol. Chem. **234**, 1575 (1960).
63. STOREY, R. T.: Arch. Biochem. **121**, 271 (1967).
64. TAGAWA, K., H. Y. TSUJIMOTO, and D. I. ARNON: Proc. nat. Acad. Sci. (Wash.) **49**, 567; **50**, 544 (1963).
65. TAKEMORI, S., and T. E. KING: J. biol. Chem. **239**, 3546 (1964).
66. VAN TAMELEN, E. E., J. P. DICKIE, M. E. LOOMANS, R. S. DEWEY, and F. M. STRONG: J. Amer. Chem. Soc. **83**, 1639 (1961).
67. TAPPEL, A. L.: Biochem. Pharmacol. **3**, 289 (1960).
68. THORN, M. B.: Biochem. J. **63**, 420 (1956).
69. TZAGOLOFF, A., P. C. YANG, D. C. WHARTON, and J. S. RIESKE: Biochim. biophys. Acta **96**, 1 (1965).
70. WENDEL, W. B.: Fed. Proc. **5**, 406 (1946).

V. Cytoplasmic Compartmentation

The Inhibition of Adenine Nucleotide Translocation by Atractyloside

H. W. Heldt

Institut für Physiologische Chemie und Physikalische Biochemie der Universität München

With 9 Figures

Origin and Chemical Structure of Atractyloside

Atractyloside occurs in the rhizomes of *Atractylis gummifera* (in German Mastix-Distel or Leim-Distel), a thistle growing in the southern mediterranean area. The ancient Egyptians already knew this drug as reported by Pedanios Dioskurides in "De Materia Medica", Vol. III, which was written about 80 A.D. Dioskurides listed the drug as "Chamaileon Leukos". Later it was known as an abortive agent. The isolation and crystallisation was reported in 1867 by Lefranc, who then named it atractylic acid.

Atractyloside is a glycoside, the glucose moiety being esterified with two molecules of sulfuric acid and one molecule of isovaleric acid (Lefranc, 1868; Angelico, 1910; Wunschendorf et al., 1931). The aglycon, which is called atractyligenin, has been characterized by Piozzi et al. (1966) to be a derivate of norditerpenoic acid, containing one free carboxylic group and two hydroxyl groups, one of the latter being attached to the glucose moiety. The most probable structure of atractyloside is shown in the *Appendix*. Thus atractyloside contains three anionic groups. The double bond between C-16 and C-17 appears to be essential for its inhibitory effect; hydration renders the compound inactive (Santi et al., 1962).

Pharmacology of Atractyloside

For a long time, the effect of atractyloside was regarded as being similar to that of strychnin. The investigations on the pharmacological effect were largely stimulated after a serious accident had happened in Sicily: a class of school children was severely poisoned after having eaten the sweetish rhizomes. Three of the children died. Extensive investigations by SANTI and coworkers (see SANTI, 1958) showed that injection of atractyloside into mammals caused a decrease of oxygen consumption, a mobilisation of liver glycogen with a short period of hyperglycemia, followed by hypoglycemia (MARRAS, 1935) when the liver glycogen was exhausted. Apparently the resynthesis of glycogen was inhibited. Furthermore, an acidosis, due to a rise of lactic acid in the blood, was observed. Usually the animals died in a convulsive crisis, this being typical for hypoglycemia. The convulsions disappeared after administration of glucose and bicarbonate, but the animals died anyway in a state of deep depression. Thus the metabolic block appeared to be irreversible. These data indicated that atractyloside might exert its inhibitory effect on the respiratory system.

Effect of Atractyloside on Mitochondrial Phosphorylations

From subsequent studies with rat liver mitochondria it was shown that atractyloside inhibited oxidative phosphorylation (BRUNI, BISTOCCHI et al., 1958) and uncoupler or Mg^{++}-stimulated ATP hydrolysis (BISTOCCHI et al., 1960, VIGNAIS et al., 1961; BRUNI and LUCIANI, 1962), but did not inhibit uncoupler-stimulated respiration (BRUNI et al., 1961). From these findings the effect of atractyloside appeared to be rather similar to the effect of oligomycin (see SLATER, this symposium). But soon important differences were noted between the effects of these inhibitors. Whereas oligomycin maintains its effect in disrupted mitochondria, the effect of atractyloside disappears on disintegration of the mitochondria. Thus pretreatment of the mitochondria with desoxycholate, hypotonic swelling (BRUNI and LUCIANI, 1962; BRUNI et al., 1962), digitonin (VIGNAIS et al., 1962) or sonication (LÖW et al., 1963), diminished the inhibition of oxidative phosphorylation and ATPase by atractyloside. Unlike oligomycin, atractyloside was shown to inhibit, in addition to the oxidative phosphorylation, the substrate level phosphorylation linked to ketoglutarate oxidation (BRUNI et al., 1964). In contrast to oligomycin, the inhibitory effect of atractyloside on oxidative phosphorylation and uncoupler-stimulated ATPase was competitively reversed by ADP or ATP respectively (Bruni et al., 1962; Vignais et al., 1964; Bruni, Luciani et al., 1965). From these data, and from studies of adenine nucleotide "binding" (Bruni, Luciani et al., 1964) which had been actually exchange measurements, but were not recognized as such at that time, it was concluded that atractyloside acts at the level of the final phosphorylation reaction of the mitochondrial energy transfer system, presumably as a competitive inhibitor of the adenine nucleotides (Bruni and Azzone, 1964; Vignais and Vignais, 1964). As shall be dealt with in the following, this explanation turned out to be incorrect.

Adenine Nucleotide Translocation

Investigations into the functional compartmentation of mitochondrial phosphorylation, as carried out in our laboratory, proved to be highly useful for elucidating the inhibitory effect of atractyloside. For this reason, some of the results are summarized here. Isolated mitochondria contain a certain amount of endogenous adenine nucleotides (Siekevitz and Potter, 1955) which were shown to be the primary reactants in oxidative phosphorylation (Heldt et al., 1965; Heldt, 1966). At low temperatures the phosphorylation of exogenous ADP proceeds much more slowly than the phosphorylation of endogenous ADP (Heldt, 1966; Heldt and Klingenberg, 1968). It was also shown that the endogenous adenine nucleotides are exchanged with external ADP or ATP (Klingenberg et al., 1964; Klingenberg and Pfaff, 1966), the velocity of which is comparable to the rate of phosphorylation of external ADP. This exchange is highly specific for ADP and ATP, practically no exchange being measured with externally added guanine-, uracil- or cytosine-nucleotides (Pfaff et al., 1965). Furthermore, it was found that more than half of the mitochondrial space is extremely rapidly permeated in an unspecific way by all solutes of small molecular weight, for example substrates, or free nucleotides (Pfaff et al., 1965; Klingenberg and Pfaff, 1966). The amount of permeated nucleotides was proportional to the external concentration, and these permeated molecules were removed easily by washing.

From these data we postulated a scheme for the organisation of mitochondrial phosphorylations, as shown in Fig. 1 (Heldt et al.,

1965; PFAFF et al., 1965). According to this scheme, only the endogenous ADP, being located in the matrix space, reacts with the ATP synthase of the respiratory chain. Therefore, the oxidative phosphorylation of external ADP involves in fact three steps: firstly, ADP passes the outer membrane of the mitochondria by diffusion-limited permeation. Secondly, the ADP, now being located in the intermembrane space, is exchanged across the inner membrane with endogenous ATP in the matrix space. Thirdly, the

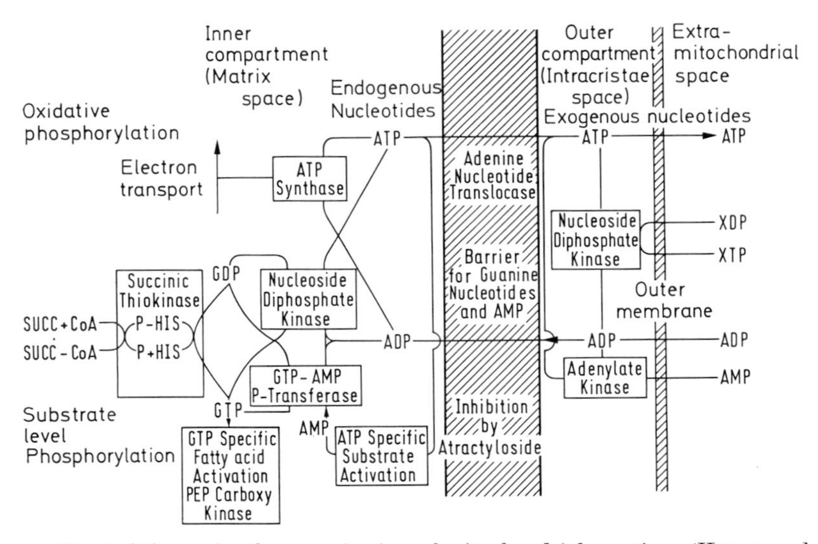

Fig. 1. Scheme for the organisation of mitochondrial reactions (HELDT and SCHWALBACH, 1968)

ADP is phosphorylated in the matrix space by the ATP synthase of the respiratory chain or by mitochondrial substrate level phosphorylation, the ATP thus formed being exchanged again with external ADP.

Regarding this operational scheme of mitochondrial phosphorylation, it was rather likely from the known data on the action of atractyloside, as conferred in the preceding pages, that atractyloside inhibits the adenine nucleotide translocation. It will be shown in the following that our working hypothesis was correct.

Inhibition of Translocation by Atractyloside

Fig. 2 shows the phosphorylation of endogenous and exogenous ADP by rat liver mitochondria at 10°, as measured by the uptake of ^{32}P-phosphate. The phosphorylation of endogenous ADP was started by adding oxygen to the anaerobic mitochondria. The phosphorylation of external ADP was initiated by the addition of ADP. It is clearly shown that atractyloside selectively inhibits the phosphorylation of external ADP only, the phosphorylation of

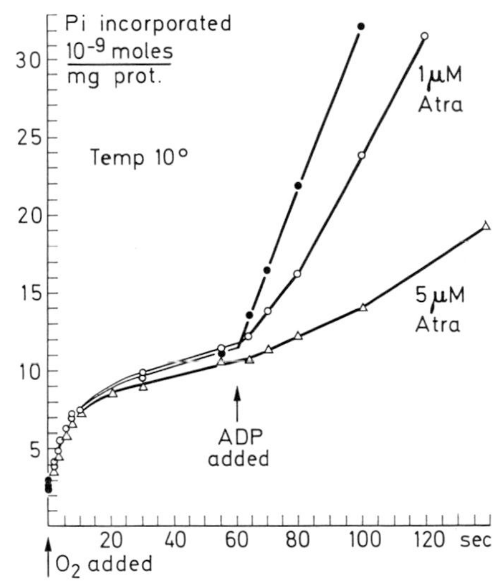

Fig. 2. Effect of atractyloside on the phosphorylation of endogenous and exogenous ADP in rat liver mitochondria (HELDT, 1967). Atractyloside was added together with the mitochondria to the incubation medium. For conditions see HELDT and KLINGENBERG (1968) and text

endogenous ADP being unaffected. Similar results were obtained independently by KEMP and SLATER (1964) and CHAPPELL and CROFTS (1965). The same holds for the reverse reaction of oxidative phosphorylation, the uncoupler-stimulated ATP hydrolysis, as shown in Fig. 3. In this experiment, both exogenous and endogenous ATP were present from the beginning. On addition of CCP, which is a very potent uncoupler, a very rapid dephosphorylation of the endogenous ATP occurs, followed by a slower hydrolysis of exogenous ATP. In analogy to phosphorylation, again atractyloside inhibits the dephosphorylation of the exogenous ATP only. From these results, either the unspecific permeation across the outer membrane or the specific exchange across the inner membrane might have been the point of inhibition by atractyloside. Table 1 shows an experiment in which unspecific permeation and the adenine nucleotide exchange were measured with and without atractyloside. It follows from these data that atractyloside inhibits the exchange only, whereas the unspecific permeation of the outer membrane is not inhibited (PFAFF et al., 1965). These results,

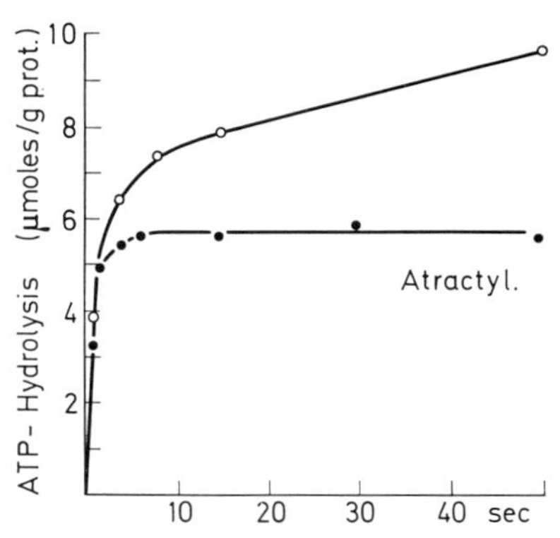

Fig. 3. Effect of atractyloside on the uncoupler-stimulated hydrolysis of endogenous and exogenous ATP in rat liver mitochondria. Temperature 4°. Atractyloside was added before the uncoupler (5 µM CCP). For conditions of assay see HELDT and KLINGENBERG (1968) and text

which have been confirmed in the meantime (DUEE and VIGNAIS, 1965; BRIERLEY and O'BRIEN, 1965; WINKLER et al., 1968), provide convincing evidence that the inhibition of mitochondrial phosphorylation by atractyloside occurs at the step of the adenine nucleotide translocation. Diverging views maintained by GREEN and co-workers [ALLMANN et al., 1966, 1967 (1, 2)] are partly due to semantic problems, and partly due to extremely high doses of atractyloside used by these authors.

Several effects of atractyloside, discussed at the beginning of this paper, are easily explained according to our scheme. Atractyloside inhibits substrate level phosphorylation, since this reaction is localized in the matrix also (HELDT, 1966). The loss of inhibitory effect of atractyloside on disruption of the mitochondria is explain-

Table 1. *Rat liver mitochondria. Incubation at 5° for 82 sec*

Conditions	Extramitoch. [14C] ADP (mM)	Mitoch. AXP (μmoles/g protein) (uncorrected)	Permeability			Exchange (%)	Extrapolated initial exchange rates (μmoles/g protein/min)
			ΔAXP (μmoles/g protein)	ΔAXP (mM)	Permeable space (%)		
Endogenous	—	11.14	—	—	—	—	—
Without atractyloside	3.65	30.43	10.03	3.12	86	74	20
With atractyloside	3.46	29.45	9.73	3.02	87	44	4

The medium contained 4 mg mitochondrial protein per ml, ± 50 μM atractyloside, ± 3.5 mM [14C]ADP (0.03 μC [14C]/ml). The exchange is given as % of the total endogenous adenine nucleotides labelled. Correcting for the levelling off of the % exchange given in this table; the initial exchange rates were calculated by extrapolating to the linear part of the time dependence curve assuming that the AXP exchange always follows the same time dependence. In the exchange rates the difference due to the inhibition by atractyloside is revealed more clearly. (After KLINGENBERG and PFAFF, 1966).

ed by a loss of the translocation step. In this case, exogenous adenine nucleotides are able to pass freely to the site of ATP synthase. This is shown in Fig. 4. In undisrupted mitochondria, the DNP-stimulated ATPase does not react with added ITP and is inhibited by atractyloside. In mitochondria disrupted by freezing and thawing, ITP is also hydrolyzed, indicating that the adenine nucleotide translocation, being responsible for the ATP specificity of the reaction, has been lost. This concurs with a loss of inhibitory

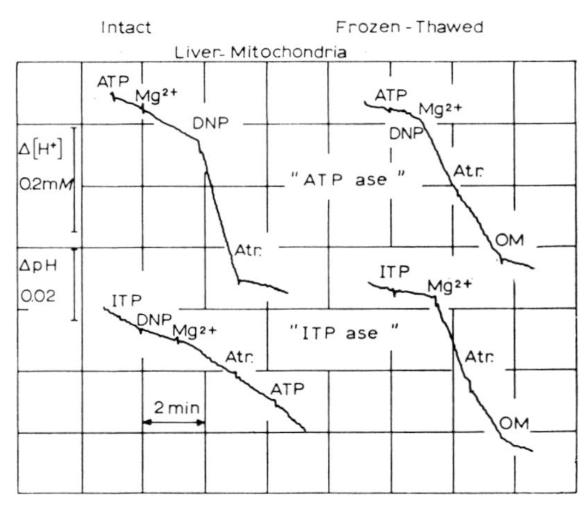

Fig. 4. Differentiation of the atractyloside sensitivity for the ATPase and ITPase in rat liver mitochondria (from KLINGENBERG and PFAFF, 1966). Recording with a pH electrode in a suspension of intact and of frozen and thawed rat liver mitochondria. Temperature 25°

effect by atractyloside. Analogous results have been obtained with oxidative phosphorylation by sonic particles (LÖW et al., 1963).

Earlier interpretations on the site of inhibitory action of atractyloside assumed that the endogenous adenine nucleotides are bound in the mitochondria. This view was supported by results of HULTIN and RICHARDSON (1964), showing binding of inorganic phosphate and of nucleotides to structural protein isolated from mitochondria. Likewise, it has been reported that binding of adenine nucleotides to structural protein from beef liver mitochondria and from yeast respiratory particles was reversed by very high concentrations of atractyloside (MORET et al., 1966).

Subsequently it has been shown, however, that binding of nucleotides to structural protein and its reversal by atractyloside was unspecific and could be reproduced with a large number of other anions, for instance succinate (PALMIERI, KLINGENBERG, 1967). It appears now that binding of nucleotides to structural protein may be an artifact due to the basic properties of this protein. From functional studies carried out in our laboratory, the endogenous adenine nucleotides seem to be in solution, confined by the inner membrane, which surrounds the matrix space (PFAFF et al., 1969; HELDT et al., 1969).

Properties of the Inhibitory Action

In view of these findings, the competitive reversal of the inhibitory effect of atractyloside by ADP and ATP, as mentioned already, has to be re-interpreted. Fig. 5 shows the competition between adenine nucleotides and atractyloside as observed by BRUNI et al. (1965). As a most simple explanation, the adenine nucleotides and atractyloside compete for a reactive site of the translocase, most probably at the outer surface of the inner membrane. From the study of net efflux (depletion) and influx (superfilling) of adenine nucleotides there is evidence that atractyloside indeed acts at the outer surface of the inner membrane. It has been mentioned already that the amount of endogenous adenine nucleotides present in the mitochondria is kept constant. This is due to a strict coupling of inward and outward translocation. This means that for each nucleotide molecule transported into the mitochondria, one nucleotide is transported out again. If this strict coupling is only released to a small extent, a net influx or efflux of adenine nucleotides would occur. A net efflux of adenine nucleotides is actually observed when the mitochondria are incubated at 30° with phosphate and Mg^{++}. If there is at the same time a very high concentration of ADP present in the medium, a net influx is observed. It is clearly shown from Table 2 that atractyloside inhibits the influx only (MEISNER, unpublished), whereas the efflux is not inhibited, or even slightly stimulated, by atractyloside (MEISNER and KLINGENBERG, 1968; VIGNAIS et al., 1968). This allows the conclusion that atractyloside selectively inhibits the reactive sites of the translocation at the outer surface of the inner membrane.

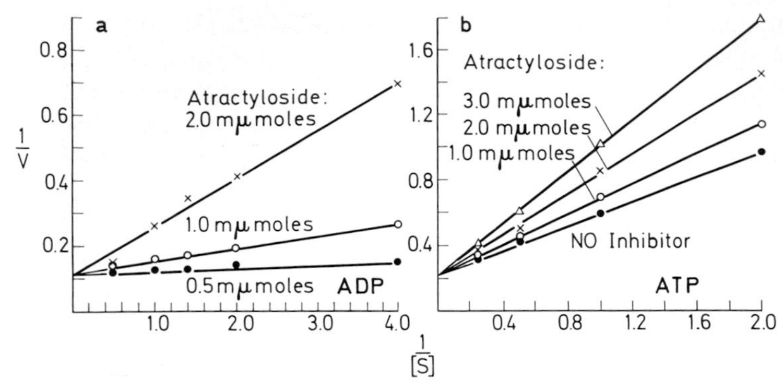

Fig. 5. Effect of varying concentrations of ADP (a) or ATP (b) on the inhibition by atractyloside of oxidative phosphorylation (a) or uncoupler-stimulated (dinitrophenol) ATPase (b). (From BRUNI, LUCIANI et al., 1965). Temperature 30°

Table 2. *The effect of atractyloside on efflux and influx of adenine nucleotides in rat liver mitochondria*

	Atractyloside (μM)	Change of endogenous adenine nucleotide
A. Efflux[a]	0	−57%
5 mM Mg^{++}	10	−63%
10 mM Phosphate	500	−63%
5 min, 30°		
B. Influx[b]		
5 mM Mg^{++}	0	+42%
10 mM Phosphate	50	+12%
5 mM ADP		
10 min, 30°		

[a] MEISNER and KLINGENBERG, 1968.
[b] MEISNER, unpublished.

It would be very interesting to know the number of active sites of the translocase, as related to mitochondrial protein. In principle, this may be achieved by measuring the amount of atractyloside bound to the mitochondria, as has been attempted by BRUNI, CONTESSA et al. (1965). Fig. 6 shows an experiment in which the binding of atractyloside was measured by incubation of the mitochondria with the inhibitor, followed by centrifugation and assay of atractyloside remaining in the supernatant by its inhibitory effect on oxidative phosphorylation. By this method, intact mitochondria were shown to bind 0.15 nmoles of atractyloside per mg protein. This value was decreased on damaging the mitochondria by treatment with phosphate or desoxycholate. The binding of oligomycin was not affected by this treatment. It should

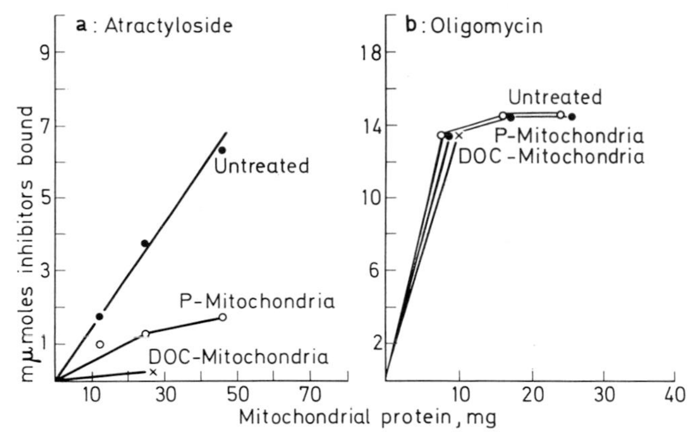

Fig. 6. Binding of atractyloside and oligomycin to damaged mitochondria. (From Bruni, Contessa et al. 1965). P-mitochondria: rat liver mitochondria incubated for 10 min at 30° with 33 mM potassium phosphate buffer (pH 7.4) and 83 mM sucrose, then centrifuged and resuspended in 0.25 M sucrose. DOC-mitochondria: rat liver mitochondria incubated for 10 min at 30° with 3 mM sodium deoxycholate, 45 mM Trisacetate buffer (pH 7.5) and 225 mM sucrose, then centrifuged, washed once and resuspended in 0.25 M sucrose

be kept in mind, however, that the method of indirect measurement employed might yield inaccurate results. It is therefore desirable to measure the binding of atractyloside directly by employing the radioactively labelled inhibitor. Unfortunately, radioactive atractyloside has not been available yet.

It was attempted in our laboratory (Weidemann, Erdelt and Klingenberg) to assay the reactive sites of translocation by preloading the mitochondria with radioactive ADP or ATP and measuring the liberation of radioactive adenine nucleotides on the addition of atractyloside. The values thus obtained are similar to those derived from the studies of atractyloside binding by Bruni, Contessa et al. (1965).

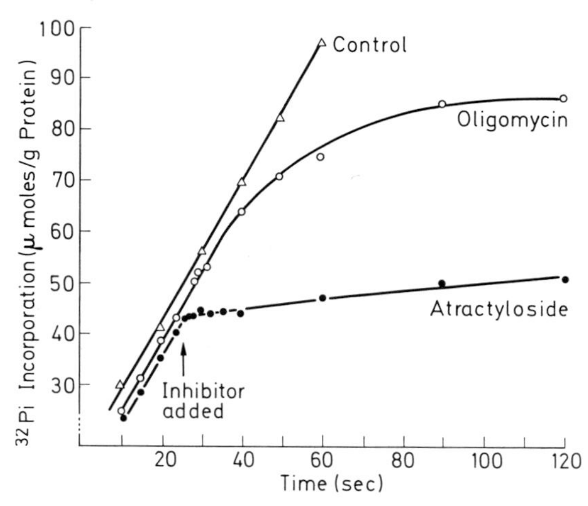

Fig. 7. Time dependence of the effects of atractyloside (40 μM) and oligomycin (12 μM) on the phosphorylation of exogenous ADP (160 μM) by rat liver mitochondria. Temperature 10° (Heldt and Klingenberg, 1968)

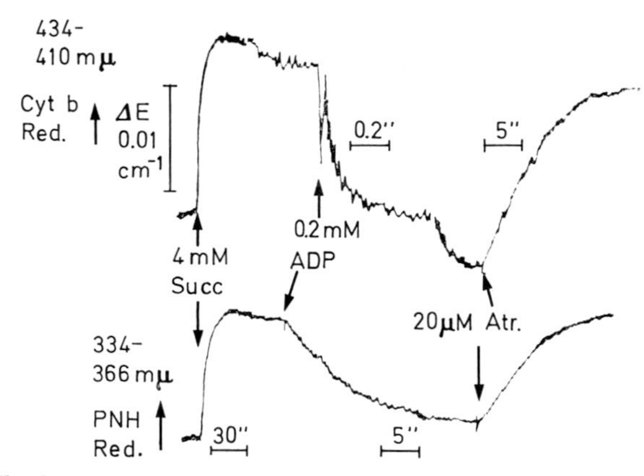

Fig. 8. The kinetic response of respiratory components to the addition of ADP and atractyloside. Additions made with the moving-mixing-chamber apparatus. Suspension of liver mitochondria in sucrose-EDTA medium (pH 7) at 11°. Separate experiments for recording the absorption of cytochrome b and NADH. (From Klingenberg 1967)

If atractyloside competes with exogenous ADP or ATP for the binding sites of the adenine nucleotide translocation, atractyloside should react very rapidly. This is actually the case. Fig. 7 shows an experiment in which the velocity of the atractyloside effect was measured. Immediately after the addition of atractyloside, i.e. within the resolution time of sampling (1 sec), the ^{32}P-uptake stops. With oligomycin, on the other hand, considerable time elapses before maximal inhibition is reached.

Essentially similar results are obtained from measuring the response of the respiratory components in the active state on the addition of atractyloside. Fig. 8 shows the recording of the reduction of cyt. b and of pyridine nucleotides. Again, the response to atractyloside occurs within the first second after the addition (KLINGENBERG, 1967).

Some Applications of Atractyloside

The rapid action of atractyloside makes it very useful for quick termination of the adenine nucleotide exchange. Using atractyloside, it was possible for the first time to obtain exact initial kinetics of the adenine nucleotide exchange. Fig. 9 shows an example of such a measurement. By preincubation of the mitochondria with ^{14}C-labelled ADP, and subsequent washing, the endogenous adenine nucleotides are homogeneously labelled. The exchange is started by injecting unlabelled ADP or ATP into the mitochondrial suspension. By a rapid technique, samples are taken and stopped by injection into a solution containing atractyloside. The mitochondria are separated by centrifugation, the radioactivity appearing in the supernatant is taken as a measure for the exchange. With this method, the first sample can be obtained as soon as 0.5 sec after starting the reaction.

Furthermore, atractyloside appears to be a valuable tool for studying the localization of mitochondrial reactions which utilize ATP. If atractyloside inhibits the reaction with externally added ATP, but does not inhibit the reaction with internally generated ATP, this reaction is characterized to be located within the inner membrane. Alternatively, if atractyloside inhibits the reaction with internally generated ATP and does not inhibit the reaction with externally added ATP, the reaction is located outside the inner membrane.

By these criteria, the citrulline synthetase (CHARLES et al., 1967), the ATP-specific fatty acid activation (CHAPPELL et al., 1965; VAN DEN BERGH, 1967) and the mitochondrial RNA polymerase (SACCONE et al., 1967) were shown to be localized within the inner membrane. Likewise, the adenylate kinase (VIGNAIS et al., 1962), phosphorylation of mitochondrial lipids (BIEBER et al., 1966; HAJRA et al., 1968), protein phosphokinase (SILIPRANDI

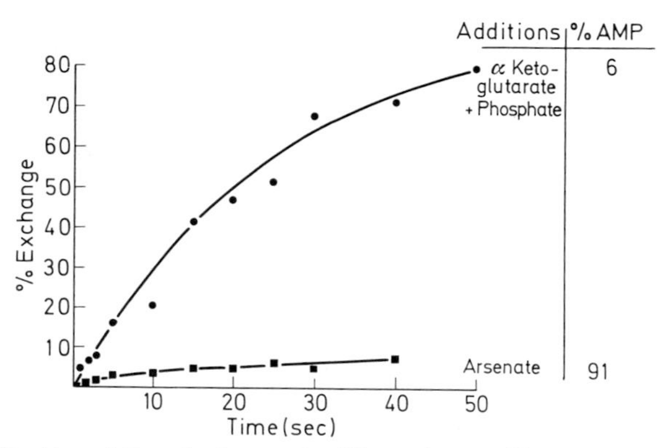

Fig. 9. Kinetics of the adenine nucleotide exchange (KLINGENBERG, HELDT and PFAFF, 1969). Rat liver mitochondria (0.7 mg prot/ml) prelabelled with 1 μC ^{14}C-ATP per 40 mg mitochondrial protein for 90 min. By preincubation with arsenate, most of the endogenous adenine nucleotides were transformed into AMP, by preincubation with ketoglutarate, most of the endogenous adenine nucleotides were transformed into ADP and ATP (HELDT and SCHWALBACH, 1967). The exchange was measured as back exchange. It was started by the addition of ADP and terminated by the atractyloside stop method. For conditions see PFAFF, HELDT and KLINGENBERG (1969). It was demonstrated by this experiment that the adenine nucleotide exchange follows a first order reaction with respect to the pool of endogenous ADP plus ATP

et al., 1966) and ATP-specific long chain fatty acid activation (YATES et al., 1966; VAN DEN BERGH, 1967) appear to be located outside the inner membrane.

In conclusion it may be stated that there has been considerable progress in our knowledge about the site of inhibition by atractyloside. However, the molecular mechanism of the action of atractyloside is still rather obscure. We cannot explain at the present time why a molecule, being so different from ADP, can act as a competitive inhibitor. Further investigation on this problem may yield important information about the molecular mechanism of adenine nucleotide translocation.

Acknowledgements

The investigations from our laboratory, which have been carried out by Prof. KLINGENBERG, Dr. PFAFF and the author, have been in part supported by grants from the Deutsche Forschungsgemeinschaft.

References

ALLMANN, D. W., L. GALZIGNA, R. E. McCAMAN, and D. E. GREEN: Arch. Biochem. **117**, 413 (1966).

—, R. A. HARRIS, and D. E. GREEN: Arch. Biochem. **120**, 693 (1967).

— — — Arch. Biochem. **122**, 766 (1967).

ANGELICO, F.: Gazz. chim. ital. **40**, 403 (1910).

BIEBER, L. L., and P. D. BOYER: J. biol. Chem. **241**, 5375 (1966).

BISTOCCHI, M., and A. MILLO: Rev. esp. Fisiol. **16**, 259 (1960).

BRIERLEY, G., and R. L. O'BRIEN: J. biol. Chem. **240**, 4532 (1965).

—, and G. F. AZZONE: VI. Int. Congr. Biochem., New York 1964, Abstr. X—9.

BRUNI, A., M. BISTOCCHI and A. R. CONTESSA: Boll. Soc. ital. Biol. sper. **34**, 459 (1958).

—, and A. R. CONTESSA: Nature (Lond.) **191**, 818 (1961).

—, A. R. CONTESSA, and S. LUCIANI: Biochim. biophys. Acta (Amst.) **60**, 301 (1962).

—, A. R. CONTESSA, and P. SCALELLA: Biochim. biophys. Acta (Amst.) **100**, 1 (1965).

—, and S. LUCIANI: Nature (Lond.) **196**, 578 (1962).

—, S. LUCIANI, and C. BORTIGNON: Biochim. biophys. Acta (Amst.) **97**, 434 (1965).

—, S. LUCIANI, A. R. CONTESSA, and G. F. AZZONE: Biochim. biophys. Acta (Amst.) **82**, 630 (1964).

— — — Nature (Lond.) **201**, 1219 (1964).

CHAPPELL, J. B., and A. R. CROFTS: Biochem. J. **95**, 707 (1965).

CHARLES, R., and S. G. VAN DEN BERGH: Biochim. biophys. Acta (Amst.) **131**, 393 (1967).

DUEE, E. D., and P. V. VIGNAIS: Biochim. biophys. Acta (Amst.) **107**, 184 (1965).

HAJRA, A. K., E. B. SEGUIN, and B. W. AGRANOFF: J. biol. Chem. **243**, 1609 (1968).

HELDT, H. W.: In: Regulation of metabolic processes in mitochondria, p. 51. TAGER, J. M., S. PAPA, E. QUAGLIARIELLO, and E. C. SLATER, Eds. Amsterdam: Elsevier 1966.

— In: Mitochondrial structure and compartmentation, p. 260. TAGER, J. M., S. PAPA, E. QUAGLIARIELLO, and E. C. SLATER, Eds. Bari: Editrice Adriatica 1967.

Heldt, H. W., H. Jacobs, and M. Klingenberg: Biochem. biophys. Res. Commun. **18**, 174 (1965).
—, and M. Klingenberg: Europ. J. Biochem. **4**, 1 (1968).
—, and E. Pfaff: Europ. J. Biochem. **10**, 494 (1969).
—, and K. Schwalbach: Europ. J. Biochem. **1**, 199 (1967).
Hultin, H. O., and S. H. Richardson: Arch. Biochem. **105**, 288 (1964).
Kemp, A., and E. C. Slater: Biochim. biophys. Acta (Amst.) **92**, 178 (1964).
Klingenberg M.: In: Mitochondrial structure and compartmentation, p. 271. Tager, J. M., S. Papa, E. Quagliariello, and E. C. Slater, Eds. Bari: Editrice Adriatica 1967.
—, H. W. Heldt, and E. Pfaff: In: The energy level and metabolic control in mitochondria. Bari: Adriatica Editrice 1969 (p. 237).
—, E. Pfaff, and A. Kröger: In: Rapid mixing and sampling techniques, p. 333. Chance, B., Ed. New York: Acad. Press 1964.
— — In: Regulation of metabolic processes in mitochondria, p. 180. Tager, J. M., S. Papa, E. Quagliariello, and E. C. Slater, Eds. Amsterdam: Elsevier 1966.
Lefranc, E.: Compt. Rend. **67**, 954 (1868).
Löw, H., J. Vallin, and B. Alm: In: Energy-linked functions of mitochondria, p. 5. Chance, B., Ed. New York: Acad. Press 1963.
Marras, A.: Studi sassaresi **13**, 75 (1935).
Meisner, H., and M. Klingenberg: J. biol. Chem. **243**, 3631 (1968).
Moret, V., M. Lorini, A. Fotia, and N. Siliprandi: Biochim. biophys. Acta (Amst.) **124**, 433 (1966).
Palmieri, F., and M. Klingenberg: Biochim. biophys. Acta (Amst.) **131**, 582 (1967).
Pfaff, E., H. W. Heldt, and M. Klingenberg: Europ. J. Biochem. **10**, 484 (1969)
—, M. Klingenberg, and H. W. Heldt: Biochim. biophys. Acta (Amst.) **104**, 312 (1965).
Piozzi, F., A. Quilico, R. Mondelli, T. Ajello, V. Sprio, and A. Melera: Tetrahedron **8**, 515 (1966).
Saccone, C., M. N. Gadaleta, and E. Quagliariello: Biochim. biophys. Acta (Amst.) **138**, 474 (1967).
Santi, R.: Nature (Lond.) **182**, 257 (1958).
—, A. Bruni, A. R. Contessa and S. Luciani: Boll. Soc. ital. Biol. Sper. **38**, 1890 (1962).
Siekevitz, P., and V. R. Potter: J. biol. Chem. **215**, 221 (1955).
Siliprandi, N., V. Moret, L. A. Pinna, and M. Lorini: In: Regulation of metabolic processes in mitochondria, p. 247. Tager, J. M., S. Papa, E. Quagliariello, and E. C. Slater, Eds. Amsterdam: Elsevier 1966.
van den Berg, S. G.: In: Mitochondrial structure and compartmentation, p. 400. Tager, J. M., S. Papa, E. Quagliariello, and E. C. Slater, Eds. Bari: Editrice Adriatica 1967.
Vignais, P. V., E. D. Duee, and J. Huet: Life Sci. **7**, 641 (1968).
—, P. M. Vignais, and E. Stanislas: Biochim. biophys. Acta (Amst.) **51**, 394 (1961); **60**, 284 (1962).

— — Biochim. biophys. Res. Commun. **14**, 559 (1964).
— — VI. Int. Congr. Biochem., New York 1964, Abstr. X—79.
WEIDEMANN, M. J., H. ERDELT, and M. KLINGENBERG: This Colloquium, p. 324.
WINKLER, H. H., F. L. BYGRAVE, and A. L. LEHNINGER: J. biol. Chem. **243**, 20 (1968).
WUNSCHENDORF, H., et P. BRAUDEL: Bull. Soc. Chim. biol. (Paris) **13**, 758 (1931).
YATES, D. W., D. SHEPHERD, and P. B. GARLAND: Nature (Lond.) **209**, 1213 (1966).

Atractyligenin and Structural Analogues

P. V. Vignais

Laboratoire de Biochimie, Centre d'Etudes Nucléaires, Grenoble, France

With 5 Figures

1. Atractyligenin as the Active Moiety of Atractyloside

I should like to sum up some lines of evidence showing that the aglycone of atractyloside, atractyligenin, is the active moiety of atractyloside and that the inhibitory effect of atractyligenin on the adenine nucleotide translocation is related to the position and the nature of some of its functional groups. (For chemical structures, see *Appendix*.)

Atractyligenin is a norditerpenoic acid, the structure of which has been elucidated [Piozzi, F., A. Quilico, T. Ajello, V. Sprio, and A. Merela: Tetrahedron Letters **23**, 1829 (1965)].

To test the effect of atractyligenin on the adenine nucleotide translocation, atractyligenin was extensively purified to minimize contamination by atractyloside. First, it was recrystallized three times from aqueous ethanol. At this stage, analysis by activation in a neutron flux was used to detect the presence of atractyloside as a contaminating impurity, since the sulfur of the sulphate moiety of atractyloside — which is missing in atractyligenin — is transformed into ^{32}P upon irradiation. Less than one molecule of atractyloside per 30,000 molecules of atractyligenin could be detected. Further purification of atractyligenin was carried out by chromatography on a thin layer of silica in the following solvent: chloroform/methanol/acetic acid/water (55:25:8:4 v/v). In this system the R_f of atractyligenin (0.95) is quite different from that of atractyloside (0.43). Atractyligenin recovered from the thin layer by extraction with ethanol (95%) was again recrystallized and used for studies on the adenine nucleotide translocation.

Like atractyloside, atractyligenin inhibits the oxidative phosphorylation of extramitochondrial ADP, but it does not alter the rate of the oxidative phosphorylation of intramitochondrial ADP. Inhibition bearing on the phosphorylation of extramitochondrial ADP is relieved by high concentrations of added ADP. All these data are reminiscent of the effect of atractyloside. Actual-

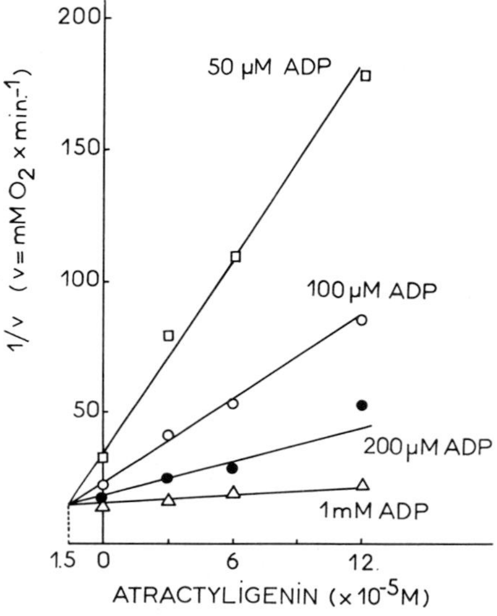

Fig. 1. Effect of various concentrations of ADP on the respiratory inhibition by atractyligenin. The rate of respiration v refers to the increase in O_2 consumption due to state 4—state 3 transition brought about by addition of ADP. The reaction medium contained: 110 mM KCl, 16 mM phosphate buffer, pH 7.3, labelled with ^{32}P, 6 mM $MgCl_2$, 10 mM glutamate and 3,4 mg of mitochondrial protein. Final volume 2 ml. Temperature: 25°

ly, the inhibitory activity of atractyligenin is 150 times less than that of atractyloside. For instance, the K_i of atractyligenin for the ADP-stimulated respiration is 1.5×10^{-5} M (Fig. 1) whereas the K_i of atractyloside determined under the same conditions is 1×10^{-7} M (Fig. 2).

It was shown later that, as in the case of atractyloside, the primary effect of atractyligenin is the inhibition of the adenine nucleotide translocation. In both cases, the inhibition of the

adenine nucleotide translocation was released competitively by ADP. Whereas it is probable that atractyligenin is the active moiety of the atractyloside molecule, it is possible that other groups in the atractyloside molecule, like glucose disulphate, potentiate the effect of the aglycone moiety (by increasing the solubility in the hydrophilic region of the membrane, for instance).

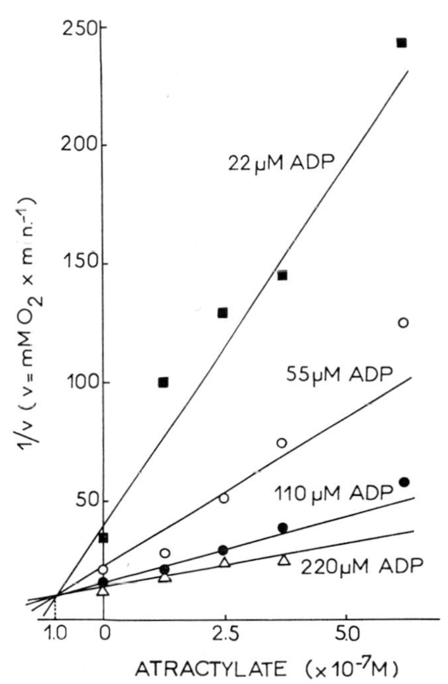

Fig. 2. Effect of various concentrations of ADP on the respiratory inhibition by atractyloside. (cf. Fig. 1)

In order to determine which functional groups of the atractyligenin molecule are involved in the inhibition of adenine nucleotide translocation, a number of analogues of atractyligenin were tested. Among them, steviol behaves, in some respects, similarly to atractyligenin. It inhibits the adenine nucleotide translocation but this inhibition is not relieved by high concentrations of added ADP as it is the case for atractyloside or atractyligenin. In other words, a small change of some functional groups in the atractyligenin molecule (additional -CH_3 at C-4 and transposition of -OH

from C-15 to C-13) leads to a significant change of the inhibitory effect on the adenine nucleotide translocation. The hydroxyl group at the C-2 position in atractyligenin is apparently not involved, since it is not free but linked to glucose in atractyloside. The reduction of the C-4 carboxyl group of atractyligenin to the corresponding alcohol (atractylitriol), as well as the replacement of -OH at C-15 by a keto-group in diketoatractyligenin leads to a loss of the inhibition of translocation. Esterification of the -COOH at the C-4 in steviol by glucose (stevioside) decreases considerably the inhibitory effect of steviol on translocation. Other diterpenoic compounds like 7-OH kaurenolide have no effect on the adenine nucleotide translocation.

The specific and competitive effect of atractyligenin on the adenine nucleotide translocation raises the interesting problem of the nature of the competition between ADP and atractyligenin. Because of the dissemblance between ADP and atractyligenin, it has been postulated [VIGNAIS, P. V., E. D. DUÉE, P. M. VIGNAIS, and J. HUET: Biochim. Biophys. Acta (Amst.) **118**, 465 (1966)] that atractyligenin (or atractyloside) is able to displace an allosteric activator of ADP translocation. It is inferred that the structure of this allosteric activator is similar to that of atractyligenin.

2. Apparent Inhibition of Oxidative Phosphorylation of Intramitochondrial ADP by Atractyloside

Conflicting results have been reported with respect to the effect of atractyloside on the phosphorylation of mitochondrial ADP (cf. A. BRUNI in Regulation of Metabolic Processes in Mitochondria, ed. by J. M. TAGER, S. PAPA, E. QUAGLIARIELLO, and E. C. SLATER, Elsevier Publ. Co, 1966, p. 275). It was noticed by BRUNI that the atractyloside effect depends on experimental conditions. Indeed it may be easily demonstrated [VIGNAIS, P. V., E. D. DUÉE, and J. HUET: Life Sci. **7** Part I, 641 (1968); DUÉE, E. D., and P. V. VIGNAIS: J. biol. Chem. (1969) **244**, 3932] that apparent inhibition of oxidative phosphorylation of mitochondrial ADP appears only under conditions which favour the leakage of internal adenine nucleotides out of the mitochondria, for instance addition of Mg^{++} to the incubation medium. The Mg^{++}-induced leakage of internal adenine nucleotides is apparently unspecific (it concerns ATP, ADP and AMP) and is not inhibited by atractyloside. As

shown in the scheme of Fig. 3, ADP which has leaked out of the matrix space is rapidly retranslocated into mitochondria by exchange with internal ADP or ATP; AMP which has been released can react outside the inner mitochondrial membrane with ATP through the action of adenylate kinase and Mg^{++} to give ADP which again is translocated into mitochondria by exchange with

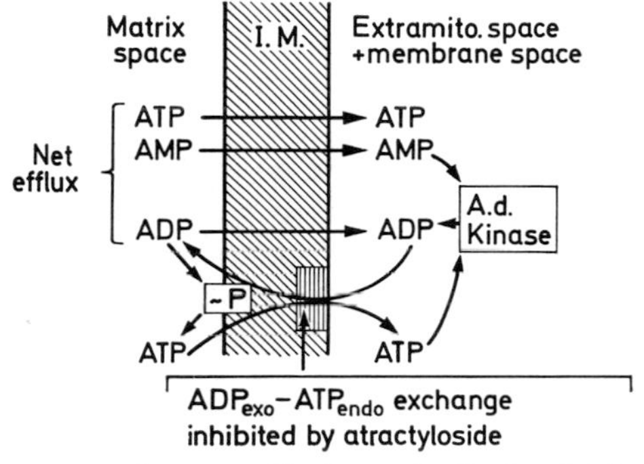

Fig. 3. Simultaneous exchange and leakage of mitochondrial adenine nucleotides

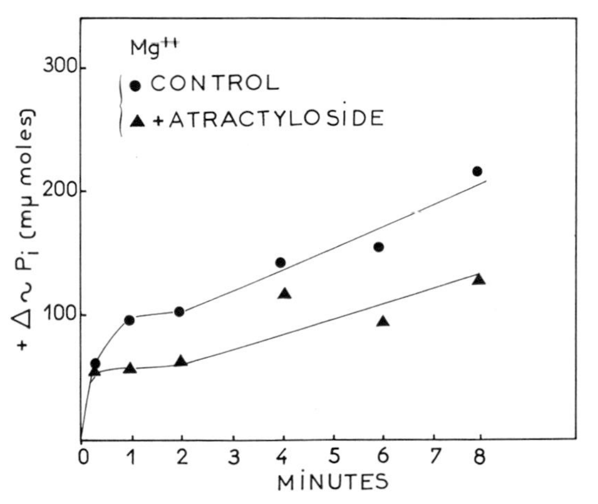

Fig. 4. Effect of atractyloside on the phosphorylation of mitochondrial adenine nucleotides in the presence of EDTA. Mitochondria (38 mg of protein) were incubated at 0° in the presence of 110 mM KCl, 10 mM succinate, 8 mM Tris, HCl, 14 mM (^{32}P) orthophosphate, pH 7.4, and 1 mM EDTA. Atractyloside, where present, was 23 μM. Incubation was stopped by addition of perchloric acid at a final concentration of 2%

internal ADP or ATP. In other words, AMP and ADP released from mitochondria are retranslocated by exchange into mitochondria and phosphorylated there to give ATP.

Atractyloside, which is a specific inhibitor of the adenine nucleotide translocation, but is without effect on the Mg^{++} induced release of internal adenine nucleotides, inhibits the replacement of AMP and ADP outside the inner mitochondrial membrane by ATP. Under these conditions, the apparent effect of atractyl-

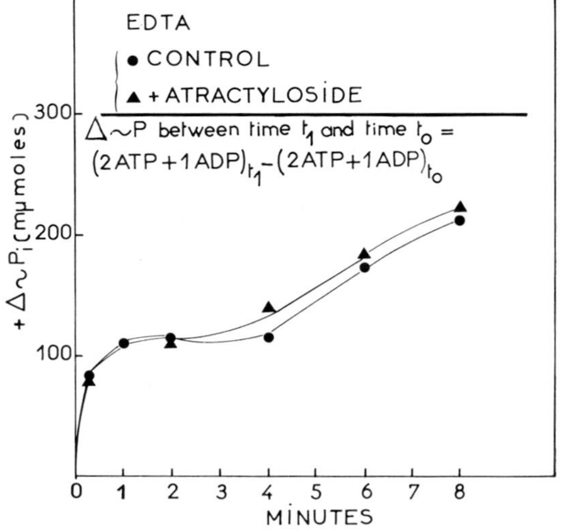

Fig. 5. Effect of atractyloside on the phosphorylation of mitochondrial adenine nucleotides in the presence of $MgCl_2$. Same conditions as in Fig. 4, except that EDTA was replaced by 6 mM $MgCl_2$

oside is an inhibition of the phosphorylation of the so called mitochondrial ADP and AMP.

Experiments, the results of which are presented in Fig. 4 and Fig. 5 illustrate the above rationale. They concern the phosphorylation of mitochondrial ADP and AMP coupled to the oxidation of succinate at a temperature of about 0 to 1°. They show that when EDTA is present in the incubation medium, atractyloside has no effect on the formation of $\sim$ P bonds. In contrast, when EDTA is replaced by $MgCl_2$, the addition of atractyloside results in an inhibition of $\sim$ P bonds in mitochondrial adenine nucleotides to an extent of about 40%.

Elucidation of a Carrier Site for Adenine Nucleotide Translocation in Mitochondria with the Help of Atractyloside

M. J. WEIDEMANN, H. ERDELT, and M. KLINGENBERG

Institut für Physiologische Chemie und Physikalische Biochemie der Universität München

With 5 Figures

Previously, the adenine translocation through the mitochondrial membrane has been shown to be mediated by a carrier system which catalyses a compulsory exchange between exogenous and endogenous adenine nucleotides. So far, the study of the adenine nucleotide translocation has been mainly concerned with a description of the overall process (specificity, kinetics, temperature dependence, regulation, etc.) [1—3]. For further understanding of the mechanism it is of interest to determine whether one can detect binding sites for adenine nucleotides and, if so, to measure the number of sites which can be attributed to the carrier per g of mitochondrial protein. As explained in detail by HELDT [4], atractyloside has been shown to be a highly specific and effective inhibitor of adenine nucleotide translocation. It can be assumed that atractyloside inhibits by way of competitive binding to the adenine nucleotide carrier site. In view of its high affinity, one type of approach for measuring the carrier sites would be to study atractyloside binding. An alternative method would be to determine the binding of adenine nucleotides (ADP or ATP) and to differentiate the specific from the unspecific binding by displacement of the adenine nucleotides with atractyloside. This approach is made possible by the unusually high affinity of the adenine nucleotide exchange for ADP or ATP. It is complicated by the fact that adenine nucleotides incorporated into the intramitochondrial space by exchange will be indistinguishable from adenine

nucleotides bound to the carrier, unless some means of identifying the bound and exchanged fractions is employed.

The experimental approach is illustrated by the scheme shown in diagram 1. In the experiments to be described we have used atractyloside to make these distinctions. In three parallel samples, atractyloside is either omitted from the incubating medium (sample 1) or is added before (sample 2) or after (sample 3) ^{14}C-labelled ADP. The time allowed for binding (5 min) is sufficient

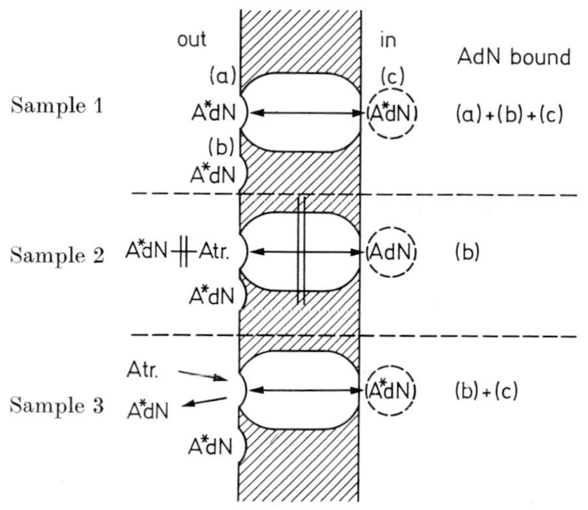

Diagram 1: Differentiation of ADP binding sites and ADP exchange in mitochondria by the use of atractyloside

for full equilibration of the added ^{14}C-ADP with the binding sites and with the exchangeable endogenous adenine nucleotide pool. This means that in the samples where atractyloside is added after ADP, full exchange can be assumed to have already taken place. This procedure is sufficient to distinguish the three different portions of the nucleotides incorporated into the mitochondrial pellet: (a) adenine nucleotides bound to the translocase carrier site; (b) adenine nucleotides bound at sites other than the translocase; and (c) exchanged adenine nucleotides. Normally, in intact mitochondria, the exchanged portion (c) would be expected to be orders of magnitude larger than the carrier bound portion (a), making such measurements very difficult. For this reason, prior to the experiment, the endogenous adenine nucleotide pool (c) is made as small as possible by depleting mitochondria in phosphate buffer.

Results and Discussion

Fig. 1 demonstrates the existence of a binding of adenine nucleotides to beef heart mitochondria incubated with ^{14}C-ADP at 0°. The fact that the pellet contains bound in excess of free adenine nucleotides is illustrated by a plot of the percentage bound versus the total adenine nucleotide concentration. This shows that at low adenine nucleotide concentration (0.1 μM)

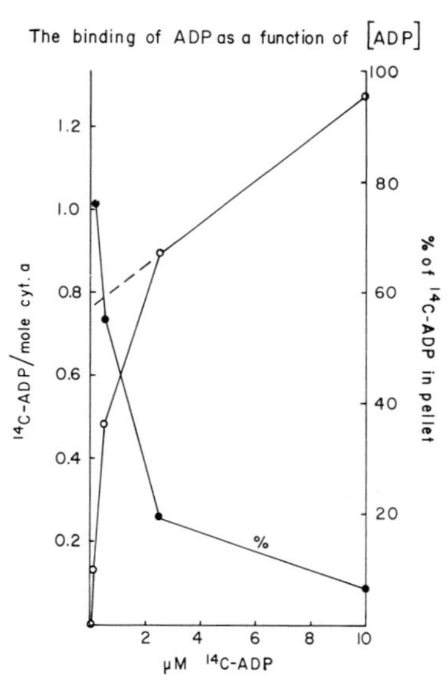

Fig. 1. The binding of ^{14}C-ADP to beef heart mitochondria as a function of ADP concentration. Beef heart mitochondria (Löw and VALLIN, 1963) were depleted of endogenous adenine nucleotides by incubation at 30° in 100 mM phosphate buffer, pH 7.5, containing 5 mM $MgCl_2$ (3 × 5 min incubations). The mitochondria (1 mg protein) were incubated at 0° in 1 ml 0.25 M sucrose containing triethanolamine buffer (10 mM, pH 7.2), EDTA (2 mM) and $MgCl_2$ (1 mM), and binding was initiated by addition of ^{14}C-ADP at the concentrations given. After 10 min the vessels were centrifuged for 2 min at 20,000 g. The supernatants were removed and radioactivity in the pellets and supernatants were determined separately following rinsing of the tubes containing the pellets and deproteinization with $HClO_4$ (0.5 ml of 1N)

nearly 80% of the added radioactivity is retained in the mitochondrial pellet. As the adenine nucleotide concentration is increased, a decreasing proportion of the radioactivity is retained, indicating that some binding sites are already saturated at ADP concentrations above 2 μM.

The differentiation of this binding according to the procedure proposed in diagram 1 is illustrated in Fig. 2. Here the concentration dependence in the binding range (up to 2 μM ADP) is differen-

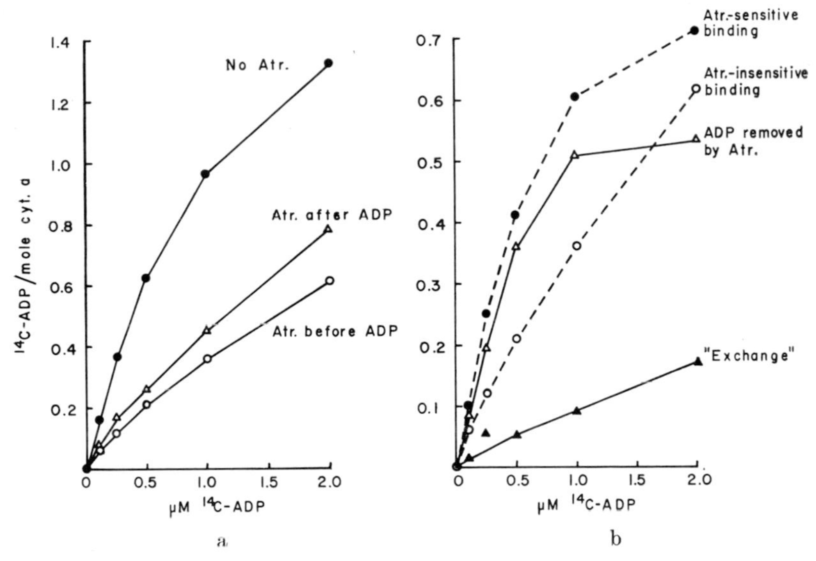

Fig. 2. Effect of atractyloside (10 μM) added before or after ^{14}C-ADP on ADP binding by beef heart mitochondria. Experimental conditions as for Fig. 1. At each concentration of ^{14}C-ADP studied, atractyloside (10 μM) was either omitted from the medium (1) or added before (2) or 5 min after ^{14}C-ADP (3). Total incubation time in each case was 10 min

tiated for the total binding (no atractyloside added) and for binding in the presence of atractyloside added either before or after ADP. In the plot derived from these data (Fig. 2b), the addition of atractyloside before ADP differentiates the binding into an atractyloside-insensitive and an atractyloside-sensitive portion. The insensitive portion may be considered to reflect extra binding sites for ADP distinct from the carrier sites. The atractyloside-sensitive portion includes both exchange and binding to the translocase carrier. The atractyloside-removable radioactivity, i.e. the difference between the total adenine nucleotides bound and the adenine nucleotides left after atractyloside addition, can be considered according to diagram 1 to give the specific binding sites of the carrier. Binding at these sites appears to reach saturation at an initial ADP concentration of approx. 1 μM. The figure also illustrates that in these experiments exchange of labelled

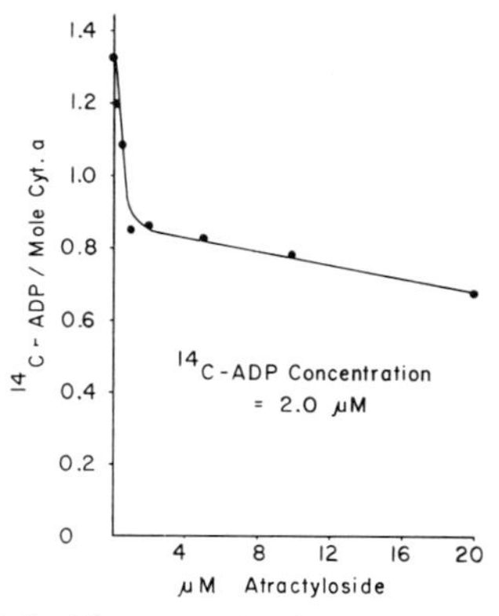

Fig. 3. Effect of atractyloside concentration on removal of ^{14}C-ADP bound to beef heart mitochondria. Experimental conditions as for Fig. 1. Binding was initiated by addition of ^{14}C-ADP (2 μM, containing 27,000 cpm) at zero time. Atractyloside at the concentrations given was added after 5 min. Total incubation time 10 min

adenine nucleotides with the endogenous pool was at most only 25% of the atractyloside-sensitive portion.

Fig. 3 shows the removability of bound ADP as a function of atractyloside concentration. The high affinity of the carrier site for atractyloside is illustrated by the very low concentration at which half the specifically-bound ADP is removed (0.5 μM).

The removability of ^{14}C-ADP by atractyloside is compared in Fig. 4 with the effect of adding a 50-fold excess of unlabelled ADP or ITP 5 min after the addition of ^{14}C-ADP. The reversibility of the ^{14}C-ADP binding is shown clearly by the exchange of 80 to 90% of the ^{14}C-ADP on the binding sites with unlabelled ADP added to the solution. A similar exchange does not occur with added ITP, which removes an amount of radioactivity equivalent only to the unspecific ^{14}C-ADP binding (approx. 20%).

For analysis of the binding characteristics according to the mass action law, the data given in Fig. 2 are replotted (Fig. 5): in this case bound ADP is plotted against the ratio of bound/free ADP [5]. The total ADP bound gives a non-linear curve, indicating that there is a mixed population of binding sites. In contrast, the atractyloside-removable portion is linear, indicating a binding of ADP to a single type of site. The straight line in this case permits

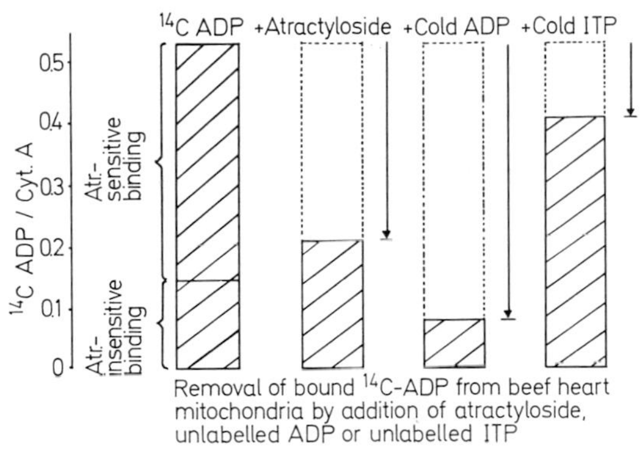

Fig. 4. Removal of bound ^{14}C-ADP from beef heart mitochondria by addition of atractyloside, unlabelled ADP or unlabelled ITP. Experimental conditions as for Fig. 1. Binding was initiated by addition of ^{14}C-ADP (0.5 μM, containing 27,000 cpm) at zero time. Subsequent additions, at 5 min, were either atractyloside (10 μM), unlabelled ADP (25 μM) or unlabelled ITP (25 μM). Total incubation time 10 min. In control vessels (extreme left-hand column) ^{14}C-ADP binding was measured in the presence and absence of atractyloside (10 μM, added before ^{14}C-ADP)

the evaluation of the dissociation constant of ADP at the binding site (K = 0.14 μM) and of the number of specific binding sites/mole of cytochrome a (N = 0.63). The binding parameters for ADP are compared in Table 1 for mitochondria from beef heart and rat liver. In rat liver mitochondria, the portion of adenine nucleotides removable by atractyloside is only 10% as compared to 53% in beef heart mitochondria, and therefore elucidation of the binding sites is more difficult. From the data obtained it appears that mitochondria from beef heart contain 2 to 3 times more translocase binding sites on a g protein basis. The affinity of the sites in beef heart (K = 0.14 μM) is considerably higher than in rat liver. In the liver experiments, the affinity of the translocase site for ADP (K = 0.9 μM) is similar to the K_m (1.3 μM) found for ADP in adenine nucleotide exchange experiments with intact mitochondria [6] and to the value for atractyloside-sensitive "binding" to membranes prepared by "Lubrol" treatment of liver mitochondria (K = 1.1 μM) obtained by WINKLER and LEHNINGER [7].

In conclusion, the present study demonstrates the existence of binding sites for adenine nucleotides at the mitochondrial mem-

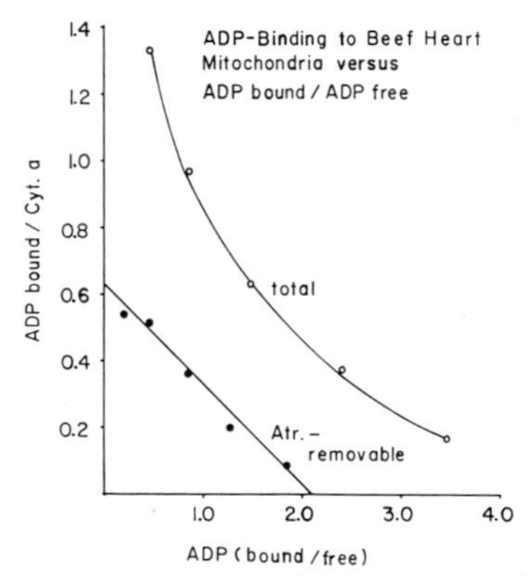

Fig. 5. Scatchard plots of ^{14}C-ADP bound to beef heart mitochondria versus the ratio of bound/free ^{14}C-ADP. The data are those from the experiment given in Fig. 2. N, moles of ADP bound per mole of cytochrome a, is determined by the y intercept, and K, the dissociation constant of ADP at the binding site, from the slope of the line and the concentration of mitochondrial cytochrome a in the reaction vessel (0.48 μMoles/g protein).

brane which can be attributed to the adenine nucleotide carrier. Further, it is possible to measure the number of binding sites, their affinity, specificity and other related kinetic and thermodynamic properties. It is evident that the method of approach we have used to differentiate ADP-binding from the residual adenine nucleotide exchange provides sufficient information to elucidate some of the properties of the binding sites.

Atractyloside-sensitivity alone, as used by WINKLER and LEHNINGER (1968) is not a sufficient criterion to identify the binding sites, as the contribution of the exchange component is not assessed. It should be emphasized that atractyloside-removability of ADP, together with a competition between nucleotide and atractyloside, is strong evidence for a common binding site. The finding of such a competition in the present experiments is in contrast to the conclusions of WINKLER and LEHNINGER, who, on the basis of no

Table 1. *Comparison of atractyloside-removable binding of ADP by beef heart and rat liver mitochondria*

	Beef heart	Rat liver
Dissociation constant K (μM)	0.14	0.90
No. of binding sites N′ (μmoles/g protein)	0.30	0.13
% of total bound ADP removable by atract. (at 1.0 μM ADP)	53	10

N′ and K were determined by SCATCHARD plots as given in Fig. 5. The number of binding sites, N′, is expressed in each case per g protein of adenine nucleotide depleted mitochondria. % removability of ^{14}C-ADP by atractyloside is given for 1 μM ADP.

removability of ADP by atractyloside, claim that there are different binding sites for ADP and atractyloside which are linked by an "allosteric" interaction.

Acknowledgements

M. J. W. thanks the Alexander von Humboldt Stiftung for the award of a Forschungsstipendium and H. E. thanks the Deutsche Forschungsgemeinschaft for an Ausbildungsstipendium.

References

1. PFAFF, E., and M. KLINGENBERG: Europ. J. Biochem. **6**, 66 (1968).
2. KLINGENBERG, M., and E. PFAFF: In: Regulation of metabolic processes in mitochondria, (TAGER, J. M., S. PAPA, E. QUAGLIARIELLO, and E. C. SLATER, Eds.). Biochim. biophys. Acta Library (Amst.) **7**, 180 (1966).
3. — — In: Metabolic roles of citrate, p. 105. GOODWIN, T., Ed. London: Acad. Press 1968.
4. HELDT, H. W.: This Mosbach Colloquium, p. 301.

5. SCATCHARD, G.: Ann. N.Y. Acad. Sci. **51**, 660 (1949).
6. PFAFF, E., H. W. HELDT, and M. KLINGENBERG: Europ. J. Biochem. **10**, 484 (1969).
7. WINKLER, H. H., and A. L. LEHNINGER: J. biol. Chem. **243**, 3000 (1968).
8. LÖW, H., and I. VALLIN: Biochim. biophys. Acta (Amst.) **69**, 361 (1963).

Discussion

HEINZ (Frankfurt): As I understand, ADP and ATP can pass the membrane only by exchange diffusion, but you showed that atractyloside affects the influx only, not the efflux. So I wonder what the effIowing nucleotide is exchanging with in that case.

HELDT (Munich): The efflux, which may be also called depletion, and the influx, which has been also called superfilling, are considered as misfunctions of the adenine nucleotide translocation, due to a partial release of the strict coupling between inward and outward translocation. Thus the efflux shown is explained by assuming that in about one in a hundred cases, the translocation of one nucleotide molecule from inside to outside is *not* accompanied by a simultaneous translocation from outside to inside, leading to depletion of mitochondrial adenine nucleotides.

HEINZ: Could you call this "leakage"?

HELDT: Yes.

KLINGENBERG (Munich): One can also say that the ratio between the rate of compulsory exchange and unidirectional translocation of the carrier is 1:100.

CHAPPELL (Bristol): How do you know it is the same carrier?

HELDT: Under these conditions, only the adenine nucleotides are released, but not the pyridine nucleotides.

KLINGENBERG: The efflux of adenine nucleotides is specific, i.e. there is no efflux of AMP.

BÜCHER (Munich): What is the biological meaning of this mechanism?

HELDT: The adenine nucleotide translocation may be regarded as a key point for the regulation of the ATP level in the cell. Our recent experiments with mitochondria in vitro have demonstrated that in the controlled state of oxidative phosphorylation the ATP potential outside the mitochondria is about 2 to 3 kcal higher than the ATP potential in the mitochondrial matrix [1], [HELDT, unpublished]. This is shown in Table 1. This finding implies that ADP is being transported against a potential into the mitochondria. It is now understood that the energy-dependent ADP specificity of the adenine nucleotide translocation into the mitochondria is responsible for this phenomenon. We know that in the muscle cell there is almost no change of the ATP level observed during muscular contraction. This is due to a rapid rephosphorylation of the ADP by creatine phosphate [2]. On the other hand, ADP is required to stimulate oxidative phosphorylation. We have recently shown that there is a strong dependence between the steady state level of ADP in the mitochondrial matrix and the rate of oxidative phosphorylation [3]. The question arises: if there is hardly any increase of the ADP level in the cytosol, how is oxidative phosphorylation in the mitochon-

Table 1. *Phosphorylation potentials of ATP in the mitochondrial matrix and in the supernatant during the state of respiratory control*

At the beginning of phosphorylation the medium contained 0.2 mM ADP, 1 mM P_i, 5 mM Mg^{++} and 5 mM succinate. Temperature 285 °K.

	$\frac{ATP}{ADP}$	P_i (mM)	K (M^{-1})	$\Delta E'$ kcal/mole
Mitochondrial matrix	3.20	16.2	197	11.8
Supernatant	20.2	1.0	20200	14.4

$$\Delta E'_{285} = \Delta E^{0\prime}_{285} + 1.29 \log K; \qquad K = \frac{[ATP]}{[ADP]\,[P_i]}$$

$$\Delta E^{0\prime}_{298} = 8.8 \text{ kcal/mole } [4]$$

dria initiated, in order to refill the "reservoir" of creatine phosphate? This points to the crucial function of translocation. By the mechanism discussed, the low increase of ADP in the cytosol causes a larger increase of ADP in the mitochondrial matrix, which may then be sufficiently high to stimulate oxidative phosphorylation. Thus, the adenine nucleotide translocation appears to have a major function in maintaining a constant level of ATP in the cell.

LARDY (Madison, Wisc.): Dr. VIGNAIS, I would like to comment on your interesting suggestion that atractyloside may occupy an allosteric site on the ADP carrier. Recently, we have found a new antibiotic which acts in every way exactly like atractyloside, except for one feature, that is: instead of being linear in its response as is atractyloside, it shows cooperative effects with the carrier. I think this would support your hypothesis.

The name of the antibiotic is bongkrekic acid. It is produced in the fermentation of cocoa products for Javanese food. When the fermentation goes badly and bongkrekic acid is produced, the food is toxic and can be fatal.

STROMINGER (Cambridge, Mass.): I just want to warn the audience that Dr. LARDY is well-known to pull huge jokes, so you should wonder whether this is really a true compound.

BÜCHER (added in proof): We may confirm the existence of bongkrekic acid [5, 6]. The substance has been provided by Dr. BERENDS, Delft, and is under investigation in Dr. KLINGENBERG's laboratory in Munich.

References

1. Klingenberg, M., R. Wulf, E. Pfaff, and H. W. Heldt: Abstr. Vth FEBS Meeting, Prague 1968 (in press).
2. Hohorst, H. J., M. Reim, and H. Bartels: BBRC **7**, 142 (1962).
3. Heldt, H. W., and E. Pfaff: Europ. J. Biochem. **10**, 494 (1969).
4. Alberty, R. A.: J. biol. Chem. **243**, 1337 (1968).
5. W. Welling, J. A. Cohen and W. Berends; Biochem. Pharmacol. **3**, 122 (1960).
6. Lijmbach, G. W. M.: Thesis, Technische Hogeschool, Delft, The Netherlands 1969.

Transport and Exchange of Anions in Mitochondria

J. B. Chappell

Department of Biochemistry, Medical School, University of Bristol, United Kingdom

With 5 Figures

Transport and Exchange of Anions in Mitochondria

To date evidence has been obtained for the existence of seven anion transporting systems located in the inner membrane of mitochondria (Table 1). It is not proposed to discuss in this paper the adenine nucleotide translocase since this will be dealt with by other speakers in this symposium. The nature of the evidence which has been provided for the remaining six carriers has been reviewed elsewhere (Chappell, 1968; Chappell, Henderson, McGivan and Robinson, 1968).

Particular attention will be paid in this paper to the probable mechanism of action of the carriers, the elucidation of which has been made possible by the use of certain specific inhibitors, and the physiological role of these carriers in cellular metabolism.

The carriers fall into two classes. The first, comprising the phosphate and glutamate transporters, do not require the presence of an added activator before entry occurs. It is postulated that these carriers catalyse an anion-hydroxyl exchange. The other carriers appear to be antiporters (Mitchell, 1967), i.e. they catalyse an anion-anion exchange (Table 2).

The phosphate transporter

Low concentrations (9 mμ moles/mg mitochondrial protein) of certain reagents (see Table 1) which react with sulphydryl groups more or less specifically, inhibit phosphate entry into and efflux from mitochondria. This has been shown in a series of elegant experiments reported by Fonyo and Bessman (1966, 1968) and

Table 1. *The Anion-Transporting Systems of Mitochondria*

Substance transported	Activators	Inhibitors	Comments
Phosphate (and arsenate) [1]	None	p-Mercuribenzoate [2] Mersalyl [3] Formaldehyde [3] 2-Chloromercuri-4,6-dinitrophenol [4] 5,5'-Dithio-bis-(2-nitrobenzoate) [4]	Non-competitive, but phosphate protects partially
ATP; ADP [5]	? Mg^{2+}	Atractyloside Atractyligenin Steviol	Competitive with ATP or ADP Non-competitive with ATP or ADP
Some dicarboxylic acids, e.g. malate, succinate, not fumarate [6. 7]	Phosphate	Butylmalonate [8, 9]	Competitive with dicarboxylic acid
Oxoglutarate [7, 8, 9, 10]	Malate or malonate, not isomalate	Butylmalonate [8, 9] Aspartate [11]	Competitive with malate activation Competitive with oxoglutarate
Citrate, isocitrate, Cis-aconitate [6, 7, 8, 9, 12]	Malate or isomalate, not malonate	Butylmalonate [8, 9] Oxoglutarate [13]	Competitive with malate activation Competitive with malate activation

Table 1 (Continued)

Glutamate [14]	Phosphate (slightly)	4-Hydroxyglutamate 2-Aminoadipate *threo*-Hydroxyaspartate	Competitive with glutamate
Aspartate [14]	Glutamate or 4-hydroxy-glutamate or 2-amino-adipate or threo-hydroxy-aspartate		

References: 1. CHAPPELL and CROFTS (1966); 2. FONYO and BESSMAN (1966); 3. TYLER (1968, 1969); 4. R. N. JOHNSON, unpublished; 5. see VIGNAIS and DUEE (1966) for references; 6. CHAPPELL and HAARHOFF (1967); 7. CHAPPELL, HENDERSON, McGIVAN, and ROBINSON (1968); 8. ROBINSON, and CHAPPELL (1967); 9. CHAPPELL, and ROBINSON (1968); 10. MEIJER, and TAGER (1966); 11. J. D. McGIVAN, unpublished; 12. CHAPPELL (1964, 1966); 13. ROBINSON (1968); 14. AZZI, CHAPPELL, and ROBINSON (1967).

Tyler (1968, 1969). Their results and some unpublished observations of Mr. R. N. Johnson of this laboratory are summarised in Table 3.

Table 2. *Exchange reactions catalysed by the anion transporters of mitochondria*

Transporter	Exchange reactions catalysed
Phosphate	? Phosphate-hydroxyl
Glutamate	? Glutamate-hydroxyl
Malate	Malate-phosphate, Malate-dicarboxylate anion, e.g. succinate, Phosphate-phosphate
Citrate	Citrate (isocitrate, cis-aconitate) - malate, Tricarboxylate-tricarboxylate
Oxoglutarate	Oxoglutarate-malate, ? Oxoglutarate-oxoglutarate
Aspartate	See text

Table 3. *The effects of Sulphydryl Reagents on Mitochondrial Metabolism*

Reactions Inhibited	Comments
Respiratory chain-linked and substrate level phosphorylation	Uncoupler stimulated respiration unaffected, therefore action is not at level of electron transport
Stimulation of oxygen uptake by Ca^{2+} in the presence of phosphate	When acetate replaces phosphate, respiration is little affected
Swelling of mitochondria suspended in iso-osmotic ammonium phosphate	Swelling in ammonium acetate unaffected
DNP-stimulated ATPase (partially)	Under these conditions phosphate efflux is inhibited and the mitochondria swell.
Swelling in ammonium succinate	Phosphate (about 1 mM) is required before swelling occurs in iso-osmotic ammonium succinate

The sensitivity of the phosphate transporter to sulphydryl reagents resembles that of the phosphate transporting system of bacteria (see Mitchell, 1959).

Phosphate can also enter mitochondria on the dicarboxylate transporter. Thus if mitochondria are allowed to hydrolyse terminally radioactively labelled ATP in the presence of N-ethyl maleimide, phosphate is accumulated within the mitochondria. If now "cold" phosphate is added outside the mitochondria, an exchange of internal radioactive phosphate for external phosphate occurs, and this exchange is inhibited by n-butylmalonate (JOHNSON and CHAPPELL, 1969). A probable explanation of these findings is shown in Fig. 1. Malate or succinate can also cause efflux of phosphate from N-ethyl maleimide-treated mitochondria and again n-butylmalonate inhibits.

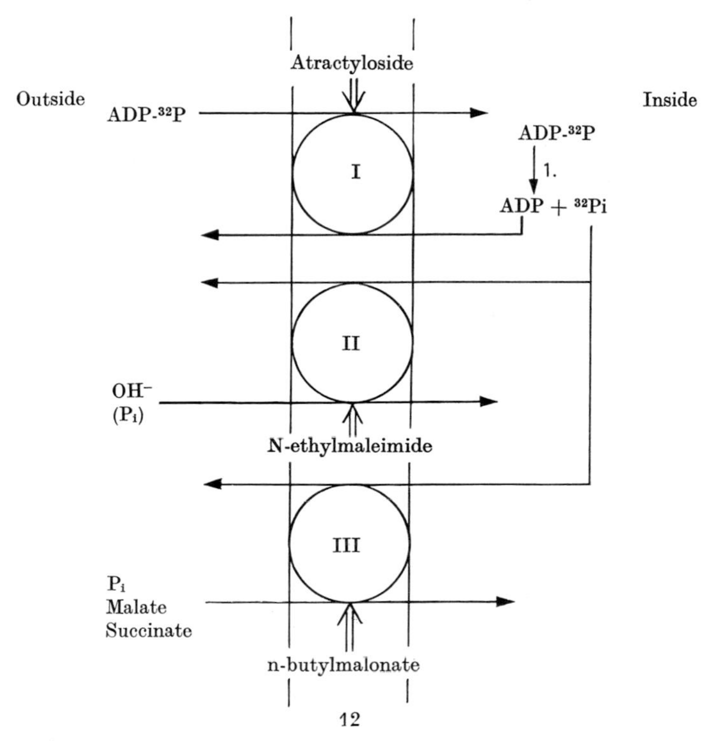

Fig. 1. Scheme to account for the exchange of internal phosphate for external phosphate and its inhibitor sensitivity. I. Adenine nucleotide translocase; II. Phosphate transporter; III. Dicarboxylate transporter; 1. Uncoupler stimulated ATPase

It appears that the phosphate transporter is capable of causing an accumulation of phosphate against a concentration gradient.

Thus in blowfly mitochondria incubated in the presence of an oxidizable substrate a four- to five-fold concentration of phosphate occurs (Fig. 2). In the presence of an uncoupling agent the concentrations of phosphate on both sides of the mitochondrial membrane is equal (HANSFORD and CHAPPELL, 1968). Liver and kidney mitochondria are also able to "actively" transport phosphate.

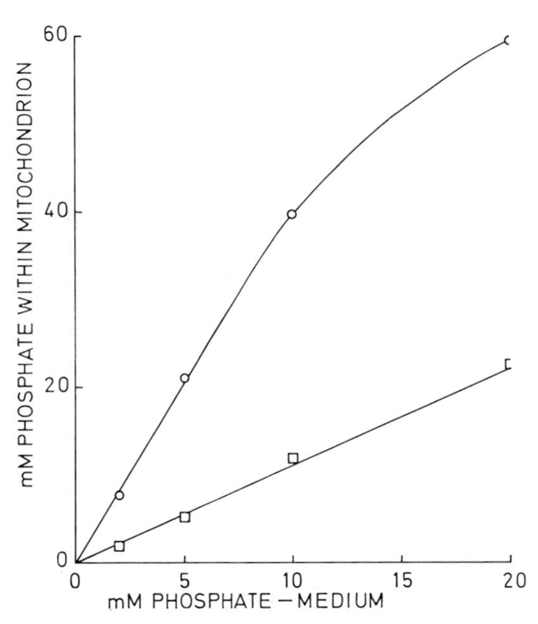

Fig. 2. The accumulation of phosphate within coupled blowfly mitochondria. The calculation of the phosphate concentration was based upon phosphate assay of the total mitochondrial pellet and determinations of ^{14}C-labelled sucrose and $^{3}H_2O$ spaces. See HANSFORD and CHAPPELL (1968) for experimental details

In two cases this ability to concentrate phosphate appears to have important metabolic consequences. Thus the NAD-linked isocitrate dehydrogenase activity of blowfly mitochondria is completely dependent on the presence of phosphate (Fig. 3). The concentration of phosphate in blowfly muscle *in vivo*, at rest and in activity, is approximately 5 mM; reference to Fig. 3 reveals that at this level of phosphate less than 5% of the NAD-linked isocitrate dehydrogenase activity is expressed. However under the conditions ikely to appertain *in vivo* in mitochondria, at an external phosphate concentration of 5 mM, the internal phosphate concentration of mitochondria would be in excess of 20 mM, which would give greater than 60% of the potential isocitrate dehydrogenase activity.

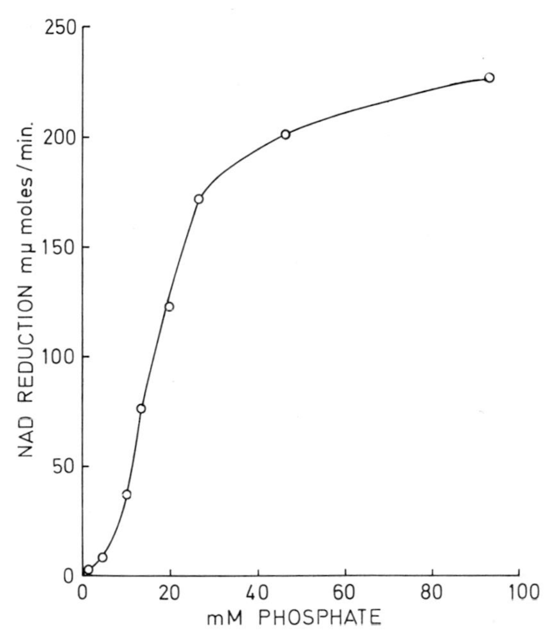

Fig. 3. The phosphate dependence of the NAD-linked isocitrate dehydrogenase of blowfly mitochondria. The activators isocitrate, NAD, Mg^{2+} and ADP were present at "maximal" concentrations. See HANSFORD and CHAPPELL (1968) for experimental details

From preliminary experiments performed in this laboratory by Dr. Z. KOVACEVIC, a similar situation appears to exist with regard to the glutaminase activity of kidney mitochondria. The soluble glutaminase activity is largely phosphate dependent, 100 mM phosphate being required for maximal activity. With intact mitochondria, in the presence of an oxidizable substrate and the absence of uncoupling agents, 30 mM phosphate induces maximal activity.

The dicarboxylate transporter

This carrier appears to have three exchange functions:

(i) Dicarboxylate anion-phosphate exchange.

(ii) Dicarboxylate-dicarboxylate exchange.

(iii) Phosphate-phosphate exchange.

Functions (i) and (iii) have been discussed previously. Function (ii) manifests itself when mitochondria oxidize succinate. The major end product with liver mitochondria is malate (CHAPPELL and HAARHOFF, 1967). Phosphate is not required for maximal rates of uncoupler-stimulated respiration. Here it is postulated that succinate entering mitochondria does so in exchange for the product of the action of succinate dehydrogenase and fumarate hydratase, malate; fumarate is a feeble penetrant of the mitochondrial membrane. This latter property explains the "latency" of mitochondrial fumarate hydratase activity.

The dicarboxylate transporter is specifically inhibited by 2-n-butylmalonate (ROBINSON and CHAPPELL, 1967). This inhibition is competitive with respect to malate (CHAPPELL and ROBINSON, 1968). 2-Phenylmalonate and 2-benzylmalonate act in the same manner, but are not as effective as butylmalonate.

Butylmalonate also inhibits the entry of oxoglutarate and tricarboxylate anions into mitochondria. This inhibition is almost certainly due to the inhibition of malate entry, which is necessary before the other anions can enter.

The oxoglutarate transporter

The oxoglutarate transporter is not only inhibited by butylmalonate, but also by L-aspartate; in this case the inhibitor is competitive with respect to oxoglutarate and not malate (McGIVAN, BRADFORD and CHAPPELL, 1969). Furthermore, aspartate appears to inhibit the entry and not the efflux of oxoglutarate. This may be of considerable physiological significance in maintaining an asymmetric distribution of oxoglutarate in the cell and thus effecting the redox potential of the NAD-$NADH_2$ couple in the cytosol and the mitochondrion (see below).

The tricarboxylate transporter

Again butylmalonate inhibits citrate, isocitrate and cis-aconitate entry, most probably by interfering with malate transport. Oxoglutarate also inhibits, and the inhibition is again competitive with malate and not the tricarboxylate anion (ROBINSON, 1968). The inhibition is not very marked and is unlikely to be of great physiological significance.

The glutamate and aspartate transporters

4-Hydroxyglutamate, 2-aminoadipate and *threo*-hydroxyaspartate are competitive inhibitors of glutamate entry into mitochondria. These same compounds, like glutamate, appear to act as activators of aspartate entry (AZZI, CHAPPELL and ROBINSON, 1967).

Possible physiological significance of the transporters

Citrate transport. The importance of citrate transport from the mitochondrion and its involvement in the cytosol has been discussed previously (CHAPPELL and ROBINSON, 1968; CHAPPELL, 1968; GREVILLE, 1969).

Transfer of reducing power from cytosol to the mitochondrion

An adequate system for the transport of reducing power was demonstrated to operate in insect flight muscle a number of years ago (ZEBE, DELBRÜCK and BÜCHER, 1957; ESTABROOK and SACKTOR, 1958). However this "glycerol phosphate shuttle" is not thought to be of importance in most mammalian tissues (BORST, 1963).

BORST (1963) suggested the possibility that a shuttle involving malate dehydrogenase and aspartate aminotransferase may operate to cause the transfer of reducing power across the mitochondrial membrane (Fig. 4). This cycle requires the presence of malate dehydrogenase and aspartate aminotransferase in both the cytosol and the mitochondria. This is the case in many if not all mammalian tissues. Thus by various techniques it has been shown that malate dehydrogenase and aspartate aminotransferase have a bimodal distribution in rat liver, brain and uterine epithelium and in the muscles and fat body of locusts (see DE DUVE, WATTIAUX, BAUDHUIN, 1962).

The system proposed by BORST (1963) requires the existence of four transporting systems, one each for malate, glutamate, aspartate and oxoglutarate. The evidence for the existence of these transporting systems in mitochondria prepared from rat liver and rat and beef heart has been provided (see CHAPPELL, 1968).

A demonstration that the shunt is capable of catalysing rapid rates of $NADH_2$ oxidation *in vitro* is possible. Liver mitochondria were suspended in a KCl medium and the oxidation of $NADH_2$ was followed by double-beam spectrophotometry. It should be noted that only a very small amount of mitochondria was used in these experiments so that redox-changes in the intramitochondrial nucleotides were only a small part of the total absorbancy changes. Addition of malate together with malate dehydrogenase caused only a slight increase in the rate of $NADH_2$ oxidation. However on addition of aspartate aminotransferase, glutamate and aspartate, high rates of $NADH_2$ oxidation were observed. All the components added were necessary for maximal rates of $NADH_2$ oxidation.

As was pointed out by BORST (1963) in considering the aspartate aminotransferase-malate dehydrogenase shunt, such a system could only lead to the equilibration of the redox potential of NAD in the cytoplasm and the mitochondria. There is a growing body of evidence that the redox potential of *free* NAD in the two compartments is very different under a wide variety of metabolic conditions. HOLZER, SCHULTZ and LYNEN (1956) and BÜCHER and KLINGENBERG (1958) provided the first evidence from a measurement of the relative concentrations of substrate and product of various dehydrogenases which are known to be located solely in the cytosol or in mitochondria. These measurements coupled with a knowledge of the values of the equilibrium constants *in vivo* enable the free $[NAD]/[NADH_2]$ ratio to be calculated. This approach has been used recently by WILLIAMSON, LUND and KREBS (1967) in a careful study of the relative redox potentials for mitochondrial and cytoplasmic NAD in liver under a variety of metabolic conditions. In every case under the metabolic conditions studied the redox potential of the mitochondrial NAD was considerably more negative than that of the cytoplasm.

It is obvious therefore that if the aspartate aminotransferase-malate dehydrogenase shuttle is to operate it is a thermodynamic necessity that energy be supplied from some source to permit a

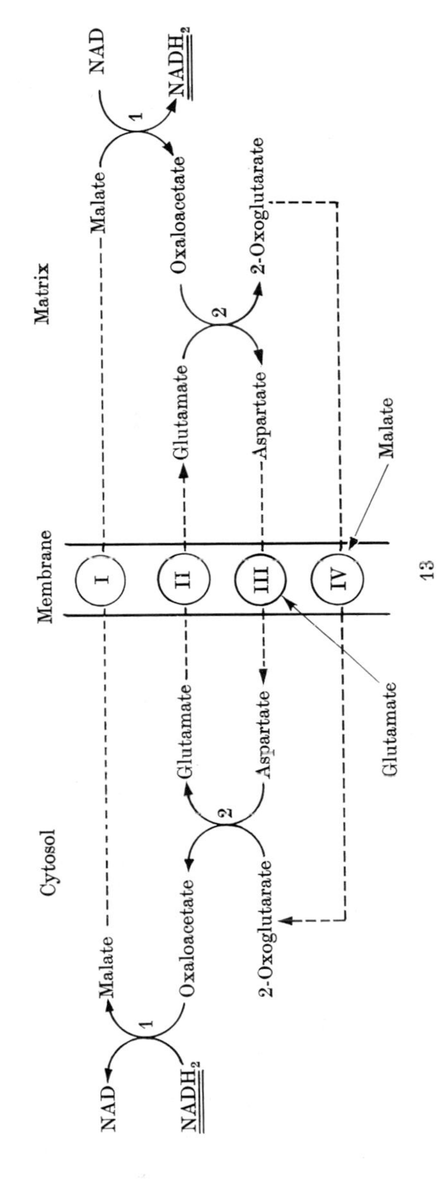

Fig. 4. I. Malate transporter; II. Glutamate transporter; III. Aspartate transporter, glutamate activated; IV. Oxoglutarate transporter, malate activated; 1. Malate dehydrogenase; 2. Aspartate aminotransferase

difference in the redox state of NAD. The situation may be represented by a consideration of equilibrium conditions:

$$\text{Let } K_{MDH} = \frac{[\text{malate}]\,[\text{NAD}^+]}{[\text{oxaloacetate}]\,[\text{NADH}]\,[\text{H}^+]} \tag{1}$$

$$\text{and } K_{AAT} = \frac{[\text{oxaloacetate}]\,[\text{glutamate}]}{[\text{aspartate}]\,[\text{oxoglutarate}]}. \tag{2}$$

It follows that:

$$K_{MDH} \cdot K_{AAT} = K' = \frac{[\text{malate}]\,[\text{glutamate}]\,[\text{NAD}^+]}{[\text{aspartate}]\,[\text{oxoglutarate}]\,[\text{NADH}]\,[\text{H}^+]} \tag{3}$$

Assuming that the enzymes involved occur in excess in both compartments, then K' must be the same on both sides of the membrane and therefore:

$$\frac{[\text{NAD}^+]_c}{[\text{NADH}]_c}\;\frac{[\text{NADH}]_m}{[\text{NAD}^+]_m} = \frac{[\text{malate}]_m[\text{glutamate}]_m[\text{oxoglutarate}]_c[\text{aspartate}]_c[\text{H}^+]_c}{[\text{malate}]_c[\text{glutamate}]_c[\text{oxoglutarate}]_m[\text{aspartate}]_m[\text{H}^+]_m}. \tag{4}$$

The subscripts m and c refer to the mitochondrial and cytosolic compartments, respectively.

The numerical value of the term on the left-hand side of Eq. (4) varies with the metabolic state and activity of the tissue, but for liver (WILLIAMSON et al., 1967) varies over the range 90—20 between well-fed and alloxan-diabetic animals. It follows therefore that the distribution of one or all of the compounds occurring on the right-hand side of Eq. (4) must be asymmetric between cytoplasm and mitochondria.

Such evidence as exists (see for example CHANCE and MELA, 1966 a, b) indicates that there is little, if any difference, in the $[H^+]$ across the mitochondrial membrane in the absence of a permeant cation, e.g. Ca^{2+}, or K^+ when valinomycin is added (CHAPPELL and HAARHOFF, 1967). If $[H^+]$ concentration were responsible, a pH difference of 2 units across the membrane would be required.

Some experiments which indicate in a preliminary fashion that anion distribution is responsible for the difference in redox potential between cytoplasm and mitochondria have been obtained. Changes in the redox state of intramitochondrial NAD(P) were followed by fluorimetry and of cytochrome *a* by double-beam spectrophotometry. Addition of glutamate together with malate caused reduction of intramitochondrial NAD(P) and addition of oxoglutarate and aspartate caused oxidation, until a steady-state was reached. Now on addition of rotenone, which blocks the oxidation of $NADH_2$ through the respiratory chain, *oxidation* of NAD(P)H_2 occurred! However, on addition of succinate, the oxidation of which is unaffected by rotenone, extensive reduction of NAD(P) occurred and was maintained until the mitochondrial suspension became anaerobic as indicated by reduction of cytochrome *a*. When oxygen was added to the suspension by stirring, reduction of NAD(P) occurred and this was maintained until the suspension became anaerobic.

That this reduction of NAD(P) was energy-dependent is indicated by the following findings:

(1) When succinate was used to cause reduction, antimycin prevented its action. In the presence of this inhibitor the addition of ascorbate together with tetramethyl-p-phenylenediamine (TMPD) caused reduction which was reversed when the suspension became anaerobic. Addition of oxygen caused reduction of NAD(P) again.

(2) ATP added in place of succinate in an experiment similar to those described above also caused reduction. Oligomycin both prevented and reversed the effect of ATP.

(3) Uncoupling agents, e.g. the carbonyl-cyanide phenylhydrazones or pentachlorophenol, both prevented and reversed the energy-dependent reduction of NAD(P) caused by oxidisable substrate or by ATP. When pentachlorophenol was used the addition of bovine plasma albumin reversed its effect, that is the NAD(P) could then be reduced on addition of oxygen or ATP.

Relationship between these findings and the energy-linked transhydrogenase

One possible criticism of the interpretation placed upon the experiments described is that the phenomena observed are due to the energy-linked transhydrogenase reaction. Thus a possible explanation might be that the addition of glutamate, aspartate, oxoglutarate and malate provides a "redox buffer" for the intramitochondrial NAD(P) (mainly through the malate dehydrogenase reaction) thus holding the NAD redox potential constant (assuming no energy-dependent anion movements) and that the increased reduction of NAD(P) observed when energy is made available, or the oxidation when it is not, is due to a change mainly in the redox-state of NADP (Fig. 5). There are two lines of evidence that this view is incorrect. These are as follows:

(1) Direct analysis, after extraction and enzymatic analysis, of the changes in NAD and NADP concentration under anaerobic and aerobic conditions in an experiment of the type described reveal that it is mainly the amount of NAD and not NADP which changes. If the hypothesis that an NAD redox buffer together with the energy-linked transhydrogenase were responsible for the reduction of NAD(P) observed by fluorimetry were responsible, then it would

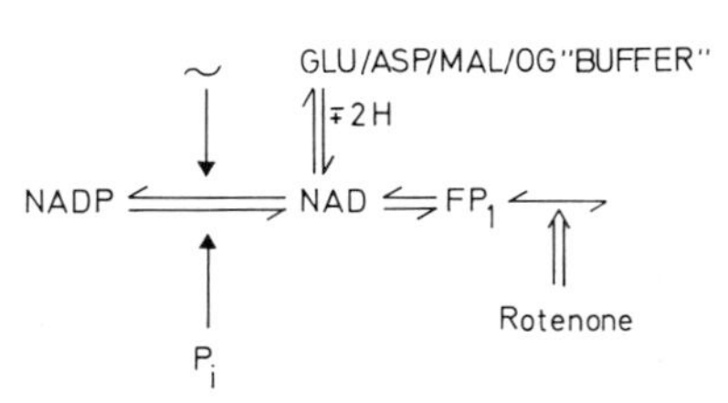

Fig. 5. The possible inter-relationship between energy-linked anion transport and the energy-linked transhydrogenase

be expected that the NADP only and not the NAD level would change. This was not the case.

(2) Similar changes to those described for liver mitochondria have been observed with both heart and kidney mitochondria. The extent of the changes observed rule out the prime involvement of NADP, and therefore of the energy-linked transhydrogenase, since the total (oxidised and reduced) NADP/NAD ratio in heart mitochondria is 0.24 and in kidney 0.19, compared with 1.7 in liver (Klingenberg, Slenczka and Ritt, 1959). Thus in heart and kidney mitochondria there is insufficient NADP present to account for the changes observed.

Other factors than the postulated energy-linked anion transport may be involved in determining the difference in redox potential between the NAD of cytosol and mitochondria. Two such factors have come to light recently:

(i) "Space" experiments of the type described by Chappell (1968) show that, even in the presence of glutamate, a putative activator of aspartate entry, aspartate as such is not found in the matrix space. However when ^{14}C-labelled aspartate is used, large amounts of ^{14}C-labelled malate are found inside the mitochondria. It would seem that aspartate as such does not occur intramitochondrially. This of course would displace the equilibrium of the aspartate aminotransferase reaction, resulting in increased mitochondrial NAD reduction.

(ii) Aspartate inhibits oxoglutarate entry but not efflux (McGivan, Bradford and Chappell, 1969). This would mean that the re-entry of oxoglutarate which had left the mitochondria would be inhibited. This in turn would displace the aspartate aminotransferase reactions in the two compartments in the required direction.

References

Azzi, A., J. B. Chappell, and B. H. Robinson: Biochem. biophys. Res. Commun. **29**, 148 (1967).

Borst, P.: In: Funktionelle und Morphologische Organisation der Zelle, p. 137. Karlson, P., Ed, Berlin-Göttingen-Heidelberg: Springer 1963.

Bücher, T., and M. Klingenberg: Angew. Chem. **70**, 552 (1958).

Chance, B., and L. Mela: (1) Nature (Lond.) **212**, 369 (1966).

— — (2) Nature (Lond.) **212**, 372 (1966).

Chappell, J. B.: Biochem. J. **90**, 255 (1964).

— Biochem. J. **100**, 43 P (1966).

— Brit. med. Bull. **24**, 150 (1968).

—, and A. R. Crofts: In: Regulation of metabolic processes in mitochondria, p. 293. Tager, J. M., S. Papa, E. Quagliarello, and E. C. Slater, Eds. Amsterdam: Elsevier 1966.

—, and K. N. Haarhoff: In: *Biochemistry of mitochondria*, p. 75. Slater, E. C., Z. Kaniuga, and L. Wojtczak, Eds. London: Academic Press 1967.

—, P. J. F. Henderson, J. D. McGivan, and B. H. Robinson: In: Interaction of drugs and subcellular components in animal cells, p. 71. Campbell, P. N., Ed. London: Churchill 1968.

—, and B. H. Robinson: Biochem. Soc. Symp. **27**, 123 (1968).

de Duve, C., R. Wattiaux, and P. Baudhuin: Advanc. Enzymol. **24**, 291 (1962).

Estabrook, R. W., and B. Sacktor: J. biol. Chem. **233**, 1014 (1957).

Fonyo, A., and S. P. Bessman: Biochem. biophys. Res. Commun. **24**, 61 (1966).

— — Biochem. Med. **2**, 145 (1968).

Greville, G. D.: In: Citric acid cycle: control and compartmentation, p. 1. Lowenstein, J. M., Ed. New York: Marcel Dekker 1969.

Hansford, R. G., and J. B. Chappell: Biochem. biophys. Res. Commun. **30**, 643 (1968).

Holzer, H., G. Schultz und F. Lynen: Biochem. Z. **328**, 252 (1956).

Johnson, R. N., and J. B. Chappell: Unpublished observations (1969).
Klingenberg, M., W. Slenczka und E. Ritt: Biochem. Z. **332**, 47 (1959).
McGivan, J. D., N. M. Bradford, and J. B. Chappell: F.E.B.S. Letters, **4**, 247 (1969).
Meijer, A. J., and J. M. Tager: Biochem. J. **100**, 79 P. (1966).
Mitchell, P.: Biochem. Soc. Symp. **16**, 73 (1959).
— In: Comprehensive biochemistry, Vol. 22, p. 167. Florkin, M., and Stotz, Eds. Amsterdam: Elsevier 1967.
Robinson, B. H.: Ph. D. dissertation, University of Bristol 1968.
—, and J. B. Chappell: Biochem. biophys. Res. Commun. **28**, 249 (1967).
Tyler, D. D.: Biochem. J. **107**, 121 (1968).
— Biochem. J. **111**, 665 (1969).
Vignais, P. V., et E. D. Duee: Bull. Soc. Chim. biol. (Paris) **48**, 1169 (1966).
Williamson, D. H., P. Lund, and H. A. Krebs: Biochem. J. **103**, 514 (1967).
Zebe, E., A. Delbrück und T. Bücher: Ber. ges. Physiol. **189**, 115 (1957).

Possible Action of n-Butylmalonate on Hydrogen Transport in Perfused Liver

R. SCHOLZ[1], R. G. THURMAN, and J. R. WILLIAMSON

Johnson Research Foundation, University of Pennsylvania, Philadelphia, USA

With 1 Figure

In experiments with perfused livers, n-butylmalonate was used as a tool for studies of transport mechanism within the complexity of intact cells. The traces in Fig. 1 represent changes in fluorescence intensity emitted from reduced pyridine nucleotides and oxidized flavins. The fluorescence of both coenzymes was simultaneously recorded from the surface of a hemoglobin free perfused rat liver [1]. An upward deflection of the traces reflects a reduction of extra- and intramitochondrial pyridine nucleotides (NADH, with little contribution of NADPH [2, 3]) and a reduction of mitochondrial flavoproteins [1]. The redox reactions of extra-mitochondrial flavoproteins are hardly detectable by this method.

After addition of ethanol, a rapid reduction of both pyridine nucleotides and flavoproteins occurred (Fig. 1) indicating extramitochondrial redox changes due to the reactions of alcohol and acetaldehyde dehydrogenases and concomitant redox changes in the mitochondrial space. Since mitochondrial acetaldehyde or acetate oxidations are negligible under these conditions, the observed redox changes presume a rapid transfer of reducing equivalents from cytosol into mitochondria. These changes were completely recovered (half time of about 15 min) when ethanol was consumed by the liver. Subsequently, n-butylmalonate and a second dose of ethanol were added. In the presence of n-butylmalonate, the initial responses to ethanol were unchanged, whereas the extent of reduction was diminished with both flavin and pyridine nucleotides.

---

[1] Present address: Institut für Physiologische Chemie und Physikalische Chemie der Universität München, Germany.

Moreover, flavoproteins became reoxidized within 2 min. The reoxidation of pyridine nucleotides appeared to be slower in the presence than in the absence of n-butylmalonate.

These observations suggest that the rate of hydrogen transport through mitochondrial membranes is decreased under the influence of n-butylmalonate. In consequence, a lower state of reduction in the mitochondrial redox systems is reached following ethanol addition. As Dr. CHAPPELL pointed out, possible sites of interaction

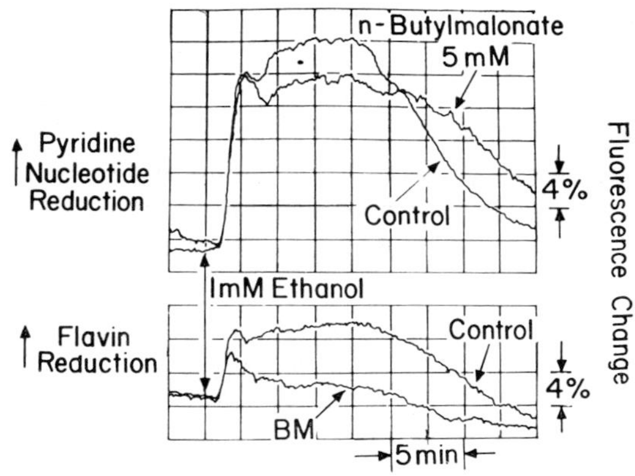

Fig. 1. Changes in fluorescence intensity simultaneously recorded from the surface of perfused rat liver. Upper traces: fluorescence of reduced pyridine nucleotides, excited at 366 mμ; lower traces: fluorescence of oxidized flavoproteins, excited at 436 mμ. Control: addition of 100 μmoles ethanol to 100 ml of perfusion fluid, after 50 min of substrate free perfusion. BM: at 110 min of perfusion, addition of 100 μmoles ethanol in the presence of n-butylmalonate (5 mM). 2-n-Butylmalonate was added 15 min prior to the second ethanol addition. The superimposed traces were recorded from the same area of the liver surface. [5, 6]

are ingress of malate and egress of α-oxoglutarate, if one assumes the existence of a shuttle mechanism involving malate dehydrogenases and aspartate aminotransferases on either side of the mitochondrial membrane [4], as depicted in his Fig. 4 (p. 345). Since the initial rates of reduction of both flavin and pyridine nucleotides were unaffected in the presence of n-butylmalonate, it is suggested that malate ingress is not inhibited. In the initial phase, the extramitochondrial hydrogen acceptor, i.e. oxaloacetate, could be provided by extramitochondrial sources, for example aspartate. In the subsequent phase, however, oxaloacetate must be regenerated from mitochondrial sources. At this point, a limitation of α-oxoglutarate egress is possible in the presence of n-butylmalonate, which secondarily results in a slower rate of malate ingress. Thus, the reoxidation of flavoproteins could reflect the decreasing rate of hydrogen transport into mitochondria.

Further experiments, however, are necessary to substantiate this speculation. Nevertheless, the presented experiment may demonstrate the existence of transport mechanisms in intact liver cells of the type discussed by Dr. CHAPPELL for isolated mitochondria. Furthermore, it also illustrates Dr. BÜCHER's previous question for the physiological importance of translocase systems. Certainly, ethanol oxidation is a physiological process. In perfused liver, it appears to be restricted in the presence of agents known to inhibit anion transport through mitochondrial membranes.

References

1. SCHOLZ, R., R. G. THURMAN, J. R. WILLIAMSON, B. CHANCE, and T. BÜCHER: J. biol. Chem. **244**, 2317 (1969).
2. —, and T. BÜCHER: Hemoglobin free perfusion of rat liver. In: Control of energy metabolism, p. 393. CHANCE, B., R. W. ESTABROOK, and J. R. WILLIAMSON, Eds. New York · London: Acad. Press 1965.
3. — Untersuchungen zur Redoxcompartmentierung bei der hämoglobinfrei perfundierten Leber, p. 22. STAIB, W., and R. SCHOLZ, Eds. Berlin-Heidelberg-New York: Springer 1968.
4. BÜCHER, T., u. M. KLINGENBERG: Angew. Chem. **70**, 552 (1958).
5. SCHOLZ, R., and R. G. THURMAN: Fed. Proc. **27**, 462 (1968).
6. WILLIAMSON, J. R., R. SCHOLZ, R. G. THURMAN, and B. CHANCE: Transport of reducing equivalents across the mitochondrial membrane in rat liver. In: Energy level and metabolic control in mitochondria. QUAGLIARIELLO, E., E. C. SLATER, S. PAPA, and J. M. TAGER, Eds. Bari : Adriatica Editrice 1969.

Discussion

LARDY (Madison, Wisc.): Could you discuss the role of maleate in permitting citrate, for example, to penetrate mitochondria, because it was included among those compounds which could not penetrate. How does it then permit the antiport to function?

CHAPPELL (Bristol): The data have been obtained by very different types of experiments. The point is that maleate is actually an inhibitor of its own entry; so, when you have isotonic maleic acid, you get a high concentration of a compound which is a weak inhibitor, and after a certain time the membrane will be blocked.

In the experiments where it is included as an activator, it is there about 2 to 3 mM for a short period of time, and it doesn't have time to inhibit. Presumably it's its sulfhydryl inhibiting function.

Slater (Amsterdam): Do you think that pyruvate goes in on a specific carrier or on one of the other carriers?

Chappell: I have no idea. We have tried to get evidence for the existence of a pyruvate carrier, but with no consistent results.

Slater: I suppose you agree that the evidence you need for a specific carrier is either a specific inhibitor or a specific activator.

Chappell: What we are trying is to produce mutants of *Neurospora* mitochondria which are lacking various of these functions.

Slater: Do you have evidence for the glycerolphosphate dihydroxyacetonephosphate carrier to be expected from the existence of the glycerolphosphate shunt in insect-muscle mitochondria, as first shown by Bücher and Klingenberg [Angew. Chem. **70**, 552 (1958)]?

Chappell: We have not, but Beechey does have some: β-methyl-α-glycerolphosphate is a strong competitive inhibitor of α-glycerolphosphate oxidation in intact, not in broken mitochondria. The K_i was about 6 μM.

Klingenberg (Munich): We have evidence that glycerolphosphate does not have to permeate, but that the glycerolphosphate oxidase looks to the outside of the inner surface of the mitochondria. There are different types of independent evidence for the localisation of the dehydrogenase to the outer surface: (a) The dehydrogenase is accessible to ferricyanide. Ferricyanide has been introduced as a means of differentiating inner or outer localisation of electron transfer components by virtue of the impermeability of ferricyanide (M. Klingenberg, in: 19th Mosbach Colloquium, p. 131. Berlin-Heidelberg-New York: Springer 1968). (b) Glycerolphosphate has been shown not to penetrate through the inner membrane in various mitochondria, although being actively oxidized.

Chappell: There is one general problem: If you have strict antiport without any uniporters, then you are not going to get penetration of the inner mitochondrial membrane by space techniques; but if you had no adenine nucleotide inside already, and add ATP, you would say that ATP was non-penetrant because there is a strict antiport. It doesn't mean to say that there is no carrier.

Heinz (Frankfurt): You obviously need for the activating effect of glutamate and malate altogether four different carriers, two of them for the uniport, and two of them for the antiport. These systems would be similar to that postulated for the so-called competitive stimulation of amino acid transport in Ehrlich ascites cells. There, upon increasing the concentration of the activating amino acids, the activation turns to an inhibition due to outside competition for the antiport carrier. Do you get this phenomenon also?

CHAPPELL: This certainly happens with the citrate antiporter. At high citrate concentrations, it inhibits its own entry.

HEINZ: Are the uniports active, and are they dependent on certain cations such as Na^+ and K^+; for instance, that of glutamate?

CHAPPELL: Not particularly. We get much the same rates of entry in a medium containing choline chloride as well as potassium chloride. Sodium is a little bit complicated because sodium does in fact enter slowly.

I should perhaps mention also — without wanting to start a battle — that some of these carriers are active, and that they will, as PRESSMAN and others have shown, cause accumulation apparently against a concentration gradient.

HEINZ: I mean really active, i.e. metabolically coupled transport, not any kind of pseudo-active transport.

CHAPPELL: Without knowledge of additional parameters you can say no more than that there is more inside than out.

BÜCHER (Munich): From ratios of redox couples in liver tissue and perfusate, one may conclude that a difference of at least 50 mV exists between the effective redox potentials of extra- and intramitochondrial NAD systems in the aerobic steady state. Thus, hydrogen transport from cytosol into mitochondria should occur against this potential difference. Do you think that the transport via malate is linked to an energy consuming process?

CHAPPELL: We have in fact done the necessary experiments. We can poise the intramitochondrial NAD at a given redox potential by adding various amounts of glutamate, aspartate and malate and oxoglutarate. So we have all 4 partners in the scheme there. When the suspension becomes anaerobic, a surprising thing happens: The intramitochondrial NAD goes very oxidized, indeed; and then, if we add some oxygen, the intramitochondrial NAD becomes extensively reduced. When the oxygen has been consumed, the NAD becomes oxidized again. If an uncoupling agent is there, then we don't get any reduction on aeration. So, there is an energy-dependent system which involves the pulling-in of glutamate and malate into the mitochondria, and the expulsion perhaps of oxoglutarate and aspartate. So if you displace those ions across the membrane, you allow this difference in redox potential between the two compartments; and I think that is where this difference resides. It is in the sidedness of these carriers, and their ability to pull in and out.

KLINGENBERG: This experiment has been done many years before that on addition of oxygen the pyridine nucleotides become reduced, and anaerobic they become oxidized again. Now only the interpretation changes. (Abstr. V. Int. Congr. of Biochem. Moscow 1961, Symp. V.,p. 46. Oxford: Pergamon Press 1963).

Cation Specificity of Inhibitors

W. Simon, L. A. R. Pioda, and H.-K. Wipf

Laboratorium für Organische Chemie der Eidgenössischen Technischen Hochschule, Zürich, Switzerland

With 3 Figures

The discovery of Moore and Pressman in 1964 [1] showing that valinomycin has an alkali cation specificity in mitochondria started a great number of studies in the field of ion transport phenomena in the presence of antibiotics. The compounds studied so far and discussed here may be divided into two classes (see Table 1; for chemical structures, see *Appendix*). Since the compounds in Table 1 show ion specific carrier properties, they have been called "ionophores" [2]. In general, the effects of members of the valinomycin group in mitochondria may be summarized as follows [3—5]:

Table 1. *Ion selective antibiotics*

Valinomycin group	Nigericin group
Valinomycin	Nigericin (= Polyetherin A)
Gramicidins (A, B, C)	Monensin
Enniatins	
Macrotetrolides	

1) Accumulation of potassium ions within the mitochondria.
2) Ejection of hydrogen ions.
3) Swelling of mitochondria.
4) Stimulation of respiration.
5) Induction of ATPase activity.
6) Uncoupling of oxidative phosphorylation.

There is some controversy as to the effects induced by compounds of the nigericin group. Lardy et al. [6] reported that nigericin compensates the effects induced by valinomycin regarding points 1) to 3) mentioned above. Some of the properties of the valinomycin and nigericin group compounds are summarized in Table 2.

So far, the macrotetrolides [7] have been studied in greatest detail [4, 5]. There is a large difference in biological activity of nonactin and monactin, the minimal inhibitory concentration being about ten times smaller for monactin [8]. A similar effect has been observed by LARDY et al. [4, 5] in metabolic studies in rat liver mitochondria. In analogy to the ion specific behaviour of

Table 2. *Properties of compounds of valinomycin and nigericin groups*

Valinomycin group	Nigericin group
— electrically neutral at physiological pH	— negatively charged at physiological pH
— induce transport of alkali metal cations into mitochondria and intact cells	— abolish uptake of alkali metal cations which was induced by antibiotics of the valinomycin group
— K^+ over Na^+ selectivity	

valinomycin [1], less ATPase activity was induced by macrotetrolides in the presence of sodium than in the presence of potassium ions [4]. In contrast to certain opinions [9], we have been able to show in 1966 [10] that the macrotetrolides as such display ion specific complex formation properties in free solution, this being one of the reasons for the ion specific EMF response of bulk membranes [10, 11]. Fig. 1 compares results obtained by EMF measurements on such membranes using antibiotics on inert supports [10, 11] with data on ATPase activity in mitochondria presented by LARDY et al. [4]. There is a striking parallel in the cation selectivity of the two systems. EMF as well as conductance measurements on experimental lipid bilayers in the presence of antibiotics give an analogous cation specificity [12]. The resistance of such membranes decreases by orders of magnitude in the presence of compounds of the valinomycin group [12].

The stability constants given in Table 3 are consistent with the larger biological activity of monactin as compared to nonactin and the preference of potassium over sodium. With the preparation of crystalline 1:1 complexes[1] AB where A is nonactin or monactin and B is NaNCS, KNCS or NH_4NCS [13] it has become possible to study the nature of the bonding between cation and macrotetrolide by X-ray analysis [14]. In the nonactin complex (Fig. 2) the K^+ ion is surrounded by four oxygen atoms from furane rings

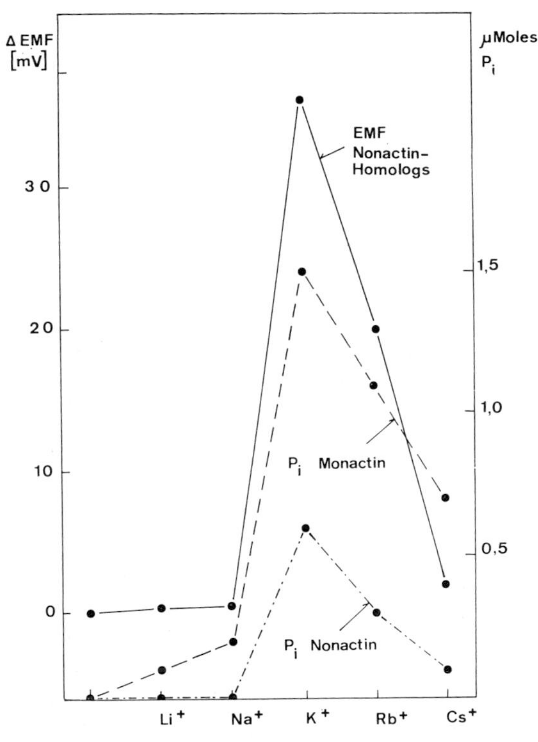

Fig. 1. Comparison of results obtained by EMF measurements with data on ATPase activity in mitochondria

and by four keto-oxygen atoms in approximately cubic 8-coordination. The observed conformation comes very close to S_4 symmetry, and the 32-membered ring can be described as resembling the seam of a tennis ball with the K^+ ion at the center of the ball and with the methyl substituents and the methylene groups of the furane

[1] It has been shown by vapor pressure osmometry that macrotetrolides form 1:1 complexes with alkali cations in organic solvents [13].

rings on the outside. This conformation is quite different from that tentatively assumed by MUELLER and RUDIN [12] on the basis of model considerations. The conformation of nonactin itself is not yet known. However, the short c periodicity clearly indicates that

Table 3

	Stability constant K [kg·mole^{-1}]		
Ligand	Na^+	K^+	K_{K^+}/K_{Na^+}
Nonactin	$(1.3 \pm 0.2)\cdot 10^2$	$(5.0 \pm 0.7)\cdot 10^3$	38 ± 5
Monactin	$(1.1 \pm 0.1)\cdot 10^3$	$(2.5 \pm 1.0)\cdot 10^5$	230 ± 70

free nonactin must adopt a conformation quite different from that of the complexed molecule, for the crystal must be built up from rather flat, plate-like molecules associated in closely stacked

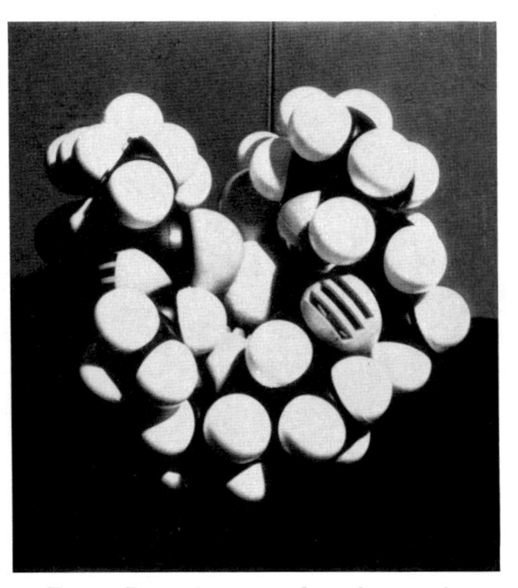

Fig. 2. Potassium complex of nonactin

columns. A transfer of cations from molecule to molecule within such stacks may be readily imagined.

In the complex of enniatin B [15] with KI the potassium ion is surrounded in octahedral coordination by six keto-oxygen atoms

of the enniatin molecule [16] showing a puckered doughnut structure (Fig. 3). Again, the polar groups are at the inner and the non-polar groups at the outer side of the complex. Whereas the macrotetrolide complex resembles a large spherical lipophilic cation, the enniatin B complex resembles a corresponding lipophilic charged disc (see also [17]). The complex of valinomycin with potassium [18] seems to be built on similar lines with a 6-coordination of the cation with carbonyl oxygen atoms [19]. Although members of the nigericin group contain a carboxyl group

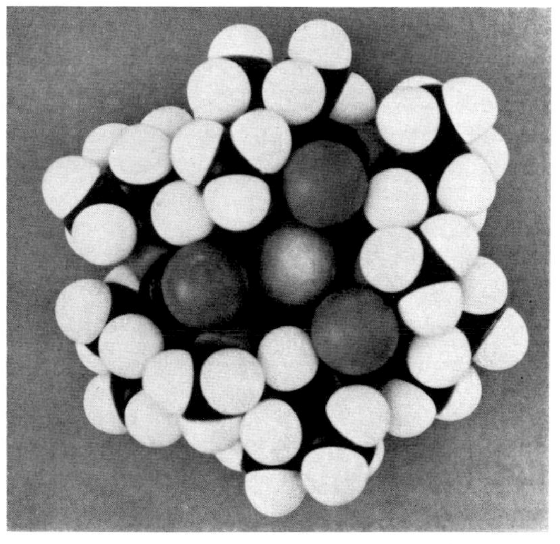

Fig. 3. Potassium complex of enniatin B

which is ionized at physiological pH, the general structures of the complexes are rather similar as shown by X-ray analysis of the silver salts of nigericin [20] and monensin [21]. The properties of the ion specific carriers can therefore be summarized as follows:

1) The external surface of the complexes is lipophilic, enhancing lipid solubility of these carrier complexes.

2) The alkali cation is not hydrated.

3) The alkali cation complexes of compounds of the valinomycin group are positively charged.

4) The alkali cation complexes of compounds of the nigericin group are electrically neutral.

The selectivity orders obtained by EMF measurements on bulk membranes are given in Table 4. They are consistent with the complex formation constants known so far [13, 15, 22, 23]. The selectivity orders to be expected for a strong and a weak binding of the alkali cation to the ligand relative to that of the solvent are also given in Table 4 [24, 25].

Table 4. *Selectivity orders (EMF)*

Nonactin:	$K^+ > Rb^+ > Cs^+ > H^+ > Na^+ > Li^+$
Enniatin B:	$K^+ > Rb^+ > Cs^+ > Na^+ > Li^+$
Valinomycin:	$Rb^+ > K^+ > Cs^+ > Na^+ > Li^+ > H^+$
Strong binding to ligand:	$Li^+ > Na^+ > K^+ > Rb^+ > Cs^+$
Strong binding to solvent:	$Cs^+ > Rb^+ > K^+ > Na^+ > Li^+$

Table 5. *Radius ratio rule*

Polyhedron	Coordination number	Radius of cage in Å
Cubo-octahedron	12	1.40
	9	1.02
Cube	8	1.02
Square antiprism	8	0.90
	7	0.83
Octahedron	6	0.58
Tetrahedron	4	0.31
Radii in Å:	Li^+ 0.6	Rb^+ 1.48
	Na^+ 0.95	Cs^+ 1.69
	K^+ 1.33	O 1.40

A simple calculation based on the assumption of rigid spheres shows that if the ratio of the radii of cation and oxygen falls below a certain value, there will occur oxygen-oxygen rather than oxygen-cation contact (radius ratio rule) [26]. This resulting minimal radius of the cage formed by oxygen atoms for different coordinations is given in Table 5. The observed K^+—O distances in the nonactin and enniatin B complexes are around 2.7 Å in perfect agreement with a cation-oxygen contact [14, 16]. Cations smaller than the cage will show a weaker bonding to the ligand relative to the situation with contact between oxygen atoms and cation, and will therefore give smaller stability constants, in agreement with

the observed selectivity orders (Table 4) [22]. The complex formation constants are around 100 to 1000 M^{-1} corresponding to free energy differences of about 3 to 5 kcal/mole, compared with hydration energies and free energies for ligand binding in the order of 100 kcal/mole. Therefore, small conformational changes in the ligand may have a large effect on the stability constants (Table 3).

In a membrane consisting of an agent complexing preferably potassium ions, a selective transport is to be expected if a potential is applied across the membrane [27] in the presence of equal concentrations of sodium and potassium ions. It has been shown that such a selective transport of potassium ions is obtained using a porous PVC membrane impregnated with macrotetrolides in octanol-2 [28]. By analogy the selective transports in biological systems may readily be imagined to be caused by potential differences across membranes in the presence of these and/or other similar complexing agents. Since the carrier complexes of the nigericin type are electrically neutral, they are not expected to migrate in a potential gradient except by diffusion. These complexes may transport cations by facilitated diffusion.

Due to the high stability constant ratio for potassium relative to sodium ions which is approximately 38, 230 and > 650 for nonactin, monactin and valinomycin, respectively, these compounds may be used in sensors for potassium ion activity. Membranes using nonactin in nujol/octanol-2 on Millipore filter show a response, as expected theoretically, in the range 10^{-1} to 10^{-3}M with a selectivity of 150 of potassium over sodium [29]. In agreement with the ratio of the valinomycin complex formation constants of potassium over sodium, liquid membrane electrodes using valinomycin in diphenyl ether on Millipore filter gives potassium-selective electrodes of high selectivity. The linear range of these electrodes is 10^{-1} M to 10^{-5} M and the selectivity of potassium over sodium around 5000. Membranes of a diameter of 5 mm show a resistance of approximately 1 MΩ and have a selectivity of potassium over hydrogen ions of about 10^4, and therefore the use of buffered sample solutions is usually not necessary. These electrodes show potassium ion selectivities which are larger by several orders of magnitude than those of conventional ion selective glass electrodes. They are suitable for analytical purposes [30].

References

1. MOORE, C., and B. C. PRESSMAN: Biochem. biophys. Res. Commun. **15**, 562 (1964).
2. PRESSMAN, B. C., E. J. HARRIS, W. S. JAGGER, and J. H. JOHNSON: Proc. nat. Acad. Sci. (Wash.) **58**, 1949 (1967).
3. HÖFER, M., and B. C. PRESSMAN: Biochemistry **5**, 3919 (1966).
4. GRAVEN, S. N., H. A. LARDY, D. JOHNSON, and A. RUTTER: Biochemistry **5**, 1729 (1966).
5. — —, and A. RUTTER: Biochemistry **5**, 1735 (1966).
   — —, and S. ESTRADA-O.: Biochemistry **6**, 365 (1967).
6. ESTRADA-O., S., S. N. GRAVEN, and H. A. LARDY: J. biol. Chem. **242**, 2925 (1967).
   GRAVEN, S. N., S. ESTRADA-O., and H. A. LARDY: Proc. nat. Acad. Sci. (Wash.) **56**, 654 (1966).
7. CORBAZ, R., L. ETTLINGER, E. GÄUMANN, W. KELLER-SCHIERLEIN, F. KRADOLFER, L. NEIPP, V. PRELOG, and H. ZÄHNER: Helv. chim. Acta **38**, 1445 (1955).
   BECK, J., H. GERLACH, V. PRELOG, and W. VOSER: Helv. chim. Acta **45**, 620 (1962).
   DOMINGUEZ, J., J. D. DUNITZ, H. GERLACH, and V. PRELOG: Helv. chim. Acta **45**, 129 (1962).
   GERLACH, H., u. V. PRELOG: Liebigs Ann. Chem. **669**, 121 (1963).
   KELLER-SCHIERLEIN, W., u. H. GERLACH: Fortschr. Chem. org. Naturstoffe **26**, 161 (1968).
8. MEYERS, E., F. E. PANSY, D. PERLMAN, D. A. SMITH, and F. L. WEISENBORN: J. Antibiot. (Tokyo), Ser. A **18**, 128 (1965).
9. PRESSMAN, B. C., and E. J. HARRIS: Abstracts Volume, Seventh International Congress of Biochemistry, Tokyo, August 19—25, 1967.
10. ŠTEFANAC, Z., u. W. SIMON: Chimia (Switz.) **20**, 436 (1966).
11. — — Microchem. J. **12**, 125 (1967).
12. MUELLER, P., and D. O. RUDIN: Biochem. biophys. Res. Commun. **26**, 398 (1967).
13. PIODA, L. A. R., H. A. WACHTER, R. E. DOHNER, and W. SIMON: Helv. chim. Acta **50**, 1373 (1967).
14. KILBOURN, B. T., J. D. DUNITZ, L. A. R. PIODA, and W. SIMON: J. molec. Biol. **30**, 559 (1967).
15. WIPF, H.-K., L. A. R. PIODA, Z. ŠTEFANAC, and W. SIMON: Helv. chim. Acta **51**, 377 (1968).
16. DOBLER, M., J. D. DUNITZ, and J. KRAJEWSKI: J. molec. Biol. (in press).
17. LARDY, H. A., S. N. GRAVEN, and S. ESTRADA-O.: Fed. Proc. **26**, 1355 (1967).
18. PIODA, L. A. R., H.-K.WIPF and W. SIMON: Chimia (Switz.) **22**, 189 (1968).
19. PINKERTON, M., L. K. STEINRAUF, and P. DAWKINS: Biochem. biophys. Res. Commun. **35**, 512 (1969).
20. —, M. PINKERTON, and J. W. CHAMBERLIN: Biochem. biophys. Res. Commun. **33**, 29 (1968).

21. Agtarap, A., J. W. Chamberlin, M. Pinkerton, and L. K. Steinrauf: J. Amer. chem. Soc. **89**, 5737 (1967).
22. Simon, W.: NRP Work Session on "Carriers and Specificity in Membranes", MIT, Brookline, Mass., February 9—11, 1969.
23. Shemyakin, M. M., Yu. A. Ovchinnikov, V. T. Ivanov, V. K. Antonov, A. M. Shkrob, I. I. Mikhaleva, A. V. Evstratov, and G. G. Malenkov: Biochem. biophys. Res. Commun. **29**, 834 (1967).
24. Eisenman, G.: Symposium on membrane transport and metabolism, special copy of communication. Prague: Publishing House of the Czechoslovak Academy of Sciences 1961.
25. Diebler, H., M. Eigen, G. Ilgenfritz, G. Maass, and R. Winkler: Private communication.
26. Pauling, L.: The nature of the chemical bond. New York: Cornell University Press 1952.
27. Eisenman, G., J. P. Sandblom, and J. L. Walker Jr.: Science **155**, 965 (1967).
Bloch, R., A. Katchalsky, O. Kedem, and D. Vofsi: Brit. Pat., Nr. 1,049,041 (1966).
28. Wipf, H.-K., and W. Simon: Biochem. biophys. Res. Commun. **34**, 707 (1969).
29. Pioda, L. A. R., u. W. Simon: Chimia (Switz.) **23**, 72 (1969).
30. Simon, W.: 135th National Meeting, The Electrochemical Society, New York City, N.Y., May 4—9, 1969.

Stereochemical Aspects of Macrotetrolide Action and Biosynthesis

W. Keller-Schierlein

Eidgenössische Technische Hochschule, Zürich, Switzerland

With 1 Figure

The complex ion of nonactin potassium shows a highly regular spheric structure which was deduced from an X-ray structural analysis, as shown by Prof. Simon. The macrocyclic ligand is folded in the manner of the seam of a tennis ball. It can easily be seen, and it can be shown by means of models, that such a regular shape (and hence a high complex stability) is only possible if the building stones of nonactin are arranged in a stereochemical manner which is unique in natural products: The macrocyclic ring is composed of 4 nonactinic acid residues, two of them have the (+)-configuration, the other two the enantiomeric (−)-configuration, so that nonactin itself is, in spite of the presence of 16 asymmetric carbon atoms, an achiral meso-compound.

An analogous unusual stereochemistry is found in all biologically active macrotetrolides (homologues of nonactin), eight of which have been analyzed up to now (Fig. 1). And although we have investigated macrotetrolide mixtures from many strains of actinomycetes (several of them very carefully), we never could isolate any compound with diastereomeric nonactinic acids. Nature seems to produce only the two enantiomeric forms, differing in the chirality of all four asymmetric centers. This fact is able to modify our thinking on biosynthesis.

It seems to be very unlikely that first one chiral form of nonactinic acid is synthesized, and then a configurational inversion takes place at all four centers of chirality. At first glance we should estimate that two separate sets of enzymes are necessary, one for the synthesis of (+)-nonactinic acid, and another one for (−)-nonactinic acid. Of course, this rather naive hypothesis is very probably not true. It is more likely that the diverse centers of chirality are introduced at once after the linkage of four achiral precursors of the nonactinic acid residues to the enzyme in an arrangement which anticipates the "tennis ball" conformation, possibly with the cooperation of a metal ion. The formation of the centers of chirality could take place simultaneously with the connection of the building stones by ester bonds.

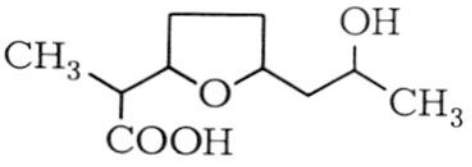

Nonactinic acid (NA) 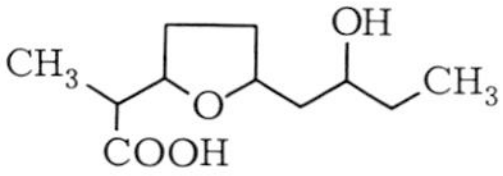 Homononactinic acid (HA) 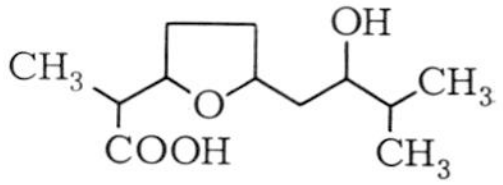 Bishomononactinic acid (BA)

<table>
<tr><th>Compound</th><th>Formula</th><th>(+)-NA</th><th>(-)-NA</th><th>(+)-HA</th><th>(-)-HA</th><th>(+)-BA</th><th>(-)-BA</th></tr>
<tr><td>Nonactin</td><td>$C_{40}H_{64}O_{12}$</td><td>2</td><td>2</td><td></td><td></td><td></td><td></td></tr>
<tr><td>Monactin</td><td>$C_{41}H_{66}O_{12}$</td><td>1</td><td>2</td><td>1</td><td></td><td></td><td></td></tr>
<tr><td>Dinactin</td><td>$C_{42}H_{68}O_{12}$</td><td></td><td>2</td><td>2</td><td></td><td></td><td></td></tr>
<tr><td>Trinactin</td><td>$C_{43}H_{70}O_{12}$</td><td></td><td>1</td><td>2</td><td>1</td><td></td><td></td></tr>
<tr><td colspan="6">BECK et al. Helv. chim. acta 45, 620 (1962)</td><td></td><td></td></tr>
<tr><td>Substance G</td><td>$C_{43}H_{70}O_{12}$</td><td></td><td>2</td><td>1</td><td></td><td>1</td><td></td></tr>
<tr><td>Substance D</td><td>$C_{44}H_{72}O_{12}$</td><td></td><td>1</td><td>2</td><td></td><td></td><td>1</td></tr>
<tr><td>Substance C</td><td>$C_{45}H_{74}O_{12}$</td><td></td><td>1</td><td>1</td><td></td><td>1</td><td>1</td></tr>
<tr><td>Substance B</td><td>$C_{46}H_{76}O_{12}$</td><td></td><td></td><td colspan="2">2</td><td colspan="2">2</td></tr>
</table>

Fig. 1

However, no experimental evidence on the biosynthesis of nonactin is available up to now.

Another biochemical aspect of the facts presented by Prof. SIMON is the following: Ion selectivity not only occurs in cells and cell particles damaged by antibiotics. It is a general process in living systems. It seems that similar mechanisms as those presented by Prof. SIMON are playing a role in the ion transport in normal cells. What are the ion carriers (corresponding to these antibiotics) in normal cells?

First, we have to consider that these antibiotics are active in extremely high dilutions, up to 10^{-10} M. If ion carriers are present only in concentrations necessary for a normal operation of life, it is nearly hopeless to detect them without an extremely sensitive test (which is not available at present).

On the other hand, actinomyces strains producing macrotetrolides or valinomycin are found very frequently. Similarly frequent are fungi which produce enniatins. We could assume from these facts that these antibiotics are the normal alkali ion carriers present in nondetectable dilution in all cells of microorganisms. The fact that many strains produce them in biologically and chemically detectable quantities could be explained by a defect in a regulation mechanism.

Nuclear Magnetic Resonance Studies of Valinomycin, Alamethicin and Gramicidin S, and Their Interaction with Phospholipids

E. G. Finer, H. Hauser, and D. Chapman

Molecular Biophysics Unit, Unilever Research Laboratory Colworth/Welwyn, The Frythe, Welwyn, Herts, England

With 1 Figure

Valinomycin and alamethicin are both examples of cyclic molecules which induce transport of ions across biological [1] and artificial membranes [2a, b]. Their action differs in two important ways: firstly, valinomycin shows potassium/sodium ion specificity, whereas alamethicin transports both ions with the same ease [1], and secondly, alamethicin (but not valinomycin) induces in black lipid films electrical properties analogous to excitability in nerve membranes [2a]. We have used high resolution nuclear magnetic resonance spectroscopy (NMR) to investigate the properties of these molecules in solution, their interaction with ions, and the way they interact with phospholipids which are present in model membrane systems [2b] and in natural membranes where ion transport properties have been demonstrated [3]. We have also investigated the interaction of the related molecule gramicidin S with phospholipids. Gramicidin S is similar to alamethicin and valinomycin in many ways (it is a cyclic surface active polypeptide antibiotic containing 10 amino acid residues, whereas alamethicin contains 19, and valinomycin contains 6 amino acid and 6 hydroxy acid residues), but it does not induce ion transport across mitochondrial membranes [3].

We were unable to obtain much information about the interaction of alamethicin with ions using NMR, but our studies on valinomycin were much more fruitful. Firstly, we were able to show, by performing variable temperature experiments on different molar ratios of valinomycin/potassium thiocyanate dissolved in $CDCl_3$, that the valinomycin-K^+ complex is remarkably stable in a hydrophobic environment and that the potassium ion is bound without a hydration shell. These results have also been obtained by HAYNES, KOWALSKY and PRESSMAN [4]. Secondly, we found that the potassium/sodium ion differential transport properties of valinomycin probably do not arise from great differences in structure of the complexes formed by valinomycin and these ions. Spectra of the two complexes are similar in many respects. The ion selectivity may arise from other factors — perhaps the greater energy of hydration of the sodium ion leads to less easy displacement of water by valinomycin. Thirdly, we have obtained a considerable amount of data about the conformation of free and complexed valinomycin in chloroform and chloroform/methanol solutions by measuring the chemical shifts and coupling constants of the valinomycin molecule. This gave us information about various dihedral angles and barriers to internal rotation of various groups. Although free valinomycin changes its conformation as methanol is added to a chloroform solution, the structure of the complex remains fixed. Infra-red studies of valinomycin and the potassium complex have given us further information about how the ion is bound — the carbonyls of the ester linkages seem to play an important role.

In our NMR studies of the interaction of valinomycin, alamethicin and gramicidin S with aqueous dispersions of phosphatidylserine and egg yolk lecithin, we found two distinct types of behaviour exemplified by valinomycin and alamethicin on the one hand and gramicidin S on the other. Fig. 1 shows how the 60 MHz proton spectrum of a sonicated dispersion of 1% phosphatidylserine in D_2O is altered by the addition of a small quantity of alamethicin (molar ratio 100:1): the hydrocarbon chain signal is drastically broadened (so that it becomes lost in the baseline). This effect is due to a reduction in motion of the lipid chains, leading to increased correlation times and hence reduced relaxation times. A similar effect is observed with lecithin. We conclude that valinomycin and alamethicin interact with the hydrophobic parts of the lipids, so that each molecule by some cooperative effect inhibits the motion of considerable numbers of lipid chains (for example, we estimate that one alamethicin molecule affects

600 molecules of phosphatidylserine). In contrast to this, the addition of gramicidin S to a sonicated dispersion of lecithin does not produce any reduction in chain signal, although the choline signal is slightly reduced at high polypeptide concentrations. We interpret this result as showing that gramicidin S, which does not transport ions, interacts primarily with the head groups of the lipid molecules rather than the hydrocarbon chains.

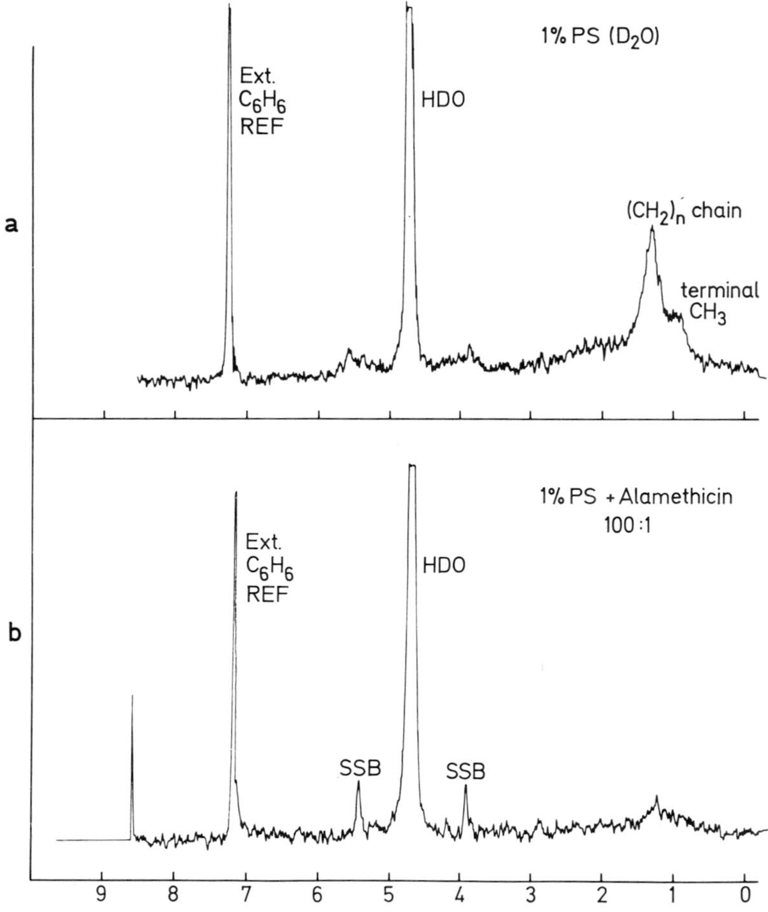

Fig. 1. (a) 60 MHz proton spectrum of 1% sonicated dispersion of phosphatidylserine in D_2O. (b) As (a) but with phosphatidylserine + alamethicin, molar ratio 100:1

We believe these studies to be important from a number of points of view:

a) Since NMR shows that valinomycin forms similar complexes with both sodium and potassium, the origin of the ion selectivity shown by this molecule may lie in some fairly subtle differences in the complex structures or ion hydration properties.

b) We have shown that related antibiotic molecules interact in different ways with phospholipids, and this may be relevant to their different actions as regards ion transport properties, as well as to their mode of action as antibiotics.

c) We have shown that hydrophobic interaction can occur between the hydrocarbon chains of phospholipids and either alamethicin or valinomycin. This is pertinent to our previous spectroscopic observations on erythrocyte membranes [5] where such an interaction was postulated to occur between proteins and lipids.

References

1. Pressman, B. C.: Fed. Proc. **27**, 1283 (1968).
2a. Mueller, P., and D. O. Rudin: Nature (Lond.) **217**, 713 (1968).
b. Henderson, P. J. F., J. D. McGivan, and J. B. Chappell: Biochem. J. **111**, 521 (1969).
3. Pressman, B. C.: Proc. nat. Acad. Sci. (Wash.) **53**, 1076 (1965).
4. Haynes, D. H., A. Kowalsky, and B. C. Pressman: J. biol. Chem. **244**, 502 (1969).
5. Chapman, D., V. B. Kamat, J. de Gier, and S. A. Penkett: J. molec. Biol. **31**, 101 (1968).

Discussion

Helmreich (Würzburg): Dr. Simon, you demonstrated very nicely to us how the cation enters and leaves the monactin ball. Your atomic model also indicates that the actins are very flexible structures. Now, I believe that Dr. Eigen has recently obtained evidence that the monactins undergo a large conformational change upon binding of the cation to the monactin carrier. Following this contraction, there is again an expansion of the monactin ball when the cation leaves.

Simon (Zürich): Dr. Eigen and his group studied in detail the kinetics of the complex formation. It turned out that this reaction is extremely fast, the rate constant being $3 \cdot 10^8$ M^{-1} sec^{-1}. This can only be explained by assuming a stepwise replacement of solvent by the ligand with a corresponding change in conformation of the ligand. If the solvent would be replaced at once, the activation energy would be of the order of 100 kcal/mole, and the reaction would be extremely slow.

Slater (Amsterdam): In some biological systems, NH_4^+ may replace K^+ in inducing effects of valinomycin. Have you any information on the binding of NH_4^+ to valinomycin and the other compounds you discussed?

Simon: From EMF studies we have to conclude that the complex formation constants of the NH_4^+ with valinomycin and the macrotetrolides are of the same order of magnitude as those with the K^+. There are, however, some differences in the behavior of the NH_4^+ in rat liver mitochondria. One explanation is simply that the accumulated NH_4^+ react differently on the hydrolysis of ATP within the mitochondria.

Heinz (Frankfurt): I couldn't see how the driving force for the K^+ to drive it in the presence of valinomycin could be anything else than pumping the H^+ outwards. If the electrical potential difference driving the positively charged valinomycin-K^+-complex inwards were created by anything else, I couldn't see how the H^+ would move *against* this potential difference outwards.

Simon: I did not comment on which is first, whether it is the potential difference or the efflux of H^+. If there is first an efflux of H^+, there will be a negative charge inside and the K^+ ions would move into the mitochondria. If the potential difference is there first, the K^+ could move into the mitochondria, and simultaneously or later H^+ could move out. The ejection of the H^+ ions may be a matter of a corresponding carrier. There is some evidence available that compounds similar to the ones described could serve as carriers for H^+.

Heinz: This possibility still implies that the H^+ move against an electrochemical potential gradient outwards, because an electrical potential gradient driving the K^+ inward can not at the same time move the H^+ outwards, unless a huge H^+ concentration gradient exists.

Simon: But there is nothing against a movement of H^+ out of the mitochondrium if there is a concentration gradient.

Heinz: But why could they move in again when you add nigericin if there is a gradient of H^+ outward?

Simon: I do not know. It might be a concentration gradient in the opposite direction developed in the meantime. To answer this question we would need to know the activity of H^+ ions within the cell.

Klingenberg (Munich): Dr. Keller-Schierlein, concerning your remark about the function of these elaborate structures which these molds produce: Do they produce these compounds for their own K^+-Na^+-transport couples, or do they want to kill enemies? What do you think of the biological significance of the production of these compounds?

Keller-Schierlein (Zurich): Although no experimental evidence is present, it is a possibility that all microorganisms produce such compounds in very low concentration for their own use as ion specific ion carriers. Only those strains which have a defect in the regulation mechanism produce them in detectable quantities.

Rink (Bonn): There are some enzymes activated by K^+ and inhibited by Na^+. Do you have any idea about the mode of action of these enzymes; it might be explained by similar complexes as those formed by valinomycin with these cations?

Simon: No, I have not.

Site-Specific Inhibitors of Gluconeogenesis

HENRY LARDY

Department of Biochemistry and Institute for Enzyme Research, University of Wisconsin, Madison, Wisconsin, USA

With 6 Figures

The synthesis of carbohydrate in mammalian liver and kidney is precisely regulated to provide the requisite supply of blood glucose. Elucidating the nature of the regulatory processes is a challenging task to anyone interested in fundamental mechanisms as well as to those who seek more effective means of treating metabolic disorders such as diabetes.

During the past few years we have found a number of naturally occurring compounds to inhibit gluconeogenesis in highly specific ways. We have also investigated the mode of action of some known hypoglycemic agents whose mechanism of action is perhaps more general and considerably more difficult to elucidate. In this paper I will summarize some of these studies in the hope that the inhibitory compounds can be of value to others studying the regulation of carbohydrate synthesis and the mode of action of hormones that affect carbohydrate metabolism.

Quinolinic Acid

In 1966, FOSTER, RAY, and LARDY [1] reported that tryptophan, in doses of 35 mg/100 gm body weight, caused the hepatic phosphoenol pyruvate carboxykinase (PEPCK) to be doubled in activity within 30 min. This rapid increase of enzyme activity was not the result of protein synthesis; it represented an activation of the enzyme present [2]. The increased activity was not accompanied by an enhanced rate of gluconeogenesis; in fact, tryptophan inhibited gluconeogenesis induced by hydrocortisone as well as that brought about by feeding pyruvate, aspartate, and malate [2].

Measuring the concentration of various intermediates of gluconeogenesis in the livers of rats treated with tryptophan demonstrated that pyruvate, lactate, citrate, malate, aspartate and oxalacetate were greatly elevated, whereas PEP, 2- and 3-phosphoglyceric acids and hexosemonophosphates were appr eciably decreased in comparison with the concentration of these intermediates in normal rat livers [3]. Thus it appeared that the block of gluconeogenesis occurred at the reaction catalyzed by PEP carboxykinase — the enzyme that is apparently activated by tryptophan administration [1].

The time sequence of metabolite changes following administration of tryptophan to rats provides some insight to the processes of gluconeogenesis (Fig. 1). Within 30 min following the intraperitoneal injection of 75 mg tryptophan per 100 g body weight, the citrate and malate concentrations in liver were greatly elevated, lactate, pyruvate and aspartate were increased two to three fold and PEP was approximately at normal. By 1 h the PEP concentration had dropped severely while the other metabolites continued to increase. Between the 6th and 8th h, when the influence of tryptophan appears to be subsiding, aspartate, malate and citrate, as well as lactate and pyruvate, decrease rapidly and PEP increases 20 fold to more than double the normal concentration. Thus during the recovery period aspartate, malate and citrate seem to be precursors of PEP, providing support for the concepts developed from *in vitro* studies [4].

Studies conducted with perfused rat livers disclosed that not only tryptophan, but also its metabolic degradation products L-kynurenine, L-3 hydroxykynurenine, 3 hydroxyanthranilic acid and quinolinic acid inhibit gluconeogenesis (Fig. 2) [5].

Since quinolinic acid is the most rapidly effective of these compounds in enhancing assayable PEP carboxykinase and since it alone can inhibit this enzyme *in vitro*, we assume that quinolinic acid is the actual inhibitor and that the other inhibitory tryptophan metabolites are active by virtue of their conversion to quinolinic acid. Nicotinic acid and several other compounds derived metabolically from tryptophan were not active. Quinaldic acid also blocks gluconeogenesis but by a different mechanism that will be discussed later in this paper.

The mechanism by which quinolinate inhibits PEP carboxykinase is interesting. It has no direct inhibitory effect when tested against the enzyme in rat liver supernatant fraction. The clue to its mode of inhibition came from studies of the metal requirements

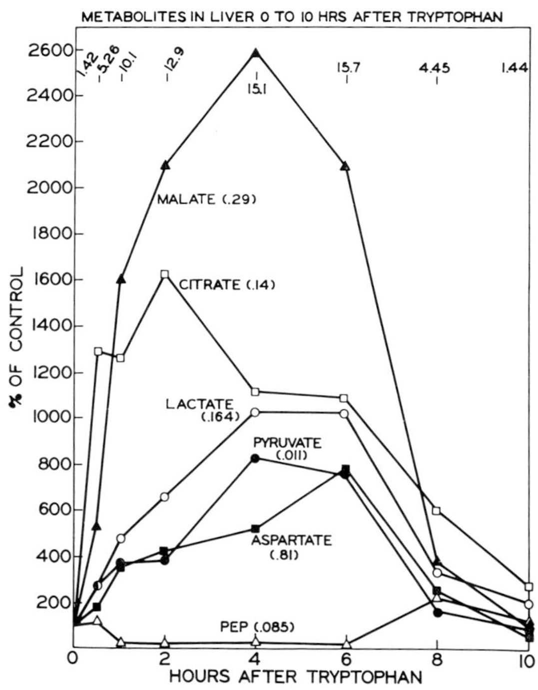

Fig. 1. The amounts of metabolites in livers of normal male rats fasted for 24 h and then given tryptophan for varying times before killing. Data are expressed as percentage of controls (24-h fasted normal male rats). Each point represents the average of data from three animals. The average concentration, in micromoles per g of liver, from control animals is given in parentheses following each substrate. The numbers across the top of the graph represent the sum of aspartate, pyruvate, lactate, citrate, and malate in micromoles per g of liver at the various times of measurement. PEP, phosphoenolpyruvate. From [3]

of this enzyme. CHANG and LANE [6] had shown that pig liver mitochondrial PEP carboxykinase was activated by Mn^{++}, and HOLTEN and NORDLIE [7] found Mn^{++} and Mg^{++} to be synergistic in activating the guinea pig liver enzyme. DAVID FOSTER in our laboratory found maximum activity with the rat liver enzyme when Mg^{++} was present in a concentration equimolar with respect to the ITP present and Mn^{++} was present in the low concentration of 50 μmolar. The increment of activity achieved in the presence

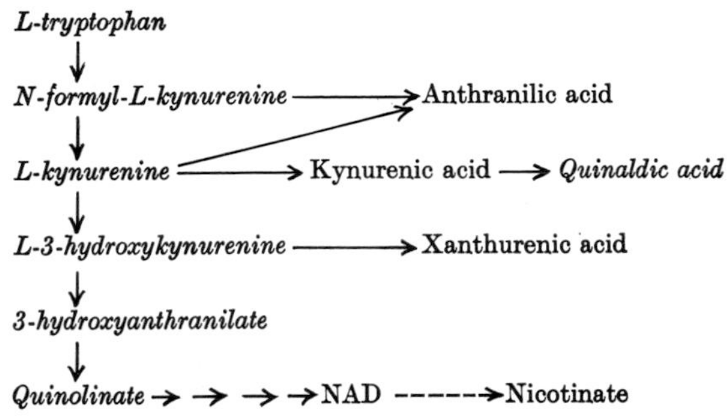

Fig. 2. Italicized compounds enhance assayable phosphoenolpyruvate carboxykinase activity and/or block gluconeogenesis in rat liver

of Mn^{++} was about 80 to 95% of the activity in the absence of added Mn^{++}. Most interestingly, this stimulation of PEP carboxykinase by Mn^{++} was completely lacking in supernatant fractions from the livers of rats that had been given tryptophan (Table 1).

Table 1. *Effects of* Mn^{3+} *and* SO_4^{2-} *in vitro on the activity of hepatic PEP carboxykinase of rats*

Treatment[a] (No. of animals)	Addition to assay mixture[b], [c]			
	None	Mn^{2+}	SO_4^{2-}	$Mn^{2+} + SO_4^{2-}$
Fed (4)	58 ± 5	110 ± 6	59 ± 4	138 ± 5
Fasted for 24 h (8)	111 ± 4	214 ± 8	112 ± 5	260 ± 9
+ L-Tryptophan (5)	331 ± 20	334 ± 25	385 ± 32	384 ± 32

[a] L-Tryptophan (75 mg/100 g) was given intraperitoneally as a suspension in 0.9% NaCl 4 h before death.

[b] Assay mixtures (1.5 ml, pH 8.0) contained: 1.6 μmoles of reduced glutathione, 6.7 μmoles of OAA, 9.0 μmoles of Na_3HITP, 22.5 μmoles of $MgAc_2$, 20 μmoles of KF, 94 μmoles of Tris (Cl), supernatant fraction of liver, and, where indicated, 0.1 mM $MnCl_2$ and/or 10 mM Na_2SO_4.

[c] Activity plus and minus standard deviation given in nanomoles of PEP formed per minute per milligram of protein.

Furthermore, although the enzyme activity from normal liver homogenates is not subject to stimulation by sulfate ion, it is stimulated by sulfate when Mn^{++} has been added; the enzyme in homogenates of tryptophan-treated rats is directly stimulatable by sulfate in the absence of added manganese [2]. Thus the activation that can be accomplished by Mn^{++} *in vitro* already appears to have been accomplished in the tissue homogenate from rats fed tryptophan.

These findings, together with studies by JAMES JOHNSTON [8] of the ion specificity of PEP carboxykinase, have led to some tentative conclusions concerning the mechanism by which quinolinic acid apparently activates the *in vitro* activity of the enzyme that it inhibits *in vivo*.

Phosphoenolpyruvate carboxykinase from the cytosol of rat liver requires the MgGTP complex as a substrate and, for maximum activity, requires in addition a low concentration of a divalent transition metal. Mn^{++}, Co^{++} and Fe^{++} activate but Fe^{+++} does not.

The addition of quinolinate to the regular assay mixture used for measuring PEP carboxykinase activity has no inhibitory effect. Likewise, in the presence of added Mn^{++}, quinolinate does not inhibit. However, if ferrous iron is used as activator, quinolinate strongly inhibits the PEP carboxykinase activity. With the high concentrations of oxalacetate used in the standard assay (4 mM), maximal inhibition (about 80%) is achieved with 5 mM ferrous quinolinate. If Mn^{++} is added to the inhibited enzyme *in vitro* or to the perfused liver in which quinolinate has blocked gluconeogenesis, there is an immediate relief of the inhibition. We take this as evidence that ferrous ion, and not Mn^{++}, is the natural activator of PEP carboxykinase, for the enzyme in liver cells is susceptible to inhibition by quinolinate.

These data explain well the inhibition of gluconeogenesis by tryptophan, quinolinate and the metabolic intermediates between these two compounds. We must now offer some explanation for the apparent activation of PEP carboxykinase activity when this enzyme is assayed in liver supernatant fractions following the administration of tryptophan to rats, and the addition of tryptophan, or its degradation products on the pathway to quinolinate, to perfused rat livers.

It must be recalled that the homogenization of liver and subsequent dilution for the enzyme assay results in a total dilution of 300 fold [1, 2]. If sufficient ferrous quinolinate is added to a 10 fold diluted liver homogenate to inhibit the enzyme by 50%, one observes that when the enzyme is diluted an additional 30 fold and allowed to incubate with the other assay mixture ingredients before addition of oxalacetate, the enzyme activity is nearly twice that of the original homogenate to which no iron salts or quinolinate were added. In separate experiments it was demonstrated

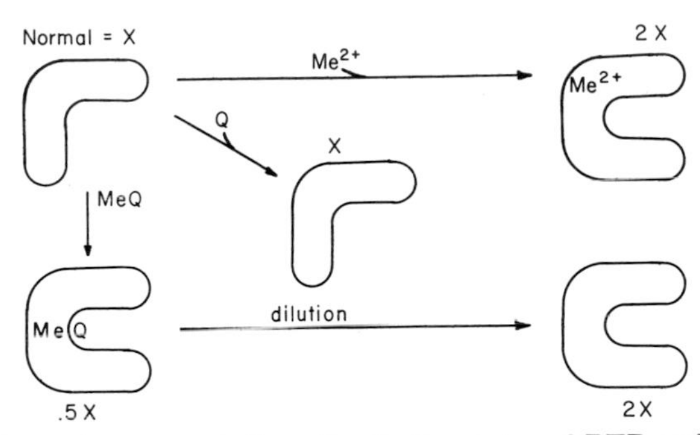

Fig. 3. Schematic representation of activity states of PEP carboxykinase. Fe^{2+} or Mn^{2+} at 5×10^{-5} M approximately double the activity of PEP carboxykinase in the soluble fraction of rat liver homogenates. Quinolinate inhibits the enzyme only when Fe^{2+} is present. The activity recovered after dilution of the inhibited enzyme is greater than the original indicating retention of a more active conformation

that the low concentration of iron quinolinate remaining after the 30 fold dilution (3×10^{-6} M) had no detectable effect on the enzyme activity in the presence of 4 mM oxalacetate. This is best depicted schematically as in Fig. 3, where the normal PEP carboxykinase activity is designated as X. The symbols arbitrarily indicate that the addition of ferrous quinolinate may bring about an alteration of the configuration of the enzyme that resembles the conformational change brought about by certain divalent transition metals alone. When the inhibited enzyme is diluted 300 fold as in the case of the livers from tryptophan-fed rats, or 30 fold as in the case of the *in vitro* inhibition by ferrous quinolinate, the ferrous quinolinate probably dissociates from the enzyme, leaving it in its more active conformation. Earlier studies [2] demonstrate that this more active conformation can be retained by the enzyme for several weeks if the enzyme is kept frozen and if dithiothreitol is present. The latter probably keeps the iron from being oxidized to the ferric state.

These findings lead us to postulate that the ratio Fe^{++}/Fe^{+++} in rat liver cytosol could well be a regulatory influence on gluconeogenesis. Reducing conditions, such as are achieved when fatty acids are available to liver, might activate PEP carboxykinase by causing the conversion of hepatic inorganic Fe^{3+} to Fe^{2+}. It is also possible that regulation of gluconeogenesis could be mediated by altering the availability of PEP carboxykinase to divalent transition metals.

To the best of our knowledge, the inhibition of gluconeogenesis by quinolinic acid is specific. We know of no other site of action save that of depressing the activity of PEP carboxykinase. Quinolinic acid in the perfused rat liver or tryptophan in the intact animal may therefore be used to study a portion of the gluconeogenic pathway. In this manner, it has been shown (P. D. RAY, D. O. FOSTER, and H. A. LARDY, detailed data to be published) that hydrocortisone more than doubles the accumulation of aspartate in the livers of rats treated with tryptophan, and has relatively little effect on glutamate and malate. We interpret this as supporting the contention of LONG, KATZIN and FRY [9] that glucocorticoids block the utilization of amino acids for protein synthesis and thus the nitrogen from these compounds is used for aspartate synthesis, but this compound cannot be converted to carbohydrate at normal rates in the tryptophan treated animal.

Tryptophan has been used also to investigate the well known feedback inhibition of gluconeogenesis that is exerted by administered glucose. One g of glucose administered together with 150 mg of tryptophan to a 200 g rat results in striking decreases in the amount of aspartate, malate, and oxalacetate that accumulates as a result of the quinolinic acid block. It appears that glucose feedback is exerted at the first unique step of gluconeogenesis, namely, the carboxylation of pyruvate to form 4-carbon dicarboxylic acids. Another way in which quinolinic acid has proved useful is in the study of the pathways by which amino acids are converted to carbohydrates. This investigation, in collaboration with Drs. VENEZIALE and GABRIELLI and Miss NANCY KNEER, has disclosed that gluconeogenesis from the carbon of those amino acids that normally give rise to 4-carbon dicarboxylic acids by degradation is inhibited by quinolinic acid in the perfused liver. The same holds for the conversion of alanine to carbohydrate as was demonstrated in the original work on quinolinic acid as an inhibitor [5]. However, serine, which has been thought to be converted to pyruvate by serine dehydratase, is not prevented from being converted to glucose by the presence of quinolinic acid in the perfusion fluid [11]. Since serine does not abolish the enhanced

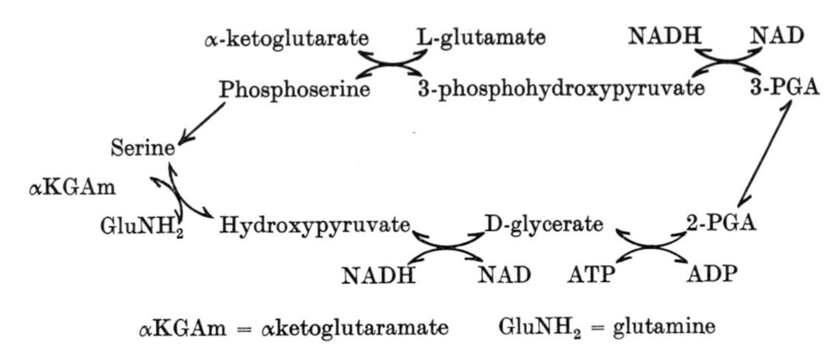

Fig. 4. Biosynthetic and possible gluconeogenic pathway of serine metabolism

accumulation of 4-carbon dicarboxylic acids in the liver treated with quinolinic acid, we assumed that it does not alter the usual inhibitory properties of the latter. Thus it appears that the carbon chain of serine bypasses the PEP carboxykinase step on its way to glucose. A possible pathway for the conversion of serine to glucose is shown at the bottom of Fig. 4 and involves essentially the reversal of a pathway previously considered for the biosynthesis of serine from glyceric acid. DICKENS and WILLIAMSON [12] have shown that hydroxypyruvate can be converted to carbohydrate in rat liver and it is possible, therefore, that serine may be transaminated rather than dehydrated in the process of gluconeogenesis. The very high Michaelis constant (70 mM) for serine dehydratase is in keeping with an alternative path for converting this amino acid to glucose. Extremely low concentrations of pyruvate are found in rat livers after perfusion with serine, which supports the concept that pyruvate is not formed directly from this amino acid. However, in very short term experiments, there is apparently some conversion of serine to pyruvate. It is, therefore, necessary to point out that the conclusions drawn from experiments with perfused livers may not necessarily apply entirely to the intact rat, for it is entirely possible that some tissue other than liver provides an allosteric activator for serine dehydratase that would permit this enzyme to function at physiological concentrations of serine. The problem therefore requires investigation in the intact animal.

Hydrazines

Hydrazine, monomethyl hydrazine and unsymmetrical dimethyl hydrazine have been known for some time to be powerful hypoglycemic agents [13, 14]. Using similar techniques to those described above, it was found [15] that hydrazine administered to rats in doses of 0.2 to 4.0 mmoles/kg resulted in elevated hepatic concentrations of malate and oxalacetate and decreased concentrations of phosphorylated intermediates of gluconeogenesis. The "crossover" point between oxalacetate and phosphoenol pyruvate is reminiscent of the inhibition at PEP-carboxykinase exerted by quinolinate. Hydrazine inhibited PEP carboxykinase *in vitro* but the mechanism has not yet been studied in detail. It is of interest that aspartate does not accumulate in increased amounts following the administration of hydrazine; this may possibly reflect an inhibition of transaminases.

Quinaldic Acid and Indole-2-carboxylic Acids

While investigating the inhibition of gluconeogenesis by tryptophan and its degradation products [5], we found quinaldic acid to inhibit gluconeogenesis from L-alanine in perfused rat livers. The pattern of metabolites accumulated in the inhibited livers was, however, greatly different from that seen in livers treated with quinolinic acid. In intact rats treated with quinaldic acid, hepatic malate, aspartate, and citrate were found in normal or less than normal amounts, but the phosphorylated, 3 carbon acids (PEP, 2PGA, 3PGA) were increased 8 fold or more [16]. Quinaldic acid was found to deplete liver glycogen and to cause severe hypoglycemia in adrenalectomized rats. During the course of these studies, BAUMAN, PEASE and HILL [17] reported the hypoglycemic activity of 5-methoxyindole-2-carboxylic acid (MICA). The similarity of the structure of these compounds suggested comparing their activities. They were found to have a similar mechanism of inhibition but MICA is the more effective.

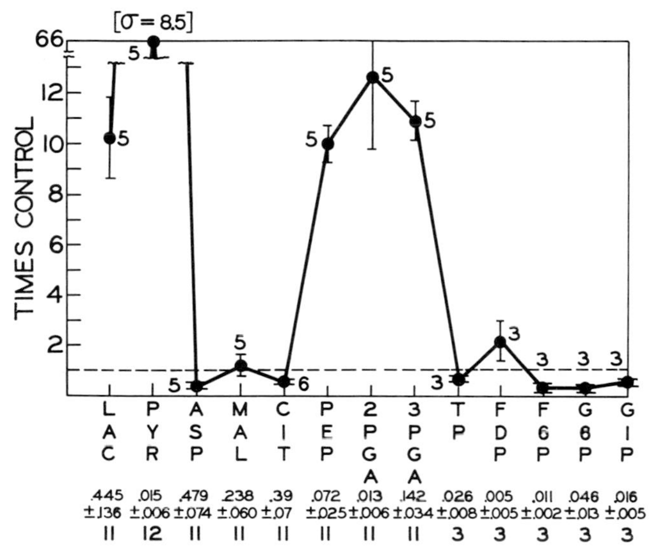

Fig. 5. Metabolites in liver 3 h after treatment with MICA. Normal male rats were fasted 24 h, treated by intraperitoneal injection with 200 mg of MICA per kg, and killed 3 h later. Data are expressed as multiples of the control values, with the number of animals contributing to each point indicated next to the point, and the standard deviation of the mean shown as a *vertical line*. Control values for lactate (LAC), pyruvate (PYR), aspartate (ASP), malate (MAL), citrate (CIT), phosphoenolpyruvate (PEP), 2-phosphoglycerate (2PGA), 3-phosphoglycerate (3PGA), triose phosphate (TP), fructose 1,6-diphosphate (FDP), fructose 6-phosphate, glucose 6-phosphate, and glucose 1-phosphate are given *along the abscissa* in μmoles per g of liver (wet weight), with standard deviations. The number of animals contributing to the average is indicated below. The standard deviation (σ) for pyruvate in MICA-treated animals is given as a number rather than a vertical bar. From [16]

The most dramatic change in hepatic metabolite concentration brought about by either quinaldic acid or MICA is the tremendous increase in pyruvate concentration [16]. For example, 3 h following

200 mg of MICA per kg body wt., pyruvate was elevated 66 times the normal concentration and lactate was 10 times normal. When smaller doses of either quinaldic acid (50 or 100 mg/kg) or MICA were given, pyruvate was elevated with no discernable effect on the other metabolites measured [16]. The greatly elevated pyruvate/lactate ratio and the accumulation of 3-phosphoglycerate in the presence of less than normal amounts of triose phosphate and hexose monophosphates indicated a decided lack of reducing equivalents in the liver cytosol of rats treated with these heterocyclic acids.

Because fatty acids are so effective in generating reducing power in the liver cytosol [18], we attempted to counteract the biochemical effects of quinaldic acid and MICA with octanoate. For these experiments, perfused rat livers were used and inhibition of gluconeogenesis was imposed by either 4.8 mM quinaldate or 0.78 mM MICA in the perfusion fluid. These concentrations of inhibitors almost completely suppressed glucose formation from lactate but did not influence the conversion of glycerol or fructose to glucose. The addition of 2 to 10 mM octanoate to the perfusion fluid completely restored gluconeogenesis in livers perfused with quinaldic acid or MICA [16] (Fig. 6).

The relationship between these heterocyclic inhibitors and fatty acids was studied also in isolated liver mitochondria. Both MICA and quinaldic acid, at 0.2 mM, strongly inhibit pyruvate oxidation as well as carboxylation to four carbon compounds. The addition of 1 mM octanoate depresses pyruvate *oxidation* as was found earlier [19], but this amount of octanoate almost completely restored pyruvate utilization for the synthesis of malate and citrate (Table 2). Thus the effects of octanoate on pyruvate metabolism in isolated liver mitochondria provide an adequate explanation of the restoration of gluconeogenesis in the perfused rat liver.

The mechanism by which octanoate reverses the inhibitory effects of MICA has been studied by my student, Miss JUTA KUTTIS. BAUMAN and HILL [20] have found that MICA inhibits pyruvate and α-ketoglutarate oxidases and that the inhibition is reversed by lipoic acid. The inhibition of ketoglutarate oxidation was confirmed by Drs. J. R. WILLIAMSON and R. SCHOLZ (personal communication) but the concentration of MICA required to inhibit significantly was considerably in excess of what we had found to be effective with intact mitochondria.

Miss KUTTIS found that mitochondria concentrate MICA from the suspension medium. A concentration of 40 fold can be readily

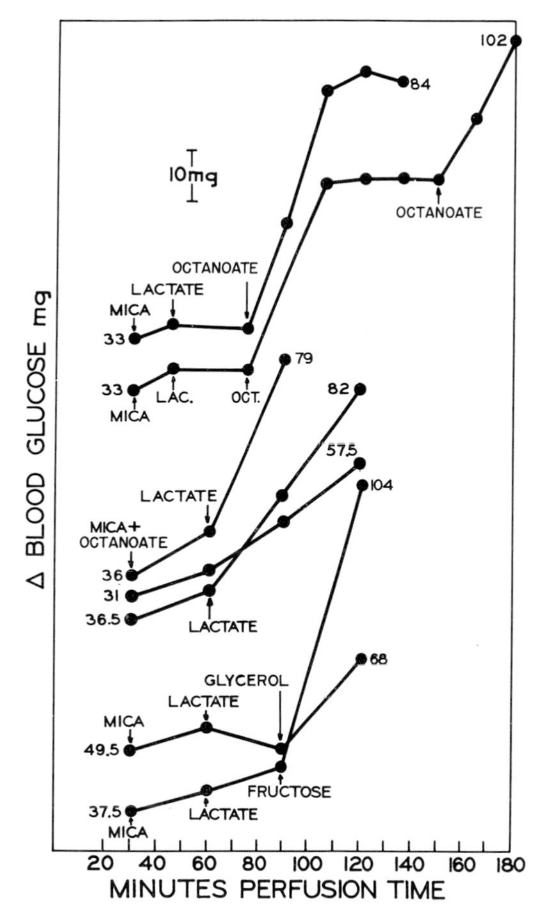

Fig. 6. Influence of MICA and octanoate on gluconeogenesis from lactate in the perfused liver. Glucose concentrations in the perfusate (100 ml) at 30 min and at the end of the perfusion are given in mg per 100 ml. Lactate (2 mmoles) was added 60 min after the start of the perfusion in each perfusion. MICA (0.078 mmole), octanoate (1 mmole), glycerol (1 mmole), and fructose (1 mmole) were added at the times indicated by the *arrows*. From [16]

effected. Thus, when mitochondria are suspended in a medium containing 0.2 mM MICA, the concentration of MICA in the mitochondrial matrix is sufficient to account for inhibition of keto acid oxidases. There are several enzymes in the keto acid oxidase

Table 2. *Influence of MICA, quinaldic acid, quinolinic acid, and octanoate on pyruvate metabolism of rat liver mitochondria*

Additions		Metabolite changes				
Inhibitor	Octanoate	Pyruvate used	Malate found	Citrate found	Total ^{14}C products	Acetoacetate found
	mM	µmoles				
		13.2	3.7	2.8	6.1	0.31
	1	11.2	5.4	2.6	9.6	2.6
MICA (0.2)		0.90	0.03	0.05	0.04	0.28
MICA (1)		0.56	0.08	0.00	0.04	
MICA (0.2)	1	10.3	5.0	2.4	9.1	2.8
MICA (1)	1	10.2	4.7	2.5	9.2	
Quinaldic acid (0.2)		2.9	0.41	0.45	0.83	0.15
Quinaldic acid (1)		1.4	0.04	0.13	0.13	0.16
Quinaldic acid (0.2)	1	10.3	5.0	2.2	8.8	2.7
Quinaldic acid (1)	1	9.5	4.6	2.1	8.2	2.7

The reaction medium contained in 3.0 ml: 4 mM potassium ATP, 10 mM $MgSO_4$, 6.7 mM potassium phosphate (pH 7.4), 6.7 mM triethanolamine (pH 7.4), 6.7 mM potassium pyruvate, 10 mM $KHCO_3$ containing ^{14}C in the amount of 4.75×10^5 dpm per µmole. It was made isotonic with sucrose, and mitochondria from 0.5 g of rat liver were used. Inhibitors were added as the sodium salts. The reactions were carried out in stoppered 25-ml Erlenmeyer flasks which were shaken in a water bath at 37°. The reactions were started by adding the mitochondria after an equilibration period of 2 min, and stopped after a 10 min reaction period by adding perchloric acid to make the final concentration 0.33 M.

From [16].

complex [21], and inhibition of any one might account for the effect of MICA on mitochondrial utilization of pyruvate. It appears that the susceptible enzyme is lipoic dehydrogenase which MICA inhibits non-competitively with respect to lipoamide.

The reversal by fatty acids of MICA and quinaldate inhibition of pyruvate metabolism is mediated at the mitochondrial membrane, not at lipoate dehydrogenase. Fatty acids prevent mitochondria from concentrating MICA against a gradient; thus this inhibitor does not reach effective concentrations and the tricarboxylic acid cycle can generate the energy required for pyruvate carboxylation.

The effect of MICA on the ratio lactate/pyruvate is a striking demonstration of the role of mitochondria in generating reducing equivalents for the cytosol compartment. When the production of malate is blocked, the cytosolic metabolites become strongly oxidized.

In conclusion, we emphasize the great utility of site-specific inhibitors for the study of complex metabolic pathways. Inhibitors of gluconeogenesis have served to clarify the pathways from pyruvate and lactate to glucose, have lent support to established concepts regarding pathways of metabolism of some amino acids and opened the possibility of new pathways for others. The inhibitors have served to locate the site of action of some agents that regulate gluconeogenesis and promise to be of value in elucidating the function of hormones that affect this process.

References

1. Foster, D. O., P. D. Ray, and H. A. Lardy: Biochemistry **5**, 563 (1966).
2. —, H. A. Lardy, P. D. Ray, and J. B. Johnston: Biochemistry **6**, 2120 (1967).
3. Ray, P. D., D. O. Foster, and H. A. Lardy: J. biol. Chem. **241**, 3904 (1966).
4. Lardy, H., V. Paetkau, and P. Walter: Proc. nat. Acad. Sci. (Wash.) **53**, 1410 (1965).
5. Veneziale, C. M., P. Walter, N. Kneer, and H. A. Lardy: Biochemistry **6**, 2129 (1967).
6. Chang, H.-C., and M. D. Lane: J. biol. Chem. **241**, 2413 (1966).
7. Holten, D., and R. C. Nordlie: Biochemistry **4**, 723 (1965).
8. Johnston, J. B., and H. A. Lardy: Unpublished data.
9. Long, C. N. H., B. Katzin, and E. G. Fry: Endocrinology **26**, 309 (1940).
10. Veneziale, C. M., F. Gabrielli, N. Kneer, and H. A. Lardy: Manuscript in preparation.
11. Lardy, H. A., C. M. Veneziale, and F. Gabrielli: 6th F.E.B.S. Meeting, Madrid 1969 Abstr. No. 21.
12. Dickens, F., and D. H. Williamson: Biochem. J. **72**, 496 (1958).

13. UNDERHILL, F. P.: J. biol. Chem. **10**, 159 (1911).
14. FORTNEY, S. R., D. A. CLARK, and E. STEIN: J. Pharmacol. exp. Ther. **156**, 277 (1967).
15. RAY, P. D., R. L. HANSON, and H. A. LARDY: Submitted for publication.
16. HANSON, R. L., P. D. RAY, P. WALTER, and H. A. LARDY: J. biol. Chem. **244**, 4351 (1969).
17. BAUMAN, N., B. PEASE, and C. HILL: Fed. Proc. **26**, 507 (1967).
18. LÖFFLER, G., F. MATSCHINSKY und O. WIELAND: Biochem. Z. **342**, 76 (1965).
19. WALTER, P., V. PAETKAU, and H. A. LARDY: J. biol. Chem. **241**, 2523 (1966).
20. BAUMANN, N., and C. J. HILL: Biochemistry **7**, 1322 (1968).
21. REED, L. J., and R. U. OLIVER: In: Structure, function and evolution in proteins. Brookhaven Symposium in Biology **21**, 397 (1968).
22. LARDY, H. A.: Harvey Lect. Ser. **60**, 261 (1966).

Discussion

O. WIELAND (Munich): You demonstrated very nicely the feedback action of glucose on gluconeogenesis. Since this was done in the whole animal, one could think of the possibility that the feedback could be mediated by hormones such as insulin which is effective in the perfused liver system as shown by MENAHAN in our laboratory. Glucagon-stimulated gluconeogenesis could be overcome by adding insulin to the medium.

Another inhibitor of gluconeogenesis which appears to have quite another mode of action is the oral antidiabetic drug glycodiazine. We learned from Dr. HASSELBLAD (Göttingen) that in liver slices it acts as an antilipolytic drug. In the liver perfusion system, during the course of studies on interaction between the liberation of fatty acids in the liver and the stimulation of gluconeogenesis supported by fatty acid oxidation, we could demonstrate that glycodiazine inhibits glucose formation, from pyruvate, for instance, and also ketogenesis; this supports the idea that the inhibitor acts by antilipolytic action in the liver.

LARDY (Madison, Wisc.): I agree with respect to the role of glucose and insulin in suppressing gluconeogenesis in the intact animal. There is no doubt that the feedback inhibition exerted by glucose is dependent on insulin. In the diabetic animal, for example, the feedback does not function. In a limited number of perfusion experiments we have failed to get a glucose feedback. Do you in fact get feedback inhibition by glucose as well as by insulin in the perfused liver?

O. WIELAND: We have not investigated feedback by glucose so far.

SEUBERT (Göttingen): In our studies on fatty acid oxidation we could demonstrate an inhibition of the caprylate activating enzyme by MICA.In addition, MICA also lowers the affinity of acetyl CoA for pyruvate carboxylase. As an alternative explanation for the inhibitory effect of MICA on gluconeogenesis from pyruvate, we could therefore offer: 1. Lowering of the intracellular concentrations of acetyl CoA by inhibition of fatty acid oxidation, 2. Inhibition of pyruvate carboxylase at concentrations of acetyl CoA below saturation of the enzyme.

Gluconeogenesis from pyruvate must in our opinion not depend on an *exclusively* intramitochondrial carboxylation of pyruvate. Contrary to our original statement of a *mitochondrial* location of this enzyme [Biochem. Z. **340**, 160 (1964)] we have concluded this from the different solubilities of glutamate dehydrogenase and pyruvate carboxylase upon extraction of liver with isotonic solutions *supplemented by monovalent cations* [Adv. Enzyme Regulation **6**, 153 (1968)]. We have extended these studies now to

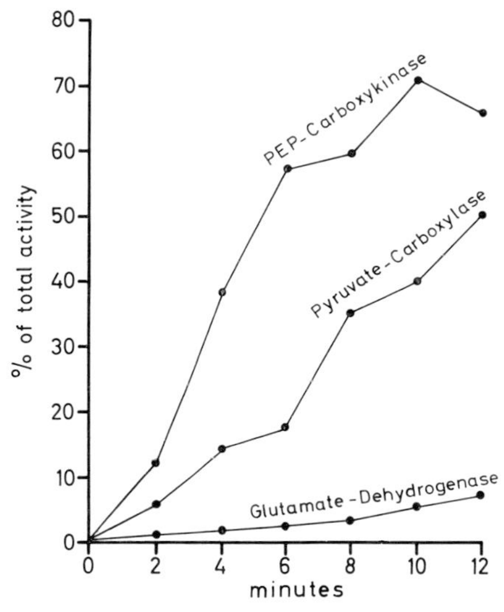

Fig. 1. Extraction of PEP-carboxykinase, pyruvate carboxylase and glutamate dehydrogenase from chicken liver mitochondria with isotonic solution supplemented by monovalent cations (B. DUGAL and W. SEUBERT, 1969).

PEP-carboxykinase, which in some species is also considered to be of mitochondrial origin. As the Fig. shows, extraction of chicken liver mitochondria (which are a mixture of all kinds of subcellular units like microbodies, lysosomes and mitochondria) with our medium results in solubilization of almost the total "mitochondrial" PEP-carboxykinase and of a great part of pyruvate carboxylase. Glutamate dehydrogenase is extracted only to a small degree. We conclude from these data that only glutamate dehydrogenase is *exclusively* located in mitochondria. In addition, isotope studies do not fit into your scheme of the pathway of carbon in gluconeogenesis. Since the hydrogen necessary for glucose synthesis is regenerated by the step lactate → pyruvate, gluconeogenesis form *lactate* should go mainly through aspartate as the transport form of the C_4-unit.

Gluconeogenesis from 3-^{14}C-aspartate (and also 3-^{14}C-malate) results, however, in complete equilibration of the radioactivity between the 1,2- and 5,6-position of glucose, while gluconeogenesis from 3-^{14}C-lactate does not. This excludes a pathway which goes *exclusively* through malate and aspartate. Also the data from Dr. BÜCHER's laboratory point to this direction.

LARDY: With respect to MICA, how do you explain the reversal by fatty acids of its inhibition of gluconeogenesis if MICA is an inhibitor of fatty acid activation?

SEUBERT: Just by competition between MICA and caprylate for the fatty acid activating enzyme. We could not determine the type of inhibition by the hydroxamate method, because MICA itself gives a hydroxamic acid. Also the optical assay with sorbic acid [Biochim. biophys. Acta **67**, 599 (1963)] cannot be employed, because MICA shows high absorbance at 300 nm.

LARDY: Whether there is a secondary inhibition of fatty acid activation, we have not examined at all. This would not be pertinent to the blockage of pyruvate entrance into the mitochondria or to inhibition of pyruvate oxidation at the lipoic dehydrogenase step.

Regarding the question of intramitochondrial or cytosolic localization of pyruvate carboxylase, I think you must agree that, apart from your laboratory, there has been no indication in the literature that this enzyme is located in the cytosol. We have done many experiments in order to determine whether pyruvate carboxylase can be demonstrated in the soluble fraction of liver or in very well purified mitochondria; we could not find it in the soluble fraction but always in the mitochondria.

At the Madrid meeting, data were presented from Dr. SOLS' laboratory [MARCO, and SOLS: 6th FEBS-Meeting, Madrid 1969, Abstract Nr. 22; Biochem. biophys. Res. Commun. **34**, 725 (1969)] that demonstrate that pyruvate carboxylase of rat liver is an enzyme of the mitochondrial matrix, not of the outer membrane, and certainly not of the cytosol.

With respect to the question of whether aspartate or malate participates in gluconeogenesis, MÜLLHOFER in BÜCHER's laboratory (6th FEBS-Meeting, Madrid 1969, Abstract Nr. 382) has very elegantly shown that malate is a precursor of both the carbon chain and of the tritium for glucose synthesis in liver perfused with lactate.

SEUBERT: Soluble forms of pyruvate carboxylase have also been described by others [Biochem. J. **111**, 263 (1969); Biochem. J. **104**, 866 (1967); J. Lipid Res. 8, 73 (1967); Enzymologia **33**, 201 (1967)]. I would like to stress that we prefer the term *extramitochondrial* location and not *cytosolic*. The former term would include also a location in other subcellular compartments like for instance peroxisomes. DEDUVE has mentioned a possible role of this compartment in gluconeogenesis [J. Cell Biology **46**, 323 (1966)].

LARDY: The role of the peroxisomes in gluconeogenesis in the DEDUVE sense is confined to those tissues possessing the malate cycle in which 2-carbon compounds are converted to 4-carbon compounds. But we are not talking about the systems which use acetate; we are talking about gluconeogenesis in the rat or the human subject.

BÜCHER (Munich): We entered experimentally into this peroxisome question, using ^{14}C-labelled formate and looking for labelled CO_2. We did not publish that because the results were negative. I think that hitherto there is no experimental evidence supporting this idea of DEDUVE.

In the experiments of MÜLLHOFER [1, 2], glucose was formed from lactate, and in principle there is no objection that glucose may be formed from aspartate. But when glucose is formed from lactate, this goes on without equivalent labelling of the aspartate pool. However, aspartate might be compartmentated, so that only a fraction of aspartate is acting. We are raising a bit the finger, but further experiments are needed. [1. MÜLLHOFER, G., O. KUNTZEN, and S. HESSE: Sixth FEBS-Meeting, Madrid 1969, Abstr. No. 382; — — —, and TH. BÜCHER: FEBS-Letters **4,** 33 (1969).]

VI. Appendix

Chemical Structures of Inhibitors

Known chemical structures of inhibitors discussed in this book are presented in alphabetical order. The page numbers in square brackets indicate where the given inhibitor is discussed.

The structures were either provided by the contributors to this volume or were taken from D. GOTTLIEB and P. D. SHAW (Editors), 'Antibiotics I, II', Berlin · Heidelberg · New York: Springer 1967.

The help by W. KELLER-SCHIERLEIN and A. SCHWAB in checking the structures is gratefully acknowledged.

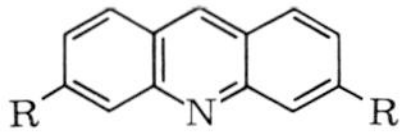

Acridines (see also Proflavin, Quinacrine) [11]

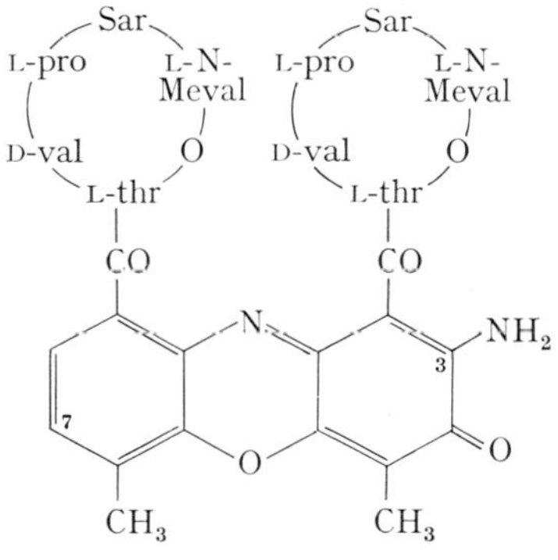

L-thr is L-threonine; D-val is D-valine; L-pro is L-proline; sar is sarcosine; and L-N-meval is L-N-methylvaline

Actinomycin C_1 (D) [11, 32, 48, 73, 126, 135, 159, 167]

$(Glu)_1$ $(Pro)_2$ $(Gly)_1$ $(Ala)_2$ $(Val)_2$ $(Leu)_1$ $(GluN)_2$ $(2\text{-methyl-Ala})_8$ [cyclic]

Alamethicin [368]

N-Lost $R-N(CH_2-CH_2-Cl)_2$

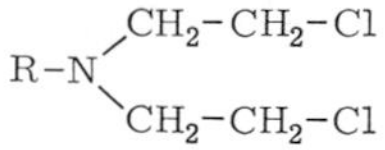

Myleran $(CH_2)_4(SO_3-CH_3)_2$

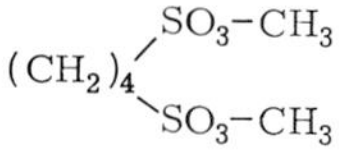

Alkylating agents [11]

$H_2N-C(=NH)-NH-R$

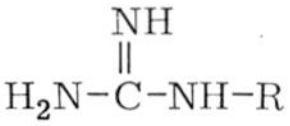

Alkyl guanidine [217]

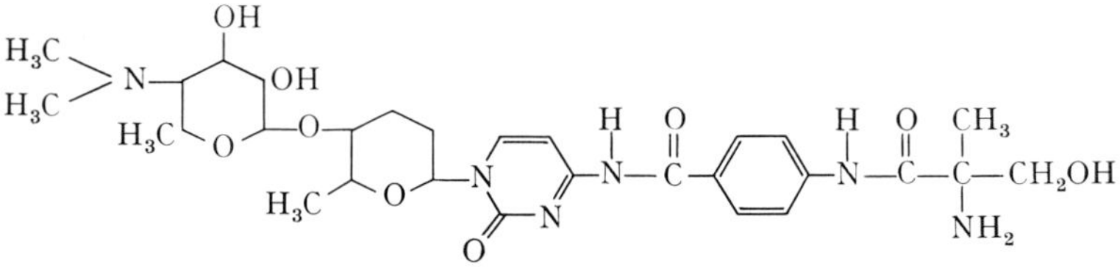

Amicetin [100]

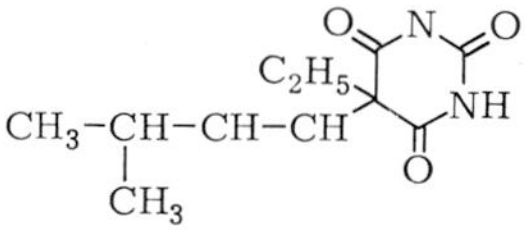

$CH_3-CH(CH_3)-CH-CH-CH$ (C_2H_5, barbituric ring: O, N, O, NH, O)

Amobarbital (= Amytal) [217, 249]

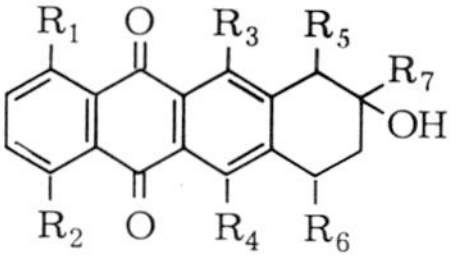

	R_1	R_2	R_3	R_4	R_5	R_6	R_7
s-Pyrromycinone	OH	OH	H	OH	$COOCH_3$	OH	C_2H_5
Aclavinone	H	OH	H	OH	$COOCH_3$	OH	C_2H_5
β-Rhodomycinone	H	OH	OH	OH	OH	OH	C_2H_5
γ-Rhodomycinone	H	OH	OH	OH	OH	H	C_2H_5
β-Isorhodomycinone	OH	OH	OH	OH	OH	OH	C_2H_5
5-Desoxy-pyrromycinone	OH	OH	H	H	$COOCH_3$	OH	C_2H_5
Daunomycinone	H	OCH_3	OH	OH	H	OH	$COCH_3$

Anthracyclines (Chromophore group) [11, 48, 73]
(see Cinerubin A, Daunomycin)

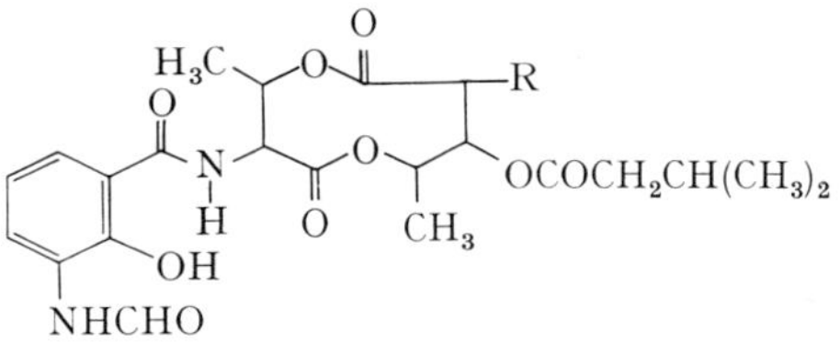

Antimycin A_1; R=n-hexyl
M.W.= 548

Antimycin A_3; R=n-butyl
M.W.= 520

Antimycins [249, 282]

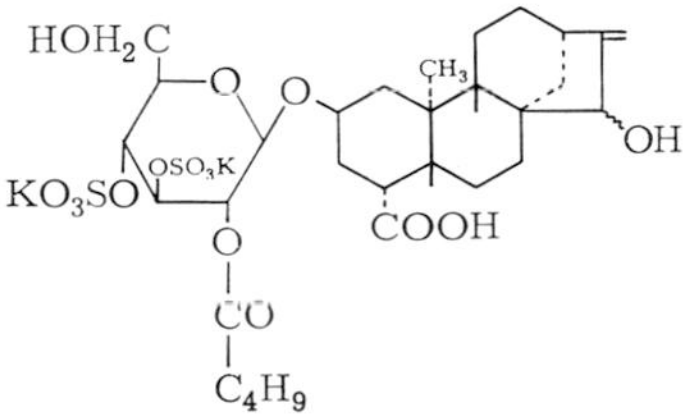

Potassium Atractylate

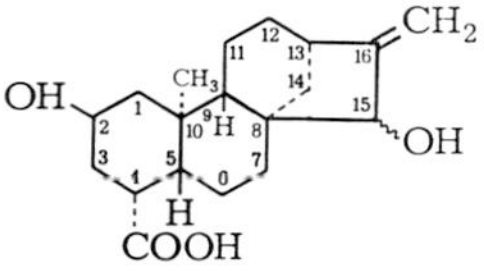

Atractyligenin

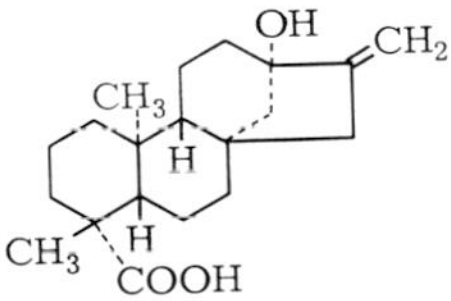

Steviol

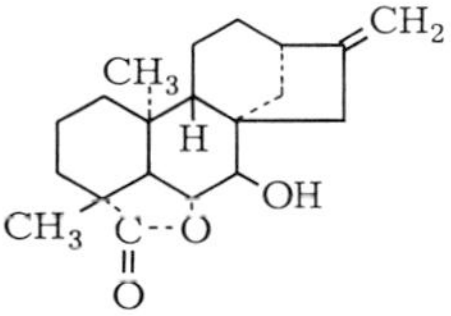

7(β)OH-Kaurenolide

Atractyloside and related compounds [301, 318, 324]

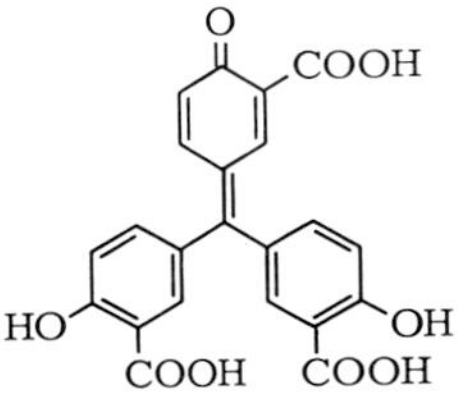

Aurintricarboxylic acid [126]

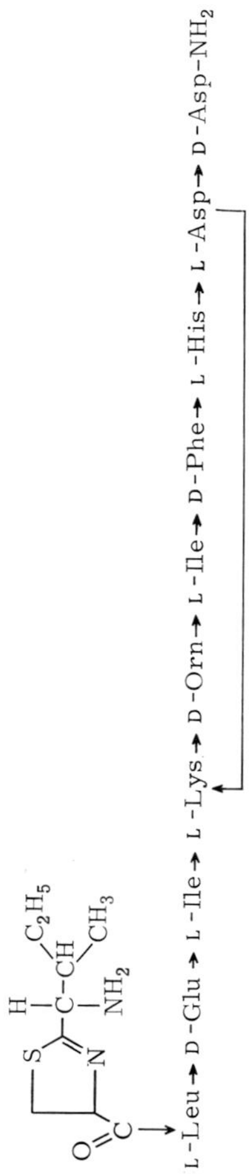

$$\text{(thiazoline ring: S, N; 2-substituent } -C(H)-CH(C_2H_5)(CH_3)\text{ with } NH_2\text{; } O{=}C- \text{ attached)} \rightarrow$$

L-Leu → D-Glu → L-Ile → L-Lys → D-Orn → L-Ile → D-Phe → L-His → L-Asp → D-Asp-NH_2

(L-Asp ⌐ linked back to L-Lys)

Bacitracin A

Bacitracin A [187, 210]

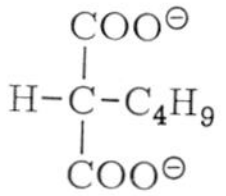

$$\begin{array}{c} COO^{\ominus} \\ | \\ H-C-C_4H_9 \\ | \\ COO^{\ominus} \end{array}$$

2-n-Butylmalonate [335, 351]

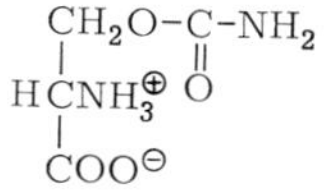

$$\begin{array}{l} CH_2O-\underset{\underset{O}{\|}}{C}-NH_2 \\ | \\ HCNH_3^{\oplus} \\ | \\ COO^{\ominus} \end{array}$$

O-Carbamylserine [187]

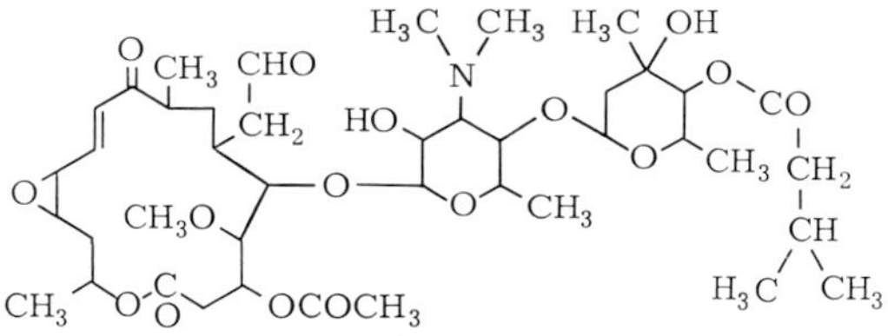

Carbomycin A [100]

1. 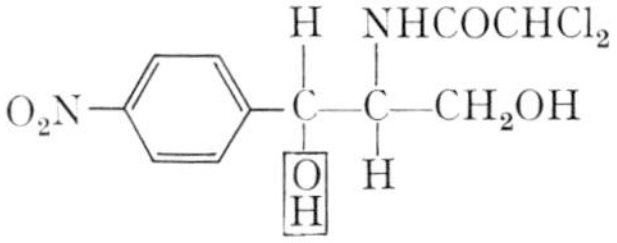 $O_2N-C_6H_4-C(H)(OH)-C(H)(NHCOCHCl_2)-CH_2OH$ D(—) Threo isomer (Chloramphenicol)

2. 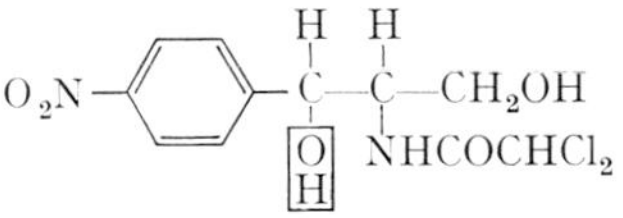 $O_2N-C_6H_4-C(H)(OH)-C(H)(NHCOCHCl_2)-CH_2OH$ L(+) Erythro isomer

3. 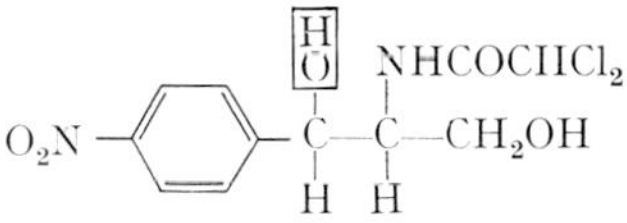 $O_2N-C_6H_4-C(HO)(H)-C(NHCOCHCl_2)(H)-CH_2OH$ D(—) Erythro isomer

4. 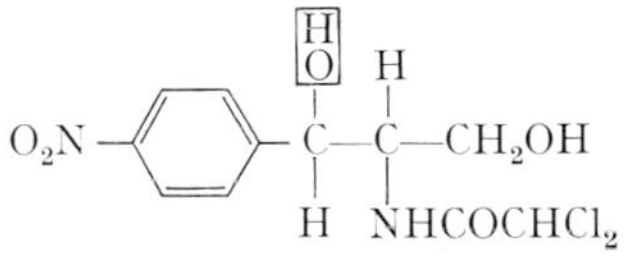 $O_2N-C_6H_4-C(HO)(H)-C(H)(NHCOCHCl_2)-CH_2OH$ L(+) Threo isomer

Chloramphenicol and its Stereoisomers [100, 140, 159]

Chloroquine [11]

chromomycinone

A —— D —— CHR —— C —— C —— B: chromomycin A_3 (AD-CHR-CCB)

derivatives:

D —— CHR —— C —— C —— B: D-CHR-CCB

D —— CHR —— C —— C : D-CHR-CC

D —— CHR : D-CHR

Chromomycin and Derivatives [11, 48, 73]

Cinerulose A 2-Desoxy-L-fucose Rhodosamine Pyrromycinone

Cinerubin A [48, 73]

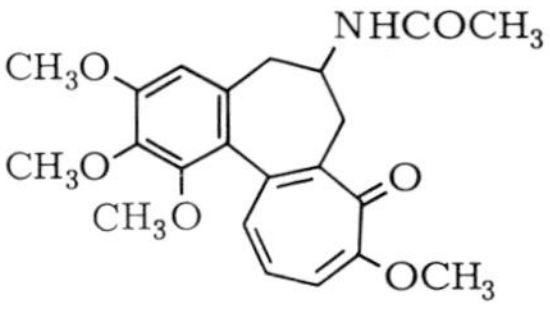

$NHCOCH_3$ CH_3O CH_3O CH_3O O OCH_3

Colchicine [167]

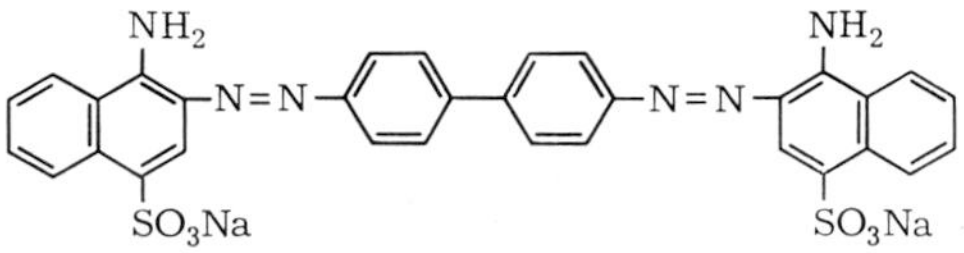

NH_2 $-N=N-$ $-N=N-$ NH_2 SO_3Na SO_3Na

Congo red [64]

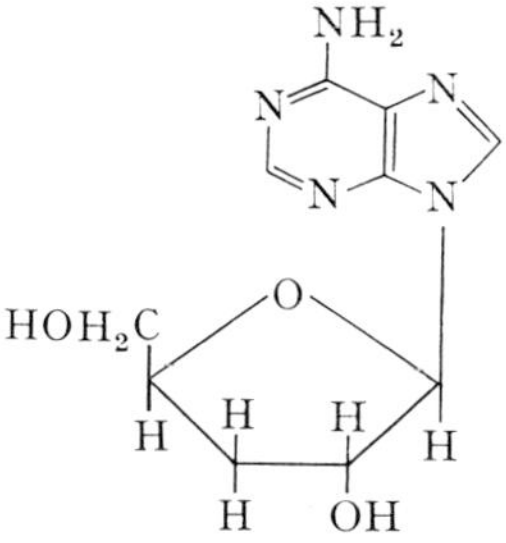

NH_2 N N N N HOH_2C O H H H H H H OH

Cordycepin (3′-deoxyadenosine) [48]

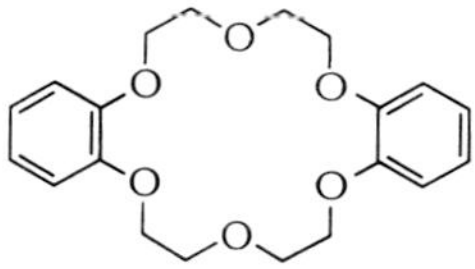

O O O O O O

Cyclic polyether [356]

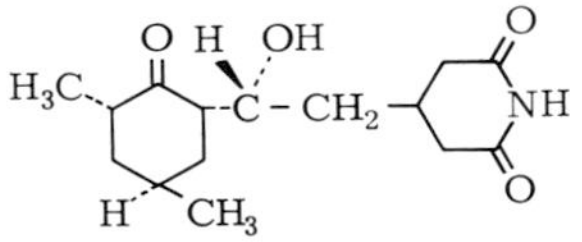

O H OH O H_3C C CH_2 NH H CH_3 O

Cycloheximide [79, 140, 159, 217]

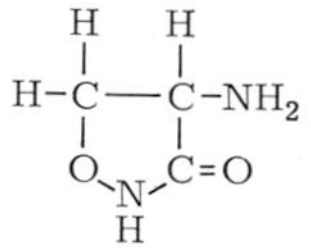

D-Cycloserine [187]

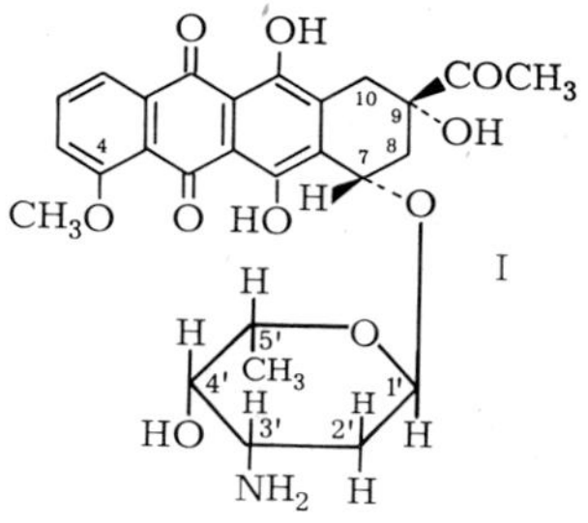

Daunomycin [48]

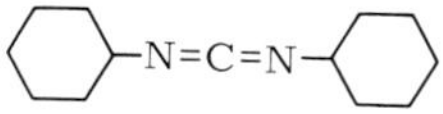

Dicyclohexylcarbodiimide (DCCD) [258]

Echinomycin [48]

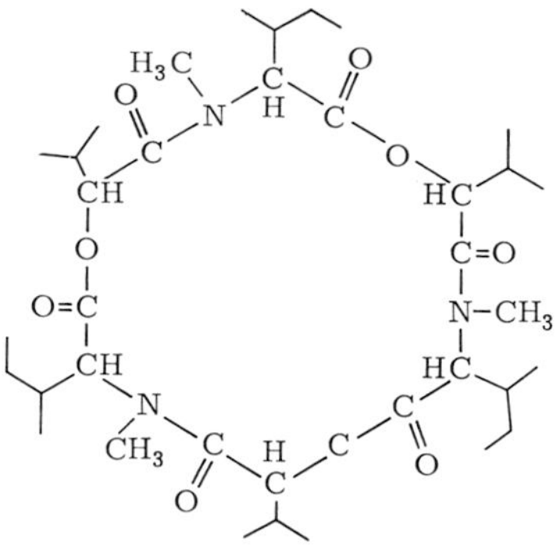

D-Hy-i-Valac-L-Me-Ile]$_3$

Enniatin A [356]

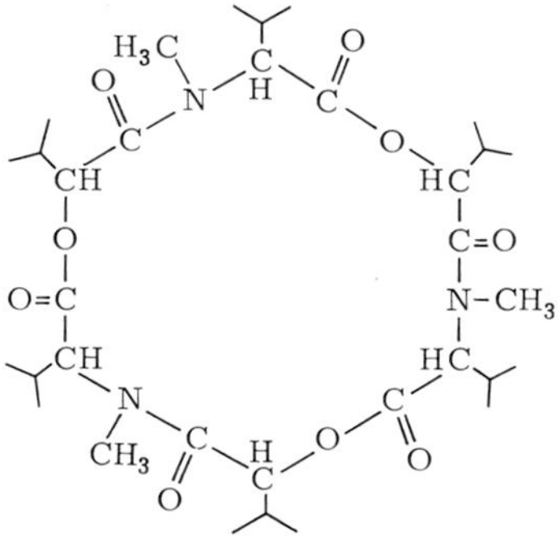

D-Hy-i-Valac-L-Me-Val]$_3$

Enniatin B [356]

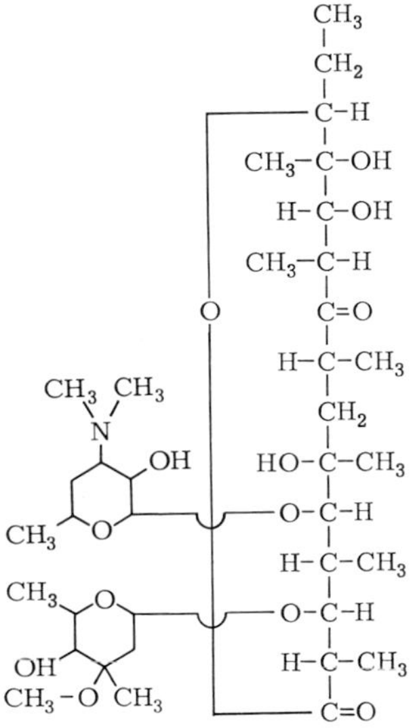

CH_3
CH_2
C-H
CH_3-C-OH
H-C-OH
CH_3-C-H
O C=O
H-C-CH_3
CH_3 CH_3
N
CH_2
desosamine OH HO-C-CH_3
CH_3 O O-C-H
H-C-CH_3
CH_3 O O-C-H
cladinose OH H-C-CH_3
CH_3-O CH_3 C=O

Erythomycin [100, 159]

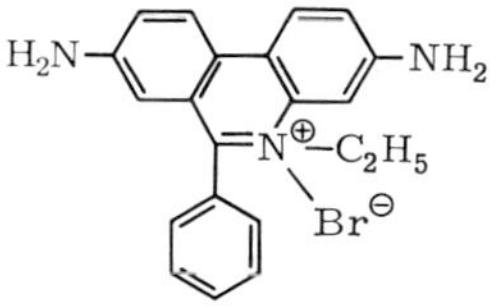

H_2N NH_2
$N^{\oplus}$-C_2H_5
$Br^{\ominus}$

Ethidium bromide [11, 48, 159]

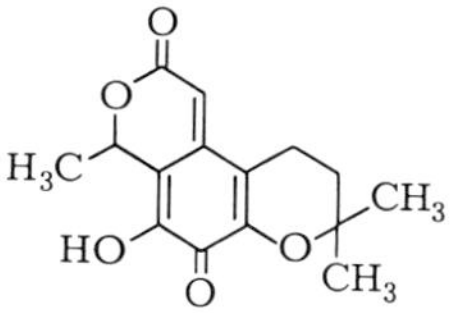

O
O
H_3C CH_3
HO O CH_3
O

Fuscin [247]

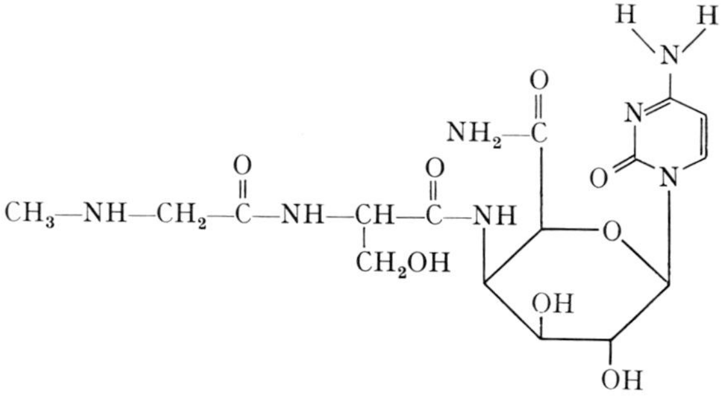

$CH_3-NH-CH_2-C(=O)-NH-CH(CH_2OH)-C(=O)-NH$ ...

Gougerotin [100]

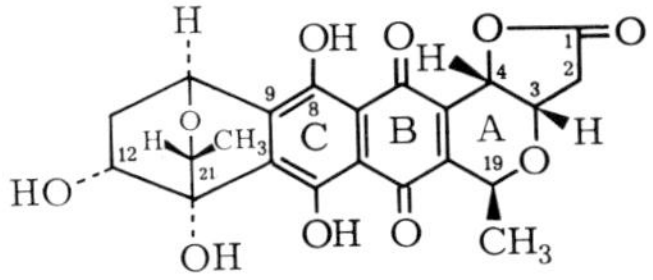

Granaticin [11]

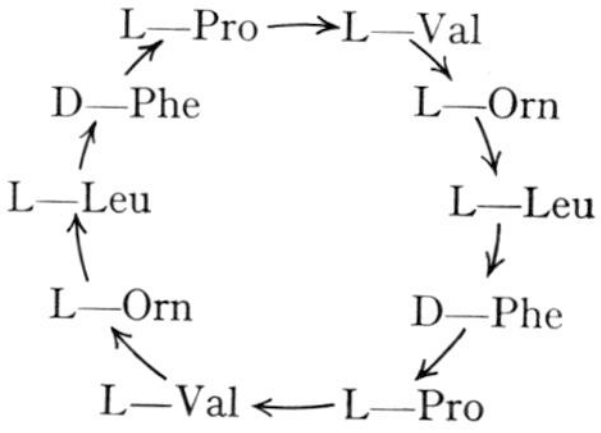

L—Pro → L—Val → L—Orn → L—Leu → D—Phe → L—Pro → L—Val → L—Orn → L—Leu → D—Phe → L—Pro

Gramicidin S [356, 368]
(see Valine-Gramicidin A)

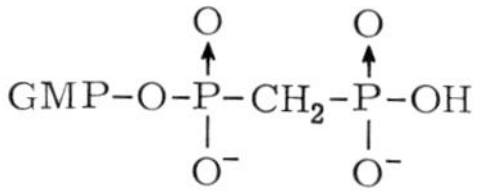

$GMP-O-P(\rightarrow O)(O^-)-CH_2-P(\rightarrow O)(O^-)-OH$

5'-Guanylyl-
methylenediphosphonate
(GMP-PCP)

[100]

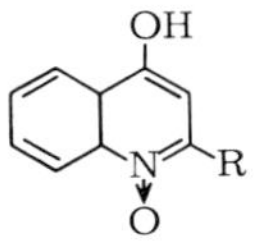

2-Alkyl-4-hydroxy-quinoline-N-oxide

R = heptyl or nonyl

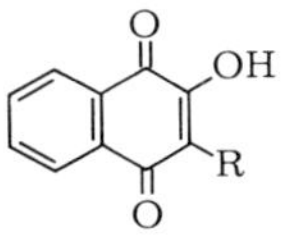

2-Hydroxy-3-alkyl-1, 4-naphthoquinone

R = 2'-methyloctyl, SN-5949
= 3',7'-dimethyloctyl, DNQ
= cyclohexyl, CNQ

Hydroxyquinoline-N-oxides and Hydroxynaphthoquinones [282]

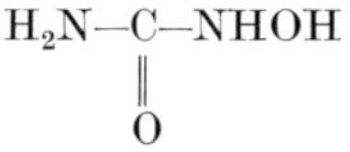

$H_2N-C(=O)-NHOH$

Hydroxy Urea [11]

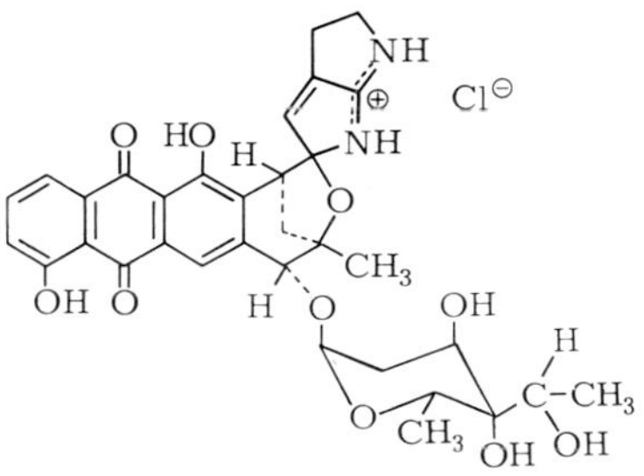

Isoquinocyclin A [48]

Kaurenolide: See Atractyloside

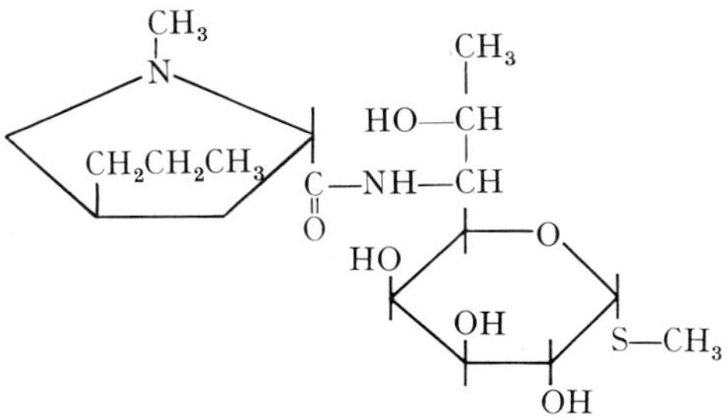

Lincomycin [100, 159]

Macrolide group: See Vazquez et al., Table 4, p. 105

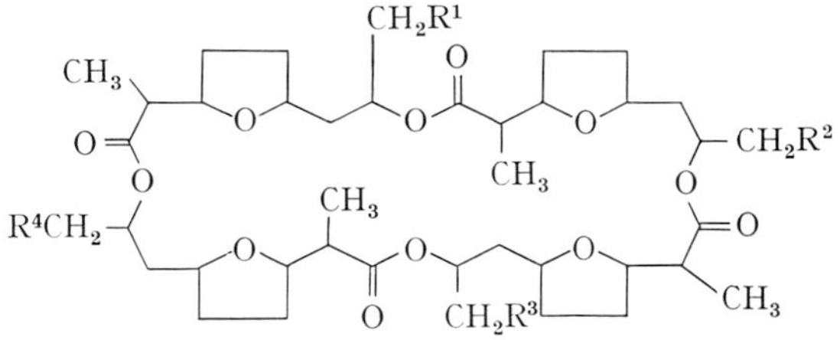

Nonactin R^1, R^2, R^3, $R^4 = H$; Monactin R^1, R^2, $R^3 = H$, $R^4 = CH_3$; Dinactin R^1, $R^2 = H$; R^3, $R^4 = CH_3$; Trinactin $R^1 = H$; R^2, R^3, $R^4 = CH_3$. The configuration about the four carbon atoms bearing $R^1 - R^4$ differ in the four antibiotics

Macrotetrolide group [356, 365]

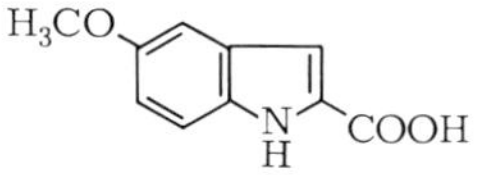

5-Methoxyindole-2-carboxylic acid (MICA) [374]

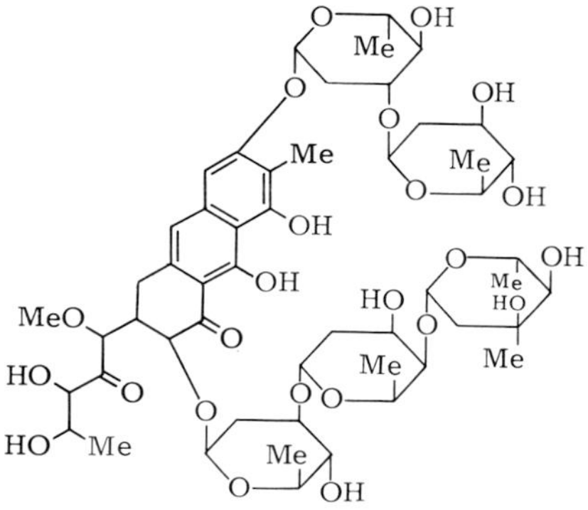

Mithramycin (= Aureolic acid) [11, 48]

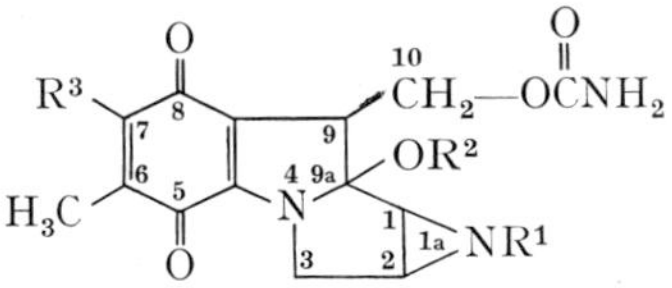

	R_1	R_2	R_3
Mitomycin A	H	CH_3	OCH_3
B	CH_3	H	OCH_3
C	H	CH_3	NH_2
Porfiromycin	CH_3	CH_3	NH_2

Mitomycins [11]

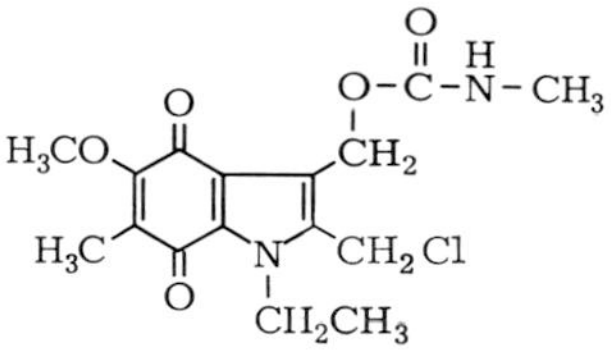

Mitomycin-derivative, lacking the aziridine ring [11]

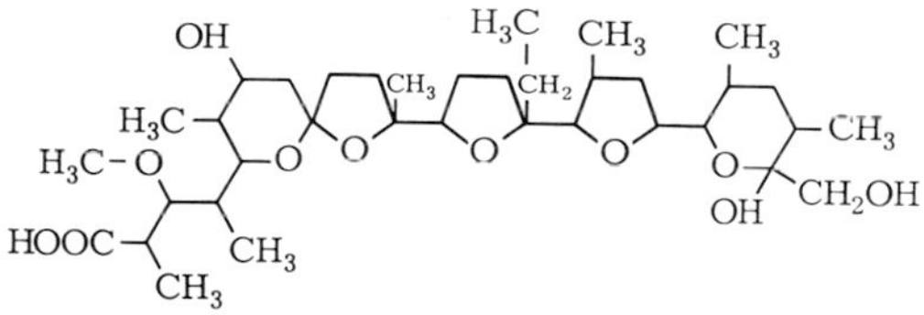

Monensin [356]

Myleran: See Alkylating agents

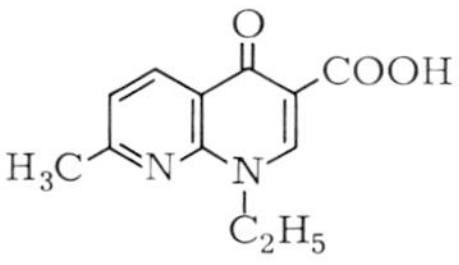

Nalidixic acid [11]

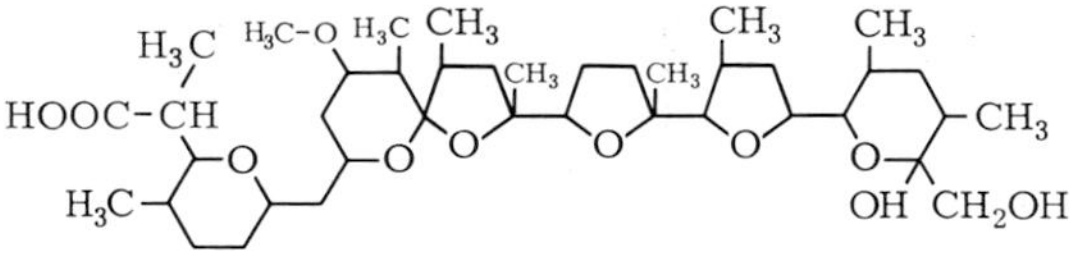

Nigericin (= Polyetherin A) [356]

N-Lost: See Alkylating agents

(+)-Nonactinic acid

(-)-Nonactinic acid

Nonactinic acid (see Macrotetrolide group) [365]

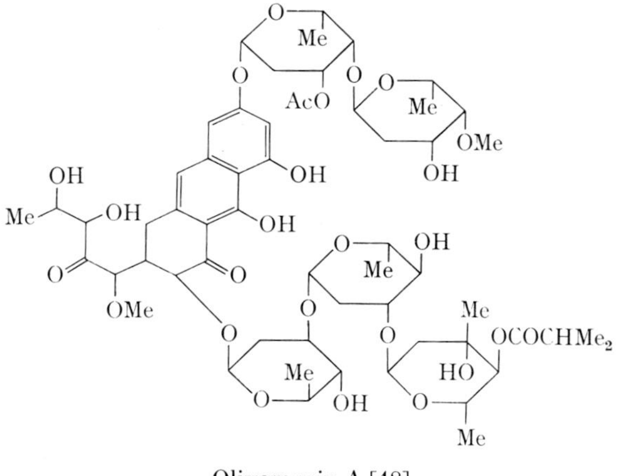

Olivomycin A [48]

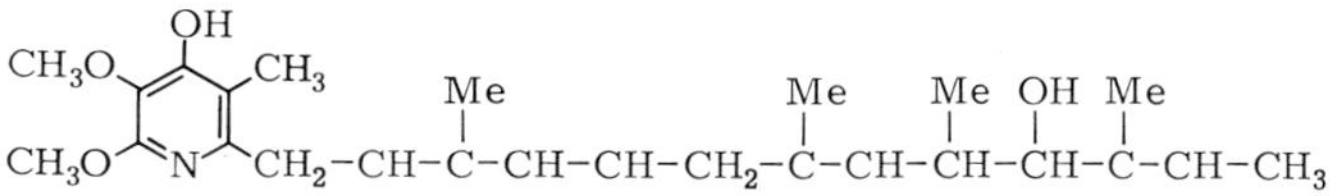

Piericidin A [217]

Penicillins [187, 208]

Proflavin [11, 32, 48]

Puromycin [100, 126, 155, 159, 167]

Quinacrine (Atebrin) [11]

Quinaldate [374]

Quinolinate [374]

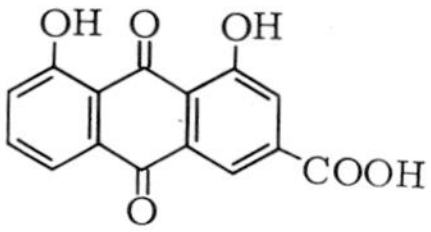

OH O OH
COOH
O

Rhein [217]

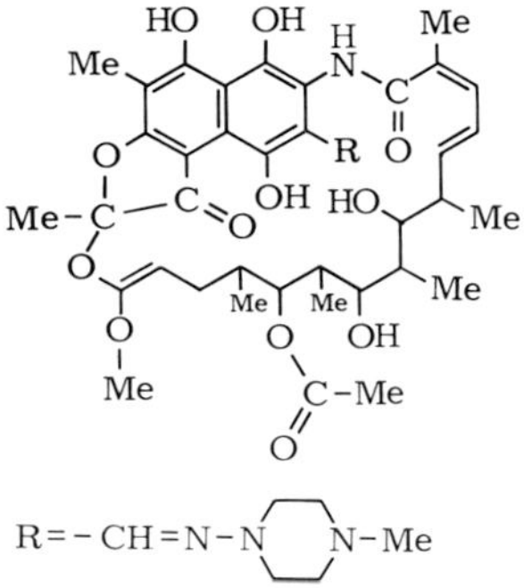

HO OH H Me
Me N C
O
O R O
Me C C O OH HO Me
O Me
Me Me OH
O O
Me C Me
O

R= – CH=N–N N–Me

Rifampicin [48, 60, 64]

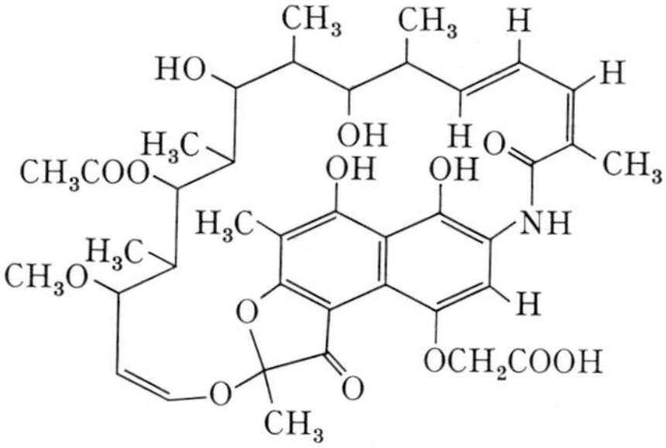

CH_3 CH_3 H
HO H
H_3C OH H O
CH_3COO OH OH CH_3
H_3C NH
CH_3O H_3C
O H
O OCH_2COOH
O
CH_3

Rifamycin B $C_{39}H_{49}NO_{14}$ [32, 48, 60]

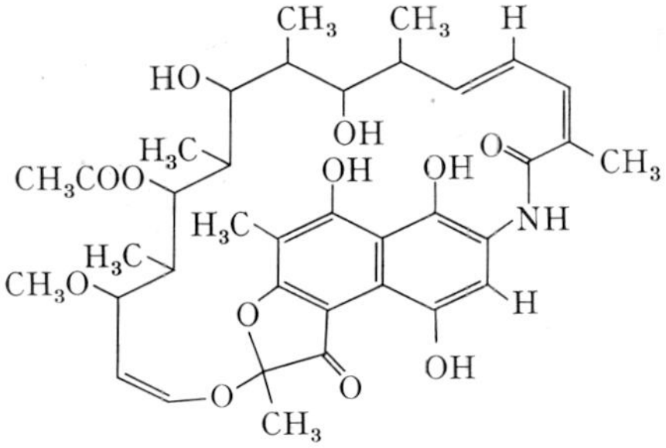

Rifamycin SV $C_{37}H_{47}NO_{12}$ [32, 48, 60]

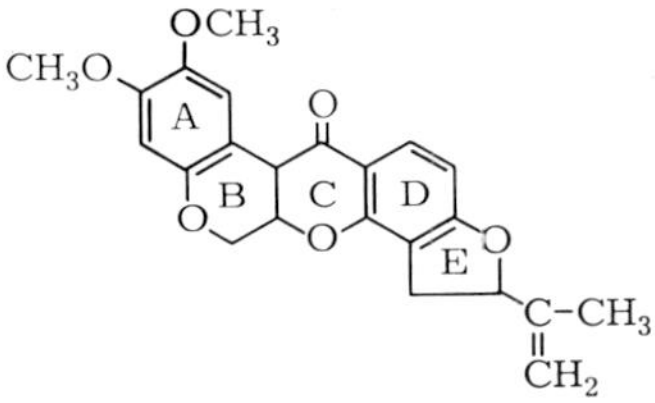

Rotenone [217, 249]

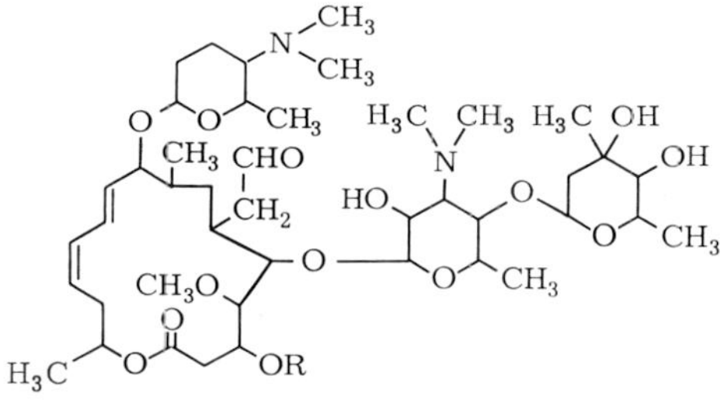

R = H : Spiramycin I
R = CH_3CO : Spiramycin II
R = CH_3-CH_2-CO : Spiramycin III

Spiramycins [100]

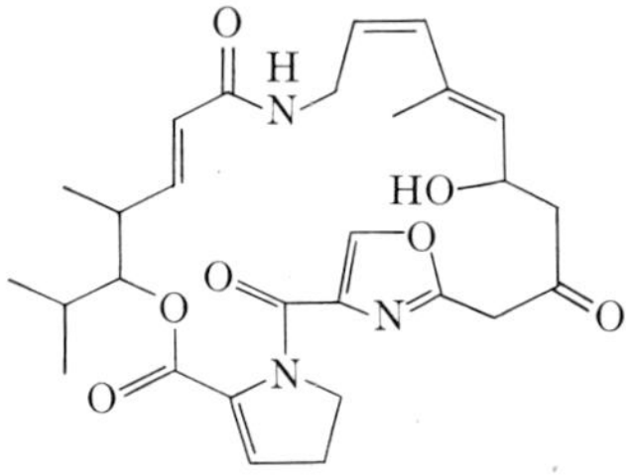

Streptogramin A [100]
(= Ostreogrycin A)

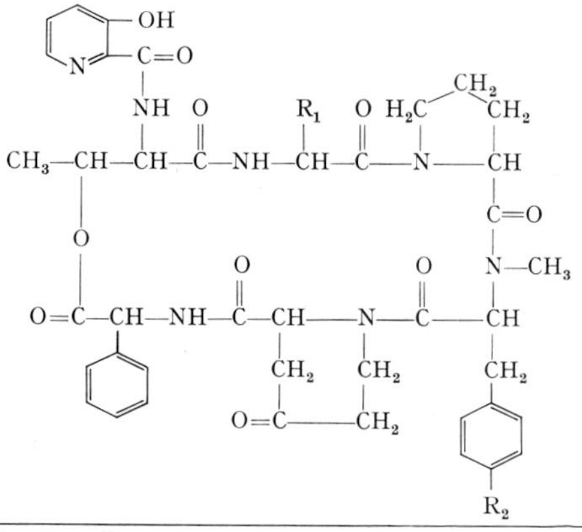

	Staphylo-mycin S	Verna-mycin B_δ	B	B_1	B_2
R_1	$-CH_2-CH_3$	$-CH_3$	$-CH_2-CH_3$	$-CH_3$	$-CH_2-CH_3$
R_2	$-H$	$-NH-CH_3$	$-N(CH_3)_2$	$-N(CH_3)_2$	$-NH-CH_3$

Streptogramin-B-group [100]

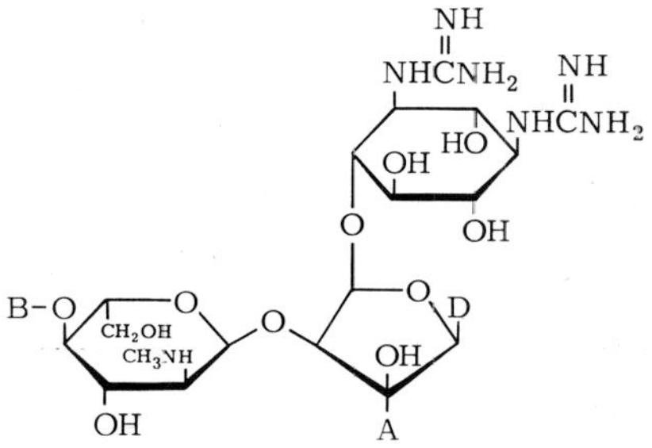

	A	B	D
Streptomycin	CHO	H	CH_3
Dihydrostreptomycin	CH_2OH	H	CH_3
Mannosidostreptomycin	CHO	See below	CH_3
Hydroxystreptomycin	CHO	H	CH_2OH

For mannosidostreptomycin, B =

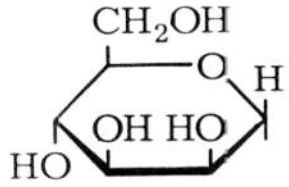

Streptomycin and analogues [79, 100, 159]

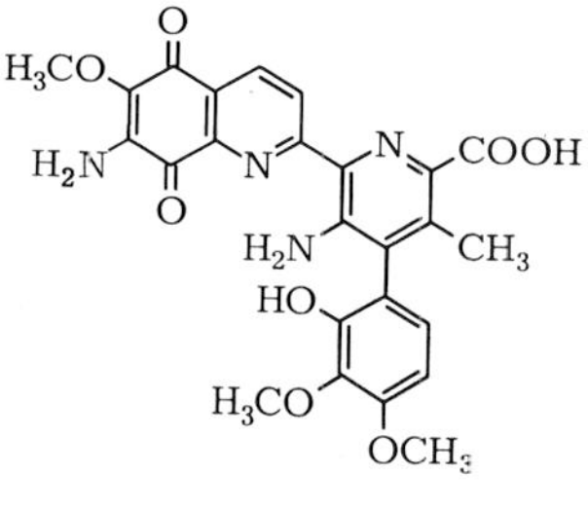

Streptonigrin [11]

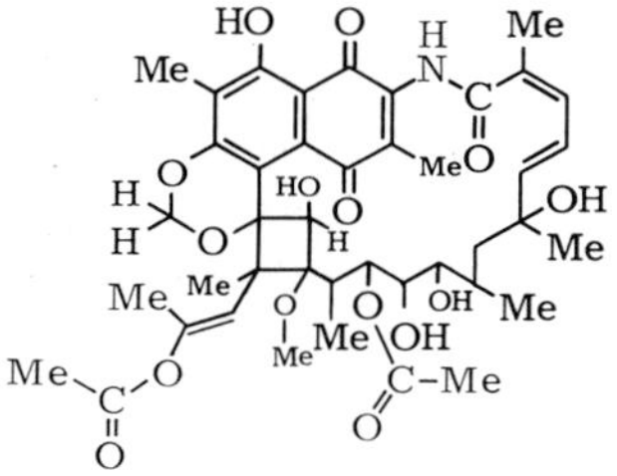

Streptovaricin A [48, 60]

Steviol: See Atractyloside

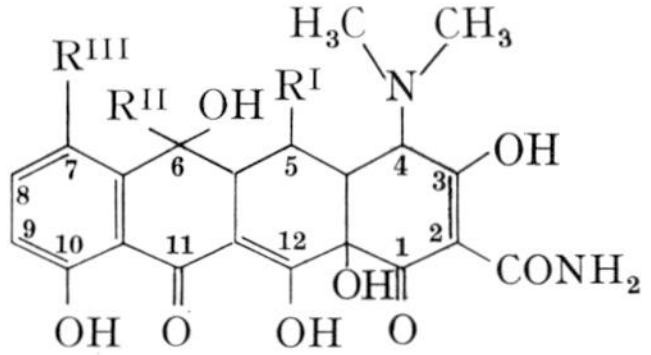

R^I	R^{II}	R^{III}	
H	CH_3	H	Tetracycline
OH	CH_3	H	Oxytetracyline
H	CH_3	Cl	Chlortetracycline
H	H	Cl	Demethylchlortetracycline

Tetracycline group [100, 159]

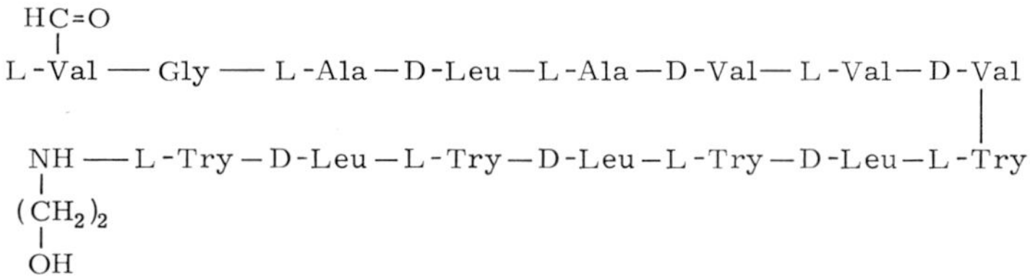

```
HC=O
 |
L-Val — Gly — L-Ala — D-Leu — L-Ala — D-Val — L-Val — D-Val
                                                        |
NH — L-Try — D-Leu — L-Try — D-Leu — L-Try — D-Leu — L-Try
 |
(CH2)2
 |
OH
```

Valine-Gramicidin A (see also Gramicidin S) [356]

```
  D-Hy-i-Valac   D-Val        L-Lac       L-Val

 ┌ H3C  CH3   H3C  CH3                  H3C  CH3  ┐
 │   \ /        \ /                       \ /     │
 │   CH         CH         CH3            CH      │
 │   |          |          |              |       │
┌│-O-CH-C--NH--CH-C--O-----CH-C---NH------CH-C-  │┐
││      ||          ||         ||              || ││
││      O           O          O               O  ││
│└                                                ┘3
└─────────────────────────────────────────────────┘
```

Valinomycin [356, 368]

Druck: Carl Ritter & Co., Wiesbaden